Happy Trails!
Jody Foss -

IN THE COMPANY OF MULES

by
Jody Foss

Illustrations by
Bonnie Shields

In the Company of Mules
by Jody Foss
Illustrated by Bonnie Shields

Published by: Mules Across America
Box 225, Tomales, California 94971

First Printing, May 2001

Library of Congress Control Number: 2001126139

ISBN: 0-9643413-2-8

Printed by Walsworth Publishing Company, Marceline, Missouri, U.S.A.
Printed in the United States of America

Publisher's Cataloging-in-Publication
(Provided by Quality Books, Inc.)

Foss, Jody, 1954-
        In the company of mules: a true western adventure/
        by Jody Foss; illustrated by Bonnie Shields; with 35
        photographs by the author. --1st ed.

        p. cm.
        ISBN 0-9643413-2-8 (softcover)

        1. Foss, Jody, 1954- 2. Women travelers--Northwest,
        Pacific 3. Oral history. 4. Mules--Northwest, Pacific.
        5. Northwest, Pacific--Description and travel. 6.
        Northwest, Pacific --History. I. Shields, Bonnie, ill.
        II. Title.

        F852.3F67 2001   917.9504'44
                                          QB101-700221

Cover photograph: Across the Coeur d'Alene
Back cover photograph: St. Marie's Old Timer

A special thank you to the people whose talent, time and patience brought this book to print:

Robert de la Vergne, editing, interior layout and design, proof reading,
Erin Hentz, cover layout and design,
Charlie Parker, Debbie Foss, Jackie Fields, proof reading.

Three cheers to Bonnie Shields, Don and Marilynn Foss, Chromographics, Color Paramount, Digitype, Walsworth Publishing, Dale Burk, Jane Healy, Dan Poynter, Daniela Sklan, Ethel Kurland, the Lutons, Joan Jones, Julie Martinoni, Phyliss Moore, Viola Waterman, Snake River Lou, Joan Kay Herres, Jay Thomas, Ken Munford, Kary Miller, Wilda Freeman, Tami Sneddon, Morrow County Museum, Oregon State Archives, Sagebrush News, Ramblin' Jack and Jan Currie Elliott, The Grit, Larry Beamer, Jenny Ruchert, Anna Lane, Pauline Shook, E.J. Kirchoff, Elaine Dauphin, Bert Dingle, Dorothy Miller, Pat Meehan, Beth Crowe, Mark Flores and Marilyn Greene, Leah at Toledo Feed n' Seed, Lew Waddle, Steve Wyatt, Carol Jensen, Bernice Waddle, Helen Miller, Dick Parks, Becky Johnson, J.D., Elizabeth Nielson, and Ken McCall—who wanted me to mention Mary's Peak is no longer open to mule travel.

Lovingly Dedicated to Paul D. Hersey
August 27, 1911–June 15, 1998

"In the Company of Mules"

Seattle

Washingto

Portland

Pendle
Pilot F

CAMP SHERMAN

Salem

Sweet Home

Newport

Corvallis

Madras

Antelope

Condon

Eugene

Bend

OREGON

Lake Pend Oreille
and Clark Fork, ID.

Spokane,
WA.

St Maries

Pullman

Potlatch
Moscow

IDAHO

n2 ≠ DAM
itsburg

Lewiston

a Walla, WA.

MAP

B. Shields

In the Company of Mules

Table of Contents

Chapter One

Between Hope and Paradise

It was my last night in town. I was riding out towards Oregon on the mules with Nina Cvetikovs in the morning. I came to town after Nina went to bed to dance the Western swing in my cowgirl skirt, partly because it would be the last time I would see those funny and friendly faces for awhile and partly because I was thirty and full of fun.

The Playhouse Bar was loud that night. The dancers filled up the dance floor and half the entryway and the country band was leaning back to avoid an over enthusiastic elbow or knee. Bow hunters and loggers in camouflage and Logger's World suspenders were shoulder to shoulder with some fishermen who were bragging about the big one that got away. Two local grandmothers sat huddled together at the end of the bar to avoid getting jostled by the oversized sportsmen. I could see they had been to the beauty parlor that afternoon. Leonard the Logger was in the middle of one of his big tree stories, the one that ended with the chainsaw wedged forever in the base of a giant cedar. He didn't tell his stories. He yelled them.

The loud music poured out the door into the chilly night air and sifted up the heavily forested canyons. The folks who lived up Spring Creek said they could sometimes hear the music above the roar of the rushing water.

Every barstool was taken and so were all of the tables. I danced all night like it was my last night on earth, swirling around in my big skirt with Stan the Mountain Man. Years before, he had come to Northern Idaho from Iowa to build a log cabin on his own land, later going into the landscaping business. He kept all the lawns in Clark Fork and those in Hope, overlooking Lake Pend Oreille, trimmed and raked and neat as a pin. And how the Mountain Man liked to dance. He was tall and strong from mowing all those lawns and I ricocheted and spun around under his direction like a top on a string.

I walked out of the Playhouse Bar into the bright light of the fullest moon. Stan came running down the road behind me, growling ferociously like the cinnamon bear that lived down by the spawning grounds. He grabbed me and tackled me right there in the middle of Highway 200. It was okay, though, because there was little or no traffic on the highway late at night and we could hear a car coming from a long way off. I only worried about my cowgirl skirt as it was my favorite, the one with the silver rickrack sewn in circles over thin turquoise fabric.

"Let's walk down to the river," he said.

"Let's go," I answered without hesitation.

The Clark Fork River ran swiftly through the town. To stand on the bridge late at night and look down at the water in the moonlight was one of my favorite things to do in town besides dance. We walked briskly towards the river, only a few blocks from the Playhouse.

"By golly, darlin'!" Stan said to me. "The river is so bright! A good sign for a good ride."

We both stood quietly on the bridge looking down at the fast silver water. When the town was quiet, the river would sing. During the day logging trucks, pickups, and station wagons full of kids with inner tubes on the top crossed this bridge, rumbling over the old ties on either end. But at night, when most people were already inside, the cold northern air came down off the mountains behind the town and you could hear nothing but the wind and the river.

"When Nina arrived yesterday with all her gear for the trip, I could see that it's good I bought that pack pony from Lottie

McClure. I just wish my horse, Cowboy, could go with us. But his ankle is still bad. It's a tendon injury so it will take some time to heal," I told Stan. I was sick about it. Cowboy had stepped in a hole in the field behind the granary only because I was trying a tie-down on his bridle and he couldn't see where he was walking.

"Where's he going to stay while you're gone?" Stan asked.

"Down at the Diamond T. He's in good hands there, but I sure wish he could come. You know, I've only ridden my new mule, Mavis, a dozen times. And that was just around the block!" Our block was two miles by two miles and crossed the border into Montana.

"So, how old did you say your friend Nina is?" he asked.

"She's seventy-two. But she's strong and full of life and walked my legs off down in Mazatlan. She would say, 'Jody, would you like to walk?' And I would say 'Yes' and arrive back at the Hotel Santa Barbara hours later, after trying to keep up with her on a six-mile walk! She's an older gal, that's for certain. But she's tough!"

"Well, she'd better be," Stan said. "How far is it out to Newport, Oregon, from here?"

"At least six hundred miles. Maybe a little more. Depends on which way we ride. At least she'll be riding Sarah Jane. You can't find a better mule," I said to him.

We both were quiet and stood looking down into the big river.

It had been a long time since I first rode up that valley in 1976 with my sister Debbie and two friends on a ninety day pack trip all the way from Utah. I had yelled back to Deb, "This is where I want to live!" as we rode on towards Spokane. We had been on the trail by then for over two months and were like two young bears in a blackberry patch. It was late fall and the fruit literally fell into our pockets from the trees as we rode along.

That place, that little cabin with the barn built of massive logs, never faded from my memory. Five years later, it was mine. I bought it with my Mr. Right; he moved back to town and we broke up before I ever ordered the wallpaper or fixed the holes in the old wood floor in the kitchen.

The cabin, built in 1918 by Finnish dairy farmers, had hand hewn walls of yellow pine, each log carved with a shipwright's adz.

The gold of the walls lit up the rooms with a warm color enhanced by the sunlight as it made its way through the cabin, changing as the sun filtered in the windows. The wood stove heated the downstairs; the wood ceilings and floors soaked up the warmth. The old cabin was chinked with every bit of lingerie imaginable, old lace and silk torn into narrow strips. For years, the residents had taken their old slips and underwear and stuffed them into the cracks to keep that cold north wind from sifting its way through the walls. The windows upstairs were long and narrow and looked out in all four directions, over the apple trees and the back pasture, over the bluffs that turned red and gold each evening at dusk. And the Clark Fork River was down there, right down the road to the spawning grounds only a quarter mile from the place.

I had galloped my horse Cowboy up that road a million times. He would really get going right before the big turn at the top of the hill and race through the gate, stopping with his nose only a foot in front of the big barn door where I could feel my heart beating out of my chest.

To the east, through the giant cottonwoods, alders, tamaracks and cedars, there was Montana just over the hill on the dirt road that followed the river. To the south, the Selkirks and Coeur d'Alene Mountains kept us from getting hit with severe weather. And to the west, out the window, I could see the sunset shining off the trees between me and Lake Pend Oreille eight miles away.

"Stan, I promise to send you a postcard from the road when we get down into Oregon." I hugged him goodbye and watched him drive off in his pickup truck with all the lawn mowers in the back until he disappeared into the darkness.

It was my last night to drive my old blue Chevy so I crept home in third gear, over the bridge, out along the potato fields, over the bluff and down into the flats. I had sold the car for three hundred dollars to Pat the bartender who had promised to bring me the money in the morning. When I finally reached the dirt road that headed down to the ranch, I stopped and looked down at the place poised there at the edge of the river at the bottom of the red bluff. The moon was so bright and I smiled and said aloud to myself, "What a place to call home." There was not a sound in the whole world right then as I turned onto the road that led to the ranch.

Next to the barn, in a big fenced area, Dorothy had her vegetable garden, a labor of love that took up a good four hours of her morning. She and Reid had moved up from a mortuary outside Sacramento where they were the caretakers. They were living in the cabin and I was living out in the granary, a stacked two by four building I had made into a home for myself. Reid and Dorothy had worked hard to get the cabin comfortable for themselves and to build up the garden, each vegetable neatly in its place with paths between everything and cabbages the size of bowling balls.

As I approached, barely stepping on the gas, gliding slowly towards home, I gasped. It was Sarah Jane, the white mule, smack dab in the middle of Dorothy's garden.

"Oh, my God. Oh, no. Please," I pleaded in a prayerful tone. Sarah stood still as a marble statue watching me approach in the old car. I rolled into the driveway as quietly as I could, turning off the headlights before they shined on the cabin.

I opened the door of the car and didn't slam it; I left it ajar and walked as quietly as I could, tiptoeing towards the garden gate. I did not call Sarah's name as I didn't want her to jump and wipe out another thing. The moon was bright on Sarah's pure white coat. She was so mischievous, an intelligence to be reckoned with. I never spoke a word to her as I tiptoed into Dorothy's garden. The vegetables looked untouched. The corn still stood in stiff rows, uneaten. Only one ear of corn had fallen prey to the white mule. It hung out of her mouth. I let her keep it and walked her slowly down the little garden path and out the gate.

"Just in time, Sarah Girl," I said to her as I hugged her warm neck and ran my hands through her long, silky white mane. I led her into the pasture with Mavis and the pack pony, Easter Boy. Mavis called out to me in a soft nicker. Their coats glowed in the moonlight.

"See you in the morning," I said to them. I tossed a little hay into the feeder and headed towards my bed, suddenly exhausted by the close call.

I tried to move quietly as I opened the big plank door of my

granary home. The hinges groaned as they always did. Nina had set up her bed in the tiny upstairs and I could hear her soft, steady breathing as I tiptoed around the downstairs room. The building was only twelve by twelve but it was twenty feet tall and with a remarkable view out the window facing the bluffs. With Stan's help, I had sheetrocked the upstairs and we had built the second floor joists out of logs from the mill. It was a cozy little home with floral wallpaper upstairs, a two-burner propane stove, an old refrigerator, and an outhouse out back plastered with pages of poetry from the old buckskin poet I had met up by Libby, Montana. On a cold night, when the temperature dropped below zero, the most difficult task in the world was coming out from under the down comforter to use the outhouse.

Nina and I had both migrated south to Mazatlan that winter. Northern Idaho was cold and icy and my old dog, Robin, desperately needed a break from the severe weather. Her arthritis was getting really bad and I could barely stand to watch her hobble around the yard in the deep snow. The change did us good, as change often does.

We boarded a plane and flew south all the way to the seaside spot on the coast of Mexico. I rented a room at the Hotel Santa Barbara where Señora Barbara didn't mind my big brown dog. Robin was quiet and well behaved and was as excited as I was to be in this new place so far away from the tumbling Idaho snows. That is when I met Nina. She, too, had a room in the Hotel Santa Barbara.

I was instantly charmed by this woman with the blue, twinkling eyes who made her own yogurt right there in her room.

"Jody dear, would you and your dear dog like to walk with me?" she had inquired with a mischievous smile as she stood in the doorway of my big stucco and tile room. By the look on her face I knew if I said yes I would be gone for quite awhile. She meant walk when she said walk, and I kept up with her for several hours as we hiked along the shoreline of the beach in Mazatlan. She was the oldest member of a Seattle mountaineering club and had climbed most of the big peaks in the northwest.

As we walked those warm beaches in Mazatlan, Nina told me stories of another world, growing up in a part of Russia that became

Latvia, a country torn apart by war. Her mother was Russian and her father was French. He was the head of the Riga-Orel Railroad and belonged to the French nobility. During the 1917 revolution, her family was separated and Nina never saw her father again. She lived with her mother and sisters in Russia and then went to England to improve her English. In 1938 she married her beloved husband, who was an architect, and then moved to Germany. She talked about her arrival in America on the Liberty Ship in the 1950s. Her husband had passed away years earlier.

She told me about a place I could only picture in my mind, a city called Riga paved with amber and filled with incredible beauty. And the soldiers. The tricks she would pull on them as she rode past on her bike. A young Nina hiding whisky to trade in her skirt.

"When asked at a checkpoint what it was I was carrying, I would answer, milk, eggs and ham...while patting myself, you know, here and there," she said with a laugh. "It was a different world, you can only imagine. I have lost everyone I have ever loved." She spoke matter of factly about her great losses. Yet she had continued to live her life to the fullest, coming up with the most clever and natural quips, finding humor in everything, always a thin, clever smile on her face. She amazed me.

As the weeks passed, as we walked up and down that gorgeous Mexican beach with the big brown dog, we became dear friends.

Chapter 2

Spilled Milk

By the time I peeked out from underneath my quilt, Nina had most of her stuff packed and placed neatly in a little pile near the door.

I turned over in my big, comfortable bed and opened my other eye to see the clock. It was six-thirty. The sun was just starting to send columns of light across the valley, the first birds in the orchard were singing without hesitation and when I opened the big plank door I could see Dorothy in the garden following the mule tracks, shaking her head.

"I think I made it home in the nick of time, Dorothy," I said sheepishly.

"That you did. There doesn't seem to be anything missing, except for one head of lettuce and an ear of corn." Dorothy was patient with me, and kind.

"I'm lucky, I guess," I said to myself.

Reid came outside and lit a cigarette. He walked out into the morning sun, squinting.

"Good morning, Reid and Dorothy!" Nina shouted to them.

"Are you sure it's a good morning?" Reid said, smirking. "You'll be plenty saddle sore by tonight."

"Well, Reid," Nina replied with a wry smile, "I would rather be sitting on the mule's back than laying at home on my own."

Reid stood around smoking cigarettes and watched us put our belongings for the trip into two piles.

"How long do you think the ride will take?" he asked.

"Probably close to two months," I answered. "After we cross the Coeur d'Alene Mountains, we'll be in the wheat lands of Washington before we cross into Oregon. I think it's about five or six hundred miles the way we plan to go." I was packing my red saddle bag which I planned to hang on the saddle horn since I didn't want to put too much weight over young Mavis' kidneys. I filled them with the things I wanted access to during the day: my camera, dried fruit, a first aid kit, maps of the National Forest, skin lotion, sunglasses, a compass, a hoof pick and a notebook.

"Well, good luck. But all I can say is, I'm glad it's you and not me." Reid walked over to the garden to give Dorothy a hand smoothing out Sarah Jane's tracks on the narrow path.

"Now, Jody," Nina said with authority, "we have a long way to travel so I think we should plan how we are ever going to make it all the way to the Oregon coast. First off, I will get up and get the coffee going since I'm an early riser. We should pack up by eight, ride until noon and stop for lunch. Let's ride two or three more hours and stop for tea, then keep riding until four or five before camping for the night."

"Sounds good," I answered. Her plan made me feel a little nervous. I was lazy in the morning and started slow. "I'm going out to get the animals ready."

Pat, a jovial man with a quick walk, showed up to get the Chevy. I hated to part with the old blue car. I could carry a bale of hay in the trunk and with its big back seat there was always plenty of room for groceries. The heavy metal body had saved my life more than once when I careened uncontrollably into the deep snow. Once I had stayed in it all night, wrapped in my old rabbit coat.

I was driving home from Hope after a night of waitressing when I slid off the road into the snow bank and no one ever came by. If it hadn't been for the heater and the nice old fashioned velour interior, I might have opted for the five mile walk home in the snowstorm. My friend Mike showed up in the morning, knocking on the window that was thick with ice. He hooked a chain to the heavy chrome bumper and pulled me out.

Pat smiled at me and held up the three hundred dollars. I grabbed it from him. "There you go," I said, nodding towards the Chevy. "She's all yours."

"Have a good trip, ladies." He started up the engine and drove slowly out of the barnyard. I looked away, back to the mules.

"Isn't Mavis a gorgeous mule?" I asked Nina, smiling as I brushed the young mule's charcoal and silver coat which glistened in the early morning sun. Mave's silver ear moved back and forth, listening to my flattery while her black ear was frozen forward in the direction of the buck deer that was leaping through the back pasture.

"Like a young girl who's too pretty and knows it," Nina answered. Everything Nina said had a ring to it.

Mavis had been raised by Smoke Bowers, an old cowboy who lived north of Spokane. He named her Thunderstorm. I had changed her name to Mavis after my neighbor's mother who, it turned out, was not flattered.

Mavis' mother, Dixie Lee, was the pride and joy of Smoke Bowers.

"The day I got out of the service," Smoke told me, "I bought that mare, saddled her up and rode all the way to Denver, Colorado, all the way from the Army base in North Dakota. It was the best time of my life and I'll never forget a minute of it. When Dixie Lee had Thunderstorm, I knew that little gray mule could go the distance. But now I don't ride much anymore. I'm too old and too tired," he said with a tear in his eye.

The day that Smoke delivered Thunderstorm to the ranch my dear dog Robin walked off into the bushes behind the apple trees. While the green broke mule stood tied up to the corral, working out the ropes, my dog was dying. I let the young mule go free in the pasture with Sarah and raced Robin to the vet in Sandpoint. He took her blood and tested it, finding cancer. All her organs were shutting down and she was in great pain. While I held her in my arms, filled with more intense sorrow than I had ever felt, the vet gave her a shot and she slipped away.

In a black plastic bag, I carried her home in the trunk of that old

Chevy. It was the longest drive home I can ever remember. I stopped by to see my friend Nancy at the Lighthouse Restaurant where we both worked as waitresses.

"It's Robin. She's dead!" I wailed. We both cried together. Nancy's dog, Jake, sniffed at the trunk. We opened it, and then the bag, and Jake cried too, the way dogs do.

Saying goodbye to Robin was the hardest parting of my life. I couldn't imagine riding in the woods without my sweet dog dancing along the forest floor by my side. My neighbor, Tony, dug a hole for me in the back pasture, under the big white pine, and I buried her there in the yard.

So Robin left my life and Thunderstorm entered it, all on the same day.

I saddled Mavis, placing a green and white blanket I bought in Mexico over a green saddle pad. Mavis didn't mind the saddle as long as I didn't try to cinch it up all at once.

Putting my saddlebag on the horn of my saddle, I smiled to myself. I had only ridden the young mule a dozen times. But she didn't buck and was not easily frightened. Sarah Jane had taught her quite a bit already, and what better way to train her than to spend twenty four hours a day together for a couple of months? She would learn on the trail. I had confidence in her. Although she was just three years old, she had strong, stocky legs, a straight back and long ears to listen with. We'd take our time in the beginning, giving us all the chance to get used to life on the trail.

I looked over at Nina in her plaid shorts and neat white blouse. Although she had lived over seventy years, her face had an expression of youthful exuberance. Sarah Jane would keep us all on the right track. We were depending on her, Nina especially. I trusted that Sarah would carry her safely all the way to Newport.

"I sure hope Sarah dear won't mind carrying all these things," she said.

"Sarah doesn't mind, Nina. She can carry you and a few extras," I answered as I picked Mavis' feet. John Fuller had been out to shoe them the day before and this was Mavis' first pair of shoes. The new metal was still shiny and I knew it wouldn't be long before those shoes would be thin and worn.

"At my tender age, I need things to keep me warm. A good down bag, padding and a small tent," Nina continued. She was standing up now looking at me, with those incredibly blue, sparkling eyes, her hands on her hips. "You know, last Sunday when I was all alone, still in Seattle, I visualized cold rain and dampness. Then I stopped thinking about the negative side. And that trip to the acupuncturist made me feel twenty years younger."

"You'll see, Nina. Everything we need we have right here in our pack. There's extra sheepskin for the tack, a first aid kit, extra horseshoes and nails. You name it, we have it. Even a travel iron in case we need to get pressed when we come into town."

"But where will we plug it in, to a current bush?" Nina asked with a laugh.

"The main thing, Nina, is to remember the first rule: if the mule or the pack pony tries to run away from you, always let go of the rope immediately. They can be caught up with later," I said seriously.

"I promise, Jody, I will let go of the rope," she answered.

I walked out across my yard towards the apple trees. I could see Reid at the window looking out at me. Dorothy was standing in the big kitchen doing dishes. Soon she would be back outside, out in the garden.

Taking a bite out of a red delicious, I looked around the grassy yard. I would miss this place, but I was ready to go. I walked out to Robin's grave under the big white pine.

"Goodbye, girl," I said softly. "I miss you."

Dorothy brought us a batch of fresh chocolate chip cookies wrapped in foil. Dorothy was one of the best bakers and gardeners I had ever met. She stayed ironed and neat looking all the time as she moved slowly but determinedly through the day, as Reid did what he could with a bad heart. Country life had proved to be not what they had expected it to be and was, in fact, nothing like retirement. Instead, it was a lot more work than the mortuary had been. And then there was Nina and me to worry about. In some ways, I'm sure they were glad we were leaving.

"And what about the pack pony? Do you think we can teach

27

him how to carry our gear?" Nina asked, worriedly.

"Sure do hope so," I answered in a tone that helped me convince myself. Lottie McClure, an old cowgirl from Sagle, had sold us Easter Boy for a pack pony when the veterinarian told us that Cowboy couldn't come with us. Lottie didn't promise anything but suggested that the pony was a quick learner. As long as we didn't try to take too much gear, he'd gladly pack for us.

Easter Boy stood quietly as I gently placed the thick saddle blanket on his back. I had already covered the breast collar and the butt breaching with sheepskin. He didn't seem to mind the packsaddle or the bags. He turned around and looked at the mound of gear as we finished up with the diamond hitch and made sure the edges of the orange tarp were tucked in. He fell asleep while we finished packing our own saddles, Nina with her saddle bags full of nut mix and teas, mine with my camera, canteen and first aid kit. Mavis looked so beautiful in her headstall with the sheepskin on it. She stood and slept, her black ear following the conversation, her silver ear whipping off the fly that was trying to rest on her forelock.

Nina finished packing her saddle bags, adjusted her reins, rolled up her jacket and tied it on the back of her saddle. She carefully took the cookies that Dorothy had given us and stored them in one side of her bag. She reached up and gave Sarah Jane a big hug.

"Oh, Sarah, Sarah, you are such a beautiful animal to carry me all the way across the mountains to the sea!" Nina said in a singsong voice.

"And my Mavis," I bragged, "is the most beautiful creature on the planet."

Mavis was beautiful and knew it. Smoky Bowers had been telling her that over corral fences her whole life. She was so young and knew very little about life outside the corral. She just watched Sarah and did whatever Sarah did.

We closed the door of the granary with a slam. I helped Nina get her foot up into the stirrup and onto Sarah Jane who stood as still as a statue, her ears cocked.

"I feel like royalty up here," Nina said, smiling.

I stuck my foot in the stirrup and held my rein in so Mavis would stand still. "Whoa girl, easy," I said softly. I held Easter Boy's

rope in my hand. He followed me around the yard hesitantly at first and then with a little more confidence. Just then, I heard the familiar missing muffler sound of Crazy and Poozie's truck.

"Hey, Jody, you wild woman you!" Crazy yelled at the top of his lungs. His voice filled the whole valley, echoing off the bluffs and the pine covered mountains to the south. The mules fluttered and the pony jumped as he and Poozie stumbled towards us in their big logger boots. They were waving a big bag of jerky.

"Don't leave without this!" he yelled. His dirty hands, stained for life, held up the bag. "Venison and elk. It's the best. It'll keep you fed all the way to Oregon."

Poozie stood quietly by as Crazy ranted on, flirting with Nina just for fun. Her long red hair hung in a braid down the back of her plaid wool logger's jacket. She and Crazy lived down the dirt road towards Montana in a small place with goats in the yard. She smiled up at me and said, "Good Luck, Jody, and have a good trip."

"Thanks. Don't have too much fun while I'm gone," I joked.

Crazy, Poozie, Reid and Dorothy all stood there in a line, looking at us. Poozie took our picture with an old camera that looked like they had found it at the bottom of the river. I knew that we had better just get moving or we'd think of something else to bring, and our saddlebags were heavy enough. I smiled at my friends and then at Nina. "Are you ready, cowgirl?" I asked her.

"You bet!" Nina answered as she gave Sarah a little encouragement with her tennis shoe. Sarah moved out ahead in front of Mavis and Easter Boy. She headed out the big wooden gate and onto the road. She'd been there before. I clicked to Mavis and whispered to her, "Here we go, girl."

Easter Boy moved slowly at first as he got used to the pack and then with a little more confidence as we headed up the dirt road to the highway and headed towards Dry Creek Road. I could see Reid and Dorothy standing near the garden watching us while we rode slowly away, until the pine trees blocked my view.

It was almost noon. We stopped to take a picture of Nina and Sarah next to the Dry Creek sign when Bev showed up with the three kids in her big green station wagon. She jumped out, her long, straight hair flying around in the sun behind her, holding out her arms yelling, "Bye Jode! Bye Nina! You girls take care of each other!"

Her kids, Hanna, Josh and Cora Lee, all smiled and waved from the back seat. Bev looked like she was going to cry.

"You guys better be careful! And don't forget to let go of the rope. If the pony starts to shy and run, just let go! Call me when you get to St. Maries. And drop us a postcard from the trail. Wherever you can, okay? Don't leave us worrying sick."

Bev was my neighbor out at the ranch but had moved into Clark Fork to raise her children in a more comfortable house. I missed her out in the valley. She was like family to me. Along with my other neighbors, Dave and Al and Mike and Dede, Bev had helped me with the huge task of roofing the massive log barn. We worked for months together grasping the bundles of shingles with frozen fingers and carrying them to the high ridge. The view from the ridge of the barn was breathtaking. We held on for our lives, moving carefully and slowly to avoid a dangerous fall off the tall wooden structure. Bev was there when I nailed the final shake to the very edge of the roof's peak. We cheered and sat there straddling the roof, on top of the world. We had finished the two-month project only one week before the first snow. It was people like Beverly that made me love my Northern Idaho home.

"We'll let you know. Don't worry."

We waved goodbye over our shoulders and headed up Dry Creek Road. It would lead us up into the Coeur d'Alene National Forest and eventually down into the St. Joe Valley east of St. Maries. We'd been pouring over the maps but never knew what it would really be like until we got there.

Sarah walked slowly up the road as if she was giving us all time to follow, and then she picked up speed. Mavis followed her confidently as I made sure I didn't wrap her tail with Easter Boy's lead. The pony followed as we rode up the road and out of sight. Bev drove off in the old green station wagon and the woods were suddenly silent.

Nina looked so happy. She was beaming. The years fell away from her face as she looked up the road and then through the forest and I pictured her, the young girl making her way through soldiers at checkpoints. The sun sent beams down through the trees as we rode in silence. I reached down and patted the sleek charcoal black neck of my mule and whispered, "Good girl, Mavis."

Nina was behind me as we started to climb up the mountain on the steep road. The pony walked quietly along, once in awhile taking a look back at the pack on his back. I watched the load to make sure it wasn't tipping to one side. It looked like it was even.

"Oh, Jody," Nina said quietly, "I have never felt such happiness."

We rode quietly along. I was off a little bit ahead of Nina and Sarah. Nina was singing a Latvian song to Sarah Jane and the mule was keeping time with her long white ears. I watched as Nina reached down with her hand to pat Sarah lovingly on the neck.

31

"My good Lachatka, my beautiful Lachatka," she said, smiling.

"What does it mean?" I asked.

"Little horse. My good little horse! Do you think Sarah minds me calling her a little horse?" she laughed.

Mavis was forging ahead of the rest, looking a little anxiously up the road and yet still leading the way. I was already hungry and reached into my saddlebag for some jerky. I started chewing on a piece and gave Mavis a little signal with the reins to slow down. For such a young mule, she was more than willing. She could feel my anticipation.

"Sure hope there aren't too many logging trucks this way," I said to Nina over my shoulder.

"What do we do if a big truck comes?" Nina asked.

"We jump off the edge into the duff!" I answered only halfway kidding. I could only hope we'd be in a wide place in the road when a truck came by.

"Well, we might as well not worry about it. I can see so much from up here on Sarah's nice back! What a nice position from which to view the world! And my Lachatka shall carry me all the way to the sea!"

"Look, Nina, the lake!" I called back to her. I led the pony down a narrow trail off the dirt road that ended on a little ridge from which we could see the whole valley. The Clark Fork River shone like mercury in the early afternoon sun. I followed it with my eyes, out to the west and the slough where it widens and empties into Lake Pend Oreille. The valley was incredibly beautiful. I would miss my home. I could see the road out to my cabin, the road that turns to dirt at the Montana line. The mountains, blanketed by trees, looked soft in the distance.

"What a beautiful place!" Nina was holding Sarah still and the two of them looked into the valley. Sarah was thinking about her horse, Cowboy, that grazed leisurely down at the Diamond T, two miles below.

I turned Mavis back onto the trail and out to the road again, said my own quiet goodbye to the horse I was leaving behind, and to my dog Robin, buried there beneath the big pine tree. Easter Boy pulled against the lead rope a little bit and then trotted to catch up with us for a second or two. The tarp made a noise and he jumped to the side pulling on the rope again. Mavis stood her ground and seemed to be pulling with me.

"Easy, now, Easter Boy," I said to him quietly.

"How far do you think we've gone so far?" Nina asked me with a smile.

"I think about four miles or so. And not one truck!" I said, adding, "I could sure stop and use the ladies' room!"

"Me, too!" Nina said.

We pulled into a small turnout that looked like it had been carved out with a big tractor.

"I'm going to tie up Sarah," Nina said.

"Okay. Can you hold Easter Boy's rope? I'm going to run out behind that big cedar over there!" I was holding on to Mavis by her reins. She was good with the reins. I could even hang them on her ears if I wanted to. She didn't mind.

Nina stood there holding Easter Boy and all our belongings under the big orange tarp. I turned to run off to the tree when Nina screamed, "No! Stop, pony!"

I spun around and watched as she struggled with the rope and the next thing I saw was my friend being dragged across the dirt, face down, as the pony took off at a dead gallop for the ranch.

When the dust settled, Nina was at least twelve feet from where she had fallen. I raced over to her, my stomach turning into a big knot as I ran. When I saw the way her arm was ripped open, from the elbow to the wrist, I felt my balance going and I struggled not to fall over. Instead, I fell to my knees next to her.

"Oh, Nina! Oh, my God!"

"Pull yourself together, Jody."

"But your arm, it's...it's...oh Nina, I'm so sorry!" I said through my tears.

"Stop crying and let's think of what we have to do next," she said quietly.

I ran to my saddlebag and pulled out the first aid kit. There was hydrogen peroxide and some gauze bandages. I opened the peroxide and poured it into the cut on Nina's elbow. Tears fell into the open wound. I tried to breathe. Her old skin had ripped open in a way I had never seen before. She winced as the peroxide started to bubble and she grabbed her arm.

"Ow!" she yelled. The quiet woods that had listened to our happy conversation as we rode up that steep dirt road now echoed Nina's cries.

"Ow! My knee! I don't know if I can walk!" Nina said as she leaned on me, getting to her feet. Even in her pain she was able to smile at me and say: "Oh, Jody, my friend, you are as white as snow."

I smiled back at her somehow, no longer staring at the huge gash on her arm. We stood quietly for a minute as she tried to put weight on her knee.

"I think my knee is not broken, just wrenched," she said. "Where is the pony? Where did he go?"

"The last I saw of him he was galloping as fast as he could go down the road towards the ranch." The weight of my friend fell heavy on my shoulders as we stood there, stunned. Sarah Jane looked over at us, her ears forward, concerned. Mavis was tied to a big pine by her lead rope.

"Do you think you can get up in the saddle?" I asked. Nina was standing up on her own now. She had been riding in a white blouse which now had blood all over it. I went over and picked up her glasses which were attached to a little pearl chain. They weren't broken. I dusted them off as best I could.

"Here, Nina," I kneeled down next to Sarah Jane. "Put your foot on my knee and try to hoist yourself up into the saddle."

"Ow!" she cried out again. Somehow we managed to get her back up on Sarah. She held the reins with her good hand and struggled to get her foot into the stirrup. She was an incredibly brave person who had survived much more than this.

I untied Mavis and put my foot in the stirrup. I felt so weak in the saddle I had to tell myself to breathe. The beautiful afternoon was no longer a comfort and a joy to me as I rode, broken hearted, back down Dry Creek Road to the ranch.

I rode along in front of Nina and Sarah. Mavis was walking at a fast pace, as mules always do on the way back home. Sarah stayed close behind.

"Look, there's the pony's tracks," I said to Nina. They were far apart and showed up clearly on the dirt because Easter Boy was not wasting any time. He was probably galloping still, I thought to myself.

"How's your knee?" I asked Nina. I looked back over my shoulder at my friend. Her bandaged arm rested across her lap and she was holding her reins with her good hand.

"It hurts. And so does my arm." Her voice was quiet and strained.

We followed the tracks of Easter Boy and finally met the highway where we had said goodbye to Bev only hours before. That was the one time I was not happy to see my cabin home, perched there in the open flat with the red bluffs behind. We road quietly towards the cabin speaking only a little bit once in a while. I could see Reid and Dorothy. Reid was lighting a cigarette. Dorothy was on the garden path looking up, concerned. Easter Boy stood there asleep in front of the big log barn and the granary. The orange tarp was pulled out on each side of the pack, but the pack had not slipped; it still perched squarely on the pony's back.

That made us both smile.

Nina joked with the doctor at the Emergency Room in Sandpoint.

"Well, doctor, I guess you won't let me ride a mule to Newport, Oregon," she joked, knowing the answer.

"Sorry," the doctor smiled and said, "but that arm took over thirty stitches and your knee will take months to heal."

"I guess I am no spring chicken, good doctor, but I know Sarah Jane would have carried me happily the whole way."

"How many miles to Newport, did you say?" the doctor asked her.

"Six hundred or so, right, Jody?" Nina asked me.

"About that," I answered.

"I so wanted to tell the young people we would meet along the way to do these things while they are young and have their vitality, to climb the mountain and enjoy life!" Nina said to the doctor. He was a little stunned when he heard of our trip and what had happened.

The doctor left the room and Nina looked at me seriously. "You know, you must get back on the trail as soon as possible, Jody, even if you are afraid. You must go. Promise me you will try."

"I will, Nina, but I wanted to go on the trip with you."

"Jody, don't cry over spilled milk. Clean up the mess."

"Nina, why did you try to hold onto the rope?"

"I guess, my friend, I've lost all of my belongings and everything that I loved too many times in my life. When the moment came, the instinct was to hold on."

"I will try to make it at least across the mountains to Cataldo," I promised my brave friend.

Later that afternoon, around five or so, I watched as Nina boarded the Greyhound bus for her home in Seattle. I kept repeating to myself, "Don't cry over spilled milk. Clean up the mess. Clean up the mess."

Chapter 3

Across the Coeur d'Alene

On the way back to the ranch in the borrowed truck, I stopped by the Diamond T to see Cowboy. He trotted towards me across the pasture he shared with a variety of horses, mostly Quarter Horses and Appaloosas. I put my face against his neck. A lump in my throat made it difficult to talk.

"Sure wish you could come with us, Boy." My voice quivered and strained as I held back my tears.

He limped, nodding his head, as he ran proudly back to the herd. He didn't look up at me again. I held onto the big rails of the lodgepole fence and wiped my involuntary tears on the sleeve of my shirt. I thought of all the times we had had together, all the adventures. Cowboy was such a young horse when we left on the big ride from Park City, Utah, that summer day in 1976. He was the perfect steed for the long ride, willing, fast walking and not afraid of his own shadow. None of this would have happened if we'd had Cowboy with us, I thought to myself. For some reason I remembered the time we raced the train.

It was a perfect summer day for a skinny dip in the spawning grounds below the old Cabinet School where Dave and Alirene lived. I took a deep breath and dove into the clear, cool water, opening my eyes as soon as I could so my swim under water could be a long one. I pushed the water with my hands, kicked my feet and swam to the edge of the current knowing that if I went any further I would be on my way to the lake. Cowboy loved to swim and I could ride him right into the river where soon his body would be weightless. I stayed on his back as long as I could until the strong river separated us. Then I'd grab his short tail and he'd pull me around. I had to watch out for his back legs and he was careful to watch out for me.

My neighbor from down the dirt road owed me one and I knew he'd take me on when I least expected it. I had borrowed his rooster to get my hens laying. The big red and white rooster brought a sense of peace to the hen house and eggs were abundant.

My neighbor seemed to have forgotten about the old rooster. That was until another neighbor's dog ate the prized bird. It somehow was transformed into an award winning fighting cock once it was dead, its head twisted back in a horrible position. After the bloody slaughter, the big white dog tried to look innocent and nonchalant. It wasn't easy with white feathers stuck in his teeth, sticking out of his mouth like feathers on a hat. His big eyes looked sad and, once he realized everyone knew, he stayed close to his owner with new desperation.

It was shortly after that that I rode Cowboy and Sarah down to the spawning grounds for a quick swim in the deep, protected pool that kept me from floating the seven miles down to town. Sarah grazed where she wished. Taking off all my clothes was habit. If anyone was coming, I could hear their vehicle from a long way off. That day the woods were silent, the only sound being the waves that lapped delightedly along the gentle riverbank. It was hot summer. The pine needles were heating up and blanketed the ground with a soft, warm mat. I relished the way my bare feet felt in those warm, dry needles as I climbed up on Cowboy's back. I didn't even have to touch his head because he wanted to go swimming, too. Down to the edge of the big river he'd go and then he'd walk slowly in.

Once I surfaced, clearing my eyes and wiping my long hair off my face, I could see that my pile of clothes was gone.

First I gasped; then I laughed. I didn't really care. I jumped out of the water, still on Cowboy's slick back. In a flash we raced up the road at a dead gallop, the water flying off of us. Sarah never let us get too far from her view. She took one last bite of the thick grass and galloped after us, her long tail flowing behind her like a white satin ribbon.

It was then that I heard the train as it rumbled through Cabinet on its way to Missoula. I felt my heart race. The engineer waved at me slowly from his window. I let Cowboy have his head and he kept up with the speeding train as we galloped along the soft dirt road to Montana.

Cowboy stretched his legs out and gave it his all. Grasping onto his short mane, I looked over my shoulder and could see that Sarah was losing ground after a mile or so. The engineer blew the whistle as he sped off towards the east, cutting through the mountain, disappearing into the tunnel. Cowboy slowed to a lope. I hoped no one would drive by as I headed for home. I blushed after that, every time I saw the train. I never did see my clothes again and was never sure who took them.

When I got home from the Diamond T, I fed the two mules and the pony some hay. I had a strange feeling, like I wasn't supposed to be there. I had already said my goodbyes. I saw Reid out in the yard and he looked over at the granary as if he was considering coming over to talk. Dorothy was quiet when she brought out another little package of cookies. I was in double trouble with the neighborhood. They were appalled by the accident with Nina, only three miles out, and upset that I was going on the trip alone with Mavis and Sarah. I crawled back under the quilt and fell asleep for twelve hours. For a moment, when I first woke up, I was afraid.

I couldn't take the pony, not after what had happened. I asked my neighbors, the Neumanns, if they could watch him for me. I walked him down there in the morning, as the first light poured into the valley, letting him go free on the eighty acres of pasture surrounded by deep blue cedars and tamaracks. He kicked up his heels as he ran away from me at a gallop and never looked back.

"See you, Easter Boy," I said to him as I walked away. I did not blame him for what had happened to Nina. As with most accidents involving animals, it was human error, all mine this time. I was filled with a sick sense of remorse about Nina's accident and felt even worse seeing Cowboy limping. I was anxious to leave. Maybe once I got back on the trail things would calm down. Out there where no one knew me.

By ten, I had Sarah packed. The load was lopsided since I decided to take my guitar in the old black cardboard case. I undid her pack twice before I tied the diamond hitch over the load.

"Well Sarah, you've been promoted to pack mule," I said to her, patting her on her muscular white head. She sniffed my hand, looking for treats. Her soft nose felt warm and tickled my hand, which made me smile. It was just the three of us now—Sarah, Mavis and me.

I waved goodbye to Reid and Dorothy who stood between the two big white pines with their arms crossed, their brows furrowed. I turned onto Dry Creek Road. Once again, Bev showed up in the station wagon. I looked at her and she smiled a sad smile. Her face was so expressive and she knew how scared I was.

"Now you better send a card and call from the other side of the mountain, from the first phone you come to. And give me Nina's address real quick, okay? I want to send her a note." Bev was digging around the front seat of the station wagon looking for a pen. I opened my saddlebag and found Nina's address.

Just then, as I was getting back in the saddle, my neighbor Tony showed up with a rifle, a little 22.

"We want you to take this gun so we don't have to worry," he said seriously, looking at me with sincere green eyes. Tony had a soft place in his heart for me even though his girlfriend lived down in Coeur d'Alene.

I didn't know what to say. I took the rifle from him and tied it on the pack. He hugged me with such conviction out there on that dirt road I almost forgot to let go.

"Got to go. Bye you guys."

I turned around one more time and Bev and Tony were still standing there talking on the corner of Dry Creek Road.

Mavis started out again and I could still see our tracks from the day before. I shuddered as I passed the spot where Nina was dragged through the rocks. I kept riding and didn't look back.

I finally reached Delyle Ridge, about seven and a half miles from home.

That first night out in the wilds I camped by the side of the logging road in a little turnout. The mules were picketed to trees and there was very little for them to eat in the pine needle covered floor of the forest. Mavis was more than a little nervous about being tied to a tree all night but she could see, by watching Sarah, that this was all part of a mule's life on the trail. It would take some getting used to. For her, life had always had a corral fence around the edges and an old man bringing her hay and grain. That was it. Her presence helped keep the old cowboy alive, as he remembered his days on Dixie Lee, riding down to Colorado.

The sounds of the deep forest kept their ears and eyes busy while I tried to find a flat place to put my red down sleeping bag. Half the night I tossed and turned, my mind racing with visions of the last few days before we left. I was unfamiliar with the thick silence of the forest. Around dark, the wind literally sang through the heavy stands of white pine and fir as I tried to think good thoughts and quiet my tired, worried mind. Somehow I fell asleep. In my dream, I was dancing with Stan, swirling around in my big cowgirl skirt.

I awoke to the sound of a logging truck rapidly approaching our camp perch on the edge of the road. Jumping up, I slipped my tennis shoes halfway on and stumbled towards Mavis. She looked terrified and listened to the sound of the approaching truck. It sounded big. It took big trucks to carry big trees and Mavis had never seen one up close. I could feel her quivering, eyes glued to the road.

"Easy, baby," I said to her. I calmed her down a little bit, which wasn't easy since I was a nervous wreck. Sarah had already walked to the end of her rope, as far away from the road as she could get. I moved Mavis up the hill and she followed too close with stiff, quick steps. The logging truck came rumbling past. The driver waved out the window to me as he drove slowly by, his truck hissing and quivering as he tried to keep it going fast enough to make the hill. The mules' eyes were wide as saucers.

"Better than a cup of coffee," I said to myself.

In about a half-hour, we were back on the steep dirt road heading south towards Windfall and Devil Peaks and one of the most densely forested areas in the West, where the deep dark trees seemed to go on forever.

We crossed through Buckskin Saddle and headed down Buckskin Creek. The high ridges were rocky and covered with lodgepole pines and the road, ridge after ridge, dropped down into narrow valleys covered with Alpine fir and Engleman spruce. Once in awhile I would ride into a lush meadow and we'd stop and rest along the side of the quiet dirt road. The tamaracks turned gold, as did the cottonwoods along the river, and the yellows and greens mixed together in a beautiful lush landscape. The scenery was so engaging it helped take my mind off the terrible accident and my heartbroken friend who was already back home in Seattle.

It was getting to be late afternoon, and the mules walked at a fast pace, up the ridges and down into the canyons. In the distance, I heard a truck coming towards me on the road. It sounded like a pickup truck. I stopped and jumped off Mavis, pulling her by the reins, leading Sarah with my other hand. My heart was racing. Who would it be? Someone I knew?

A white pickup stopped. Two handsome young men were sitting in the cab, smiling at me. They looked like Forest Service workers or geologists. Both wore flannel shirts and canvas jackets.

"Hi!" I said enthusiastically, "Do you guys know where you are?"

"Yes. Do you?" the driver answered. The other guy laughed.

"No. Not exactly," I admitted.

"You are almost to Big Meadows. You'll cross the Coeur d'Alene River pretty soon. But it will take you a couple of days to get out to the valley," the driver said.

It was a good feeling having someone say aloud where I was and where I was headed. It helped. I hadn't stopped for awhile, so I suggested we have coffee.

The two guys had some beer cans they cut in half with a knife, making coffee cups. They had a good laugh when they saw that I had a travel iron with me.

"An iron? I don't even have an iron at home," the driver said.

After the men left, I jumped back on Mavis and headed for Beaver Creek. The Douglas fir and the Grand fir stood tall and majestic in Big Meadow. It was so quiet and the slightest wind could be heard whispering through the giant trees. I felt as if they were watching us as we passed beneath them on the edge of the lush meadow. There was a big stand of Engleman spruce trees on the edge of the pasture. Wildflowers of all colors graced the floor of the meadow and I was overcome with a feeling of sheer delight at my whereabouts. Clark Fork seemed far behind me even though we had only been gone two days. It seemed like a lot longer than that. I figured that, by looking at the map, I had traveled about seven and a half miles from Delyle Ridge. So I had only gone fifteen, so far.

I camped at Beaver Creek camp next to an old log building that must've once been a nifty shelter. I put my bag down on my saddle blankets and built a little campfire, warming myself up with a cup of coffee and filling the hole in my stomach with the jerky that Crazy had sent with me. Mavis and Sarah were happy to have such luscious pasture and wasted no time, once they were unsaddled, digging into the grass with enthusiasm.

On the third day, I arrived safely at McGee camp after a seventeen-mile day. It was like heaven there in the middle of one of the largest chunks of forest in the world, by the edge of Teepee Creek. The cottonwoods crowded along the edge of the busy creek. Once I crossed Independence Creek, I dropped down into McGee. I camped on the edge of a huge lawn in the pines. The managers, Mr. and Mrs. Walt Charlton, made me welcome. Mrs. Charlton came out and had a cup of coffee with me while her husband worked on the three-acre lawn. I envied them for their warm security and I hated to pack up and leave. But I headed on down the road after oatmeal over the campfire.

Later that day, after I had walked ten miles or so, I came upon a tiny camp trailer and tree trimmers, Jack and Trudy Long. They were working a contract up there on the ridge. They had their eighty-seven year old mother with them. Trudy made me a perfect egg and potato breakfast in her tiny trailer kitchen as the grandma kept the mules company. When I rode away, the tiny grandma said, "Inch by

43

inch, it's a cinch." I repeated that to myself while I rode along. I thought about the geologists. It wasn't so lonely after all.

I rode down from McGee Creek and followed Leiburg Creek. It made a cheerful sound and I enjoyed the long ride on a good dirt road that crossed the creek every ten minutes. We crossed Van Hoosier Creek and I filled up my canteen with sweet tasting mountain water. We crossed over Porcupine Creek, New Creek and then three with very original names, Third, Second and then the larger, First Creek. Idaho folks say "crick." If you mention the word creek, you are often corrected. Before too long I was saying crick, too.

Leiburg Saddle was a high point and the vista from there is one I will never forget. We dropped down the ridge into a narrow valley along the creek, crossing Alvin and then Tie Creek before dropping down to the North Fork of the Coeur d'Alene River, a raucous river with big boulders and a powerful sound echoing off the rocks and the steep pine covered hills.

The road followed the edge of the river all the way to Bumblebee Camp. It had been an easy fifteen-mile day. The old cabin on the edge of the meadow reminded me that settlers and miners had once called that quiet place home.

The road surface was mostly dirt and not too much gravel so it was easy on the mules' feet. Since Mavis was young and still so new to being ridden, every once in awhile I would dismount and give the girl a rest by leading her. Of course, being in the saddle is by far a safer place to be most of the time.

I rode ten miles to Albert's place, an old wooden bar with a big front porch. The owner told me to camp in the trees next to the bar up the road from the old Enaville store. Albert's place had been there for close to a hundred years. It was a friendly place with deer heads on the walls and a big shiny back bar. An old wooden sign looked worn and inviting. The sound of my tired feet on the old wooden porch made me feel so happy. I'd ridden fifty miles. The Clark Fork Valley seemed really far away.

A retired logger at Albert's place told me a little bit about the area. He had logged all his life, all over Idaho. His hat looked like it was as old as the bar. It was covered with tied flies for fishing. They

44

stuck out every direction and made his hat look like some wild animal. His eyes were deep blue and he talked very slowly. I knew he had nowhere else he had to be.

"When the river was high, the loggers would roll the logs down river with a gaff hook. That was the way those old guys got them down to the mills! They even built chutes on the smaller river, loading the smaller logs on them to get them down to the big river. That was a dangerous and daring job, to ride the logs down river, and there was a real art to balancing on the logs in high water!" he said. "Sometimes those old timers would cross the logs at a dead run, leaping from log to log. I have some old pictures I wish I had with me."

"I bet that was a sight to see," I added.

"Pretty soon after the 1900's, they had the cross cut saw to replace the ax as the tool for felling the trees. That was a big improvement, I tell you. And in the early days, horse teams would skid the logs and haul the timber from the woods to the river. The loggers would wait for the snows so they could use sleighs. If there wasn't any snow, then the horses would pull flanged wheel trucks along wooden pole roads." He stopped and took a drink of his tall water glass and continued. "Each spring, these rugged loggers, many from Scandinavia, were part of the huge log drives down the Coeur d'Alene River. The logs were driven all the way into Lake Coeur d'Alene to boats that towed the logs to the mill." He was quiet for a moment, remembering back.

"The men of the driving crew wore spiked shoes and carried peaveys and poles. When not prodding the logs, they traveled in long boats, keeping the logs from going off into the side pools. My father was one of those men. There were millions of board feet of larch, Douglas fir and pine trees that went down that river. Those old guys were tough. Nothing like today. And we're still tough," he laughed.

I followed the CCC road from Albert's Place on the north side of the river to Cataldo and pictured in my mind the loggers on the islands of trees as they floated towards the lake.

It was easy riding and sixteen miles passed before I even realized it. I felt strong and well rested. As I rode along under the

cottonwoods and fir trees, I thought about the cafe I knew I'd find in Cataldo. I'd be starving by the time I got there.

"Which way you headed from here?" an old timer asked, sitting down next to me at the tiny counter in the cafe in Cataldo. Before I could answer, he repeated the question. "Where you headed? California?"

He wore a red felt hat, the kind that is revered by most old Idahoans. His jacket was a wonderful plaid, black and red. He looked up at me from under the red felt. I knew he was a fisherman. I bet he knows the river and the lake like very few people left in the valley, I thought to myself.

"Newport, Oregon," I answered. "About five or six hundred miles from here, the way I'll be going."

"All by your lonesome?" he asked as he raised a shaky coffee cup toward his lips, reaching his lips out to meet the cup.

"Yep. I had a partner but she got hurt the first day out. I need to call her and let her know I made it to Cataldo! She would have loved the trip so far. The Coeur d'Alene forest is a beauty. And so many trees, it just seems like they go on forever."

"They used to," the old timer answered, smiling. "You ought to go over and see the old mission. It's the oldest building in all of Idaho. No kidding," he said, as if he expected me not to believe him. "It was built for Father Ravalli, way back in 1848 by the Coeur d'Alene Indians. It took 'em four years to build the place, over three hundred of them. And you can guess they slaved away for nothin'. The settlers in the valley still took all of the best lands. It's built Indian style, out of straw and mud and wooden pegs. There ain't a nail in the whole thing. It's a real pretty place and they've got it fixed up real nice now. You gotta see it. It's a little bit out of your way, but it's worth it."

"Which way shall I go from here?" I asked him as I bit into the fresh blueberry muffin soaked with butter.

"Where you headed, St. Maries?" he asked.

"Yep, and then over towards Moscow."

"Well, you'd better get started," he said to me. "Ride up Latour Crick. The dirt road follows the crick, right along side of it. You'll pass Higgbe draw, crossing, let's see, there's Larch Crick, Baldy Crick, and then you will arrive at Lost Girl Crick. I suggest you camp at Lost Girl." He was taking another sip of his coffee, shakily reaching the cup to his lips.

"Do I have to?" I said, only halfway kidding. "There's something about camping at Lost Girl Creek I don't like!"

He chuckled. "Well, I'll tell you, back in the eighteen eighties these three gals went up there, all dressed up for an outing in their special outing clothes, and they never came back. Oh, one of the gals wandered in after a month or so but couldn't remember a thing about where the other two went. Later, some said, they found one of their hats in the stream." He stopped and thought a minute. I looked at him, a rosy cheeked flannel plaid logger man.

"As you ride up the road, you can look to the south at some pretty high peaks. Dad and I and my brother used to log up there at the base of Mt. Weissner, and Latour. You know them peaks are sixty-four hundred feet in the air! They are home to some of the biggest trees you have ever thought existed. Old trees that nobody's ever got to!" He took another sip of his coffee. "That is, if you go the way I tell you, you'll be going around the reservation. There are lots of roads down through the reservation you could take, too, but this way, you'll be going up around Rochat Peak which is almost as tall as Latour. The view from up there, well, all I can tell you, it's the top of the world. From up there, by golly, you can see all the way across the Palouse and into Oregon."

"Thanks for the help," I said to him, standing up and reaching out my hand. He grabbed it with his hand which felt like a rock around mine.

I had no plans of stopping at Lost Girl Creek.

Chapter 4

Coffee, Beans and Jerky

I came out of the little coffee shop in Cataldo and stared up at the bright blue summer sky and the huge white clouds that gathered like wool in a basket. I woke up the mules, standing sleeping side by side, tied to a telephone pole. That reminded me. I had to call Nina and Bev. I shuffled around in my red bag for the numbers and Mavis pawed the pavement to show her discontent. There was nothing to eat.

"Nina! I'm calling you from Cataldo, across the Coeur d'Alene. I wish you could have seen the ridge top!"

"Jody. Where are you?" Hearing her voice made me shiver.

"Oh Nina, you wouldn't have believed Big Meadows, it was so beautiful, and McGee Creek, all the ancient trees I saw!" I chattered excitedly. I felt like crying.

"You made it! And how is my Sarah?"

"Sarah's doing great. But I know she would really rather carry you than the pack," I told her. "It's a little cumbersome with the guitar and the rifle."

"Rifle? Don't tell me."

"The boys forced it on me. Everyone thought since I was alone."

"Do you know how to use the gun?"

"That's the problem. I really don't. Sure, one quick lesson before I left."

We were quiet.

"My knee feels better. But my arm is so sore. I wake up sometimes in the night and wonder where you are camping and what the place is like. I picture Mavis in her sheepskin covered gear, and my Sarah under the big orange tarp." She sounded sad.

"You should see where I'm headed next. Up a real steep ridge and down the other side towards Moscow, Idaho. The mountains are not as big as the ones we just crossed, though. I wish you could have seen the view from the top of the highest ridge."

"Keep going," Nina said. "Ride a mile for me. And give Sarah a special hug."

I hung up the phone and dialed Bev. No answer. Probably down at the lake with the kids, I thought to myself. That was her favorite place to be, down on the beach on Lake Pend Oreille. I pictured her there. She was flat on her back, eyes closed, and yet she still knew exactly where the kids were and what they were doing.

I headed out of town and the sound of the cars on the highway faded as I rode into the deep forest to the south. I could see the old Cataldo Mission across the river. I rode up Latour Creek and we started to climb the ridge.

Mavis and Sarah had lots of energy and walked at a fast pace. We rode up to the edge of Kootenai Peak and then passed Rochat Peak. The lodgepoles owned the ridge top, and the dirt road was rocky in places. I rode along quietly, stunned by the beauty all around me.

The view from Rochat Saddle stopped us in our tracks. There was the St. Joe River far, far below us. The road was so high the edge dropped off a thousand feet to the valley floor. Huge cottonwood trees could be seen following the river's edge in both directions. I could see the silver reflection of the rooftops in St. Maries. Far below me, the road down to the valley could be seen winding its way through the forest.

The old timer I met in Cataldo was right. I was on top of Idaho. As far as the eye could see, there was thick forest. The trees were crowded together on mountain after mountain, interrupted occasionally by clear cuts that looked like a hurricane had come through, and then a fire.

From the top of the ridge I could see halfway across Washington, down into Oregon and probably into Montana. The mules seemed to be in awe as well at the vastness of the land around us. I stopped on the top and let the mules graze for awhile in a grassy area next to the road. I pulled out my down jacket. There was a cold wind coming up. I stood up there and counted the ridges and lost count. There were a thousand shades of green and purple.

While the mules grazed, I pulled my blackened coffeepot out of my saddlebag. I made myself a cup of coffee and sat there for over an hour. It felt good to sit on the ground by the small fire. A cup of coffee with dried milk and sugar never tasted so good. I relished every sip.

"I think we'll be in to St. Maries by tomorrow night," I said to the mules. They could have cared less. As long as I still had grain in my bag, they didn't care about town.

We came down the ridge part way, camping in the forest in a meadow clearing. It was the best pasture I had seen since McGee Creek and Mavis and Sarah ate heartily. A big deer came into my camp. He was a buck and I was amazed at how close he came to the mules. They were nervous because they were tied up and the buck was not. That is just the kind of situation mules don't like to find themselves in. Their eyes were wide as they stared at the magnificent beast as he walked slowly through our camp, and I held my breath.

We came around St. Joe Baldy and down Phillips Draw, following a stream that originated at Tingley Spring where I filled up my canteen. The water flowed from beneath a grassy bog, like magic.

Passing an old miner's cabin in a meadow, long deserted, I loaded my saddlebags with apples from an old tree, giving Mavis and Sarah each one. They chewed them slowly as thick apple foam gushed from their lips. I learned to never stand too close when they were eating apples. One nod of their big heads and I'd be covered in apple slobber.

The draw was steep and winding and Mavis and Sarah were really moving. I got off and walked in front of them down towards the valley. At the bottom, right before I hit my first pavement in ninety miles, both mules came to a halt as if to say, "Let's camp here."

51

It was a dry, powdery, dusty road. I barely had the chance to get Sarah's pack off before she fell to her knees to roll in the soft dirt. I was covered with fine dust.

I rode up the river toward St. Maries, dwarfed by the huge cottonwoods that line the St. Joe. I camped down by the river, setting out my saddle blankets at the edge, with the mules picketed nearby. The power of the river moving through town gave this place a good feeling. The St. Joe is a big, beautiful river and it felt so good to camp on its banks.

"I could sure go for a shower tonight," I said aloud. For the mules, a good roll was like a good shower. They were already eating their dinner, which consisted of thick green pasture and some wild oat on the side. I went to sleep that night on my back, staring for hours at a billion stars. I stared at a sky so deep and dark and there were more stars than I had ever seen. Finally, I started to doze off, my eyes could stay open no longer. My down jacket made a fine pillow. I drifted to sleep listening to the sound of the big river. I could hear Mavis and Sarah grazing in the deep pasture near my camp. It was comforting to know they were close by and getting plenty to eat. "In the morning," I said aloud to myself, "I'll walk uptown and have an egg and potato breakfast and coffee from a real cup." I was so happy we had made it to our first town. I curled up in my sleeping bag, wrapped the down jacket around my head and fell asleep.

I awoke at dawn, which was unusual. The mules were staring at me expectantly. I looked up at two bald eagles circling overhead. Their size astounded me; they were so big they looked prehistoric. The day began with the golden light spreading first through the trees overhead and then gracefully it crossed the river and lit up the opposite bank. My stomach growled and I was excited to get up to town and have a nice breakfast at the coffee shop.

The town is just a few streets with, of course, one main one with the bars, the coffee shop and a few stores. This was a town that had seen boom and bust many times over, once brimming with miners and loggers, then quiet. Old timers sat on a bench in front of the bar and watched the world go by, trading stories.

I met one old man as I walked out of the store. He had big black pants on, held up by suspenders, and a ragged old white tee-shirt. His cheerful smile made me love him. His eyes twinkled in the old wrinkled face. I walked with him up the street and to his ancient house right behind Main Street. It had a tiny, rickety porch that was painted light green and had one single light bulb hanging from a cord. He held Sarah by the reins while I took their picture.

"I've logged these hills and worked in the mill for over fifty years," he told me. "As a kid, I mined with my dad. In fact we made out fine! Mining was a good life, but not one that the women liked. Therefore, I never married. Then, the logging life suited me fine. Worked in the snow up on the ridge and took down some mighty big trees. I'm an Idaho man, worked in the woods and worked in the mines. Yep, did 'em both and lived to tell the tale. Now I just walk to the store and try to keep from falling over!" he laughed. He grabbed the railing of his little porch and held on, trying to catch his breath.

There was a group of old timers who hung out in the mornings and then again in the afternoon at Bud's Burger Barn.

"Why you goin' alone? Don't you get scared at night?" one guy in Logger's World suspenders asked me.

"Not yet," I answered. "So far I've had some pretty nice camps. I've met some nice people, too."

"Well, good luck little lady. You take care of yourself."

There was no shortage of directions. All the old guys had a suggestion on which way to get down to Potlatch and Moscow and were still arguing about it as I walked back to camp to pack up.

I took a dirt road that was said to cut off a good ten miles, the way they figured it. Somehow I missed the main road and ended up riding in a big confusing circle on logging roads. It took me awhile to figure out I was lost, and it wasn't a great feeling. The pine trees all started to look the same. I felt great relief when I found a dirt road going off towards what I hoped would be somebody's home.

Then I saw the cabin. It was an old wood place with a screened-in porch full of boots and coats and old overalls hanging on big hooks. I tied the mules up to a post in front and walked slowly up the stairs, knocking on the screen door which banged against the wooden frame and made me jump. I could hear someone shuffling around inside.

"Come in," a voice called from inside. "Come in," he repeated, louder this time.

I opened the door slowly and saw a very old man sitting in an old ragged chair.

"Well, I'll be! A pretty girl! Come right in. It's not every day I get this kind of company!"

He had a long white beard and bushy white eyebrows and blue eyes twinkling out at me from his old face. The eyes of a much younger man that told of a lifetime lived. A plastic tube attached him to an oxygen tank. I looked around at more than twenty of them standing like silver soldiers in the middle of the room.

"No lungs left, honey," he said. "Oh, forgot to tell you. My name's Frank Burger. You see, they've tried to kill me off in the hospital more than once. But I wouldn't die. I'm more stubborn than a mule. I was down sick four days up here last year and no one knew it. Now I cart around this air. Keeps me goin'."

"So you live here all alone? Way up here?" I asked him, smiling.

"Yep. Can't handle town. I'm kind of a hermit, see? One guy gets my groceries and another gets my oxygen filled. And you can see, I have every kind of booze here."

Frank took a minute to stand up, taking care not to step on the oxygen tube. He walked over to the table, which didn't have an inch of uncovered space, and poured us each a brandy in old shot glasses with the decals worn off.

"I don't drink much but my brandy, but I have every kind of booze you can get. Have it for all the folks that show up here lost." He looked at me and smiled.

He drank down his shot and I sipped mine.

"So where did you drive from?" he asked me.

"I rode up here on my mule. I'm riding one and packing one. Heading for the Oregon coast. Started near Clark Fork a couple of weeks ago."

"Well, I swear!" Frank said as he walked in slow, deliberate steps to the window, dragging the tank with his good arm.

"Well, I'll be! Look at those mules! A black one and a pure white one!" I could see Mavis and Sarah were enjoying the thick green grass around the fence posts across the driveway.

Frank was standing there, quiet, looking out the dirty old window with the stained calico curtain. Then he spoke. "Yep, honey, I spent fifty years in the saddle. I've been everywhere except Russia, working some, bumming some. Once I rode from Pilot Rock, Oregon, to Salinas, California, with a buddy. We did it on a dare. He got off his horse there and I rode on to Hermasillo and Mexico City."

"What did you carry?" I asked him.

"Coffee, beans and jerky. We didn't need much. I gave my horse to a Mexican girl and got on a cattle barge to South America. Every time it rocked, it leaked. I was a kid then and I never, I mean never have been as scared since."

He walked away from the window, leaning on his cane and dragging the heavy silver tank behind him. "What kind of mule is the gray? An Arab?"

"Half Arab, half Quarter," I answered. Her name is Mavis. She's pretty young for a trip like this, but she seems to be enjoying it!"

"I've loved my life," he continued with a far away look in his eye. He looked away from me and said, "I couldn't pinpoint one particular time that was the best in my life. I couldn't pinpoint a thing! I have no regrets and I loved every bit of it. My only gripe is that I'm running out of time. They try to put me here or there, in a rest home down in town, but I won't let 'em. I want to live out my life on my own plot of ground, in my own cabin, no matter how humble. I wake up here, make coffee, look out and check the weather, turn on the radio for awhile, maybe read an old book and wait for somebody to show up. Rarely a day goes by without somebody showing up lost, or with my groceries, or with a letter or two from the post office. I always invite a stranger in to my cabin, because that is always the way it was for me on the road."

Frank showed me which way to go towards Alder Creek. I could feel the brandy. It was such a warm cabin, just a messy old place, home to a stubborn old man.

I rode off down the dirt road thinking of a young Frank Burger riding towards Mexico. What a different world it must've been. I hesitated to leave, but then I reminded myself: tomorrow someone would come with Frank's mail. And he was a lucky man living his life out the way he wished, up on a lonely mountaintop off a rocky dirt road. I wondered how anyone ever found the place. I wondered how long he stood at the window after I was gone.

Chapter Five

St. Maries to Moscow

The weather was threatening that afternoon. I rode along and I watched for the sign to Alder Creek.

"Don't want to miss that road, Mavis, or we may end up down in the Clearwater," I said aloud to my mule. Frank had told me that if I missed it I could end up lost on any number of unmarked logging roads, and Alder Creek was the best way to go towards Moscow.

It was getting late when I saw the nice wood cabin on the left side of the road past Happy Creek. Across the road from the cabin was some thick pasture. We'd already traveled a good fifteen miles from St. Maries and were all three more than ready to quit for the day. I stopped and tied up Mavis and Sarah across the wide dirt road from the cabin, walked up to the door and knocked softly. A man rumbled to the door and answered it. He was a big man in an oily cowboy shirt, and he was rubbing his eyes.

I knew right away that I woke him up.

"Sorry to bother you, but I was wondering, could I leave the mules across the road for the night?" I asked, timidly.

"Absolutely not!" he said, laughing, scratching his head for a minute. "You go ahead and bring those mules into our corral. We can feed them some hay and give 'em a chance to move around for a night without their halters on. Oh, excuse me, my name is Sam.

Been working graveyard at the mill. Can't seem to be able to catch up on my sleep. It's not easy to sleep when everyone else is up."

Sam grabbed his coat and slipped on some deerskin slippers and we walked outside. He led me over to the corral.

"Those are my bear dogs," he said proudly. He grabbed some hay from the shed and threw it over the fence to the mules. I hung their halters on the corral gate. Sam and I had a laugh, watching the mules roll in the soft corral dirt. Once they were through rolling, they got to their feet and started to eat.

"Come on in and have some coffee and tell me all about your trip," Sam said. His wife, Edie, made us some coffee and brought out fresh cookies. Their daughter Tia, who was around thirteen, came in and sat with us at the table.

The phone rang.

"My neighbor needs my help with a dog that's been shot. I'm a little like the neighborhood vet up here. Got to go. You make yourself at home," Sam said as he grabbed his hat and headed out the door.

I cooked up the hamburger I had bought in St. Maries. It had been frozen when I first put it in the pack, but it was already warm.

Edie and I looked at the map, trying to figure out how to get all the way to Moscow on dirt roads. She was an energetic woman, not much older than I was. She had dark black hair and eyes to match. Living out in what I considered to be the middle of nowhere looked easy, if you watched Edie. She had the whole place rigged for comfort.

"You know, Jody, it's supposed to rain cats and dogs the next few days. You are more than welcome to camp here until it quits!" Edie said as she poured me another cup of coffee.

"Thanks, but I've got to keep going, even if it rains. I haven't been stuck riding in the rain yet, and I'm not looking forward to it. Everything gets pretty soaked, and after awhile it's impossible to get dried out without a laundromat!" I said to Edie. We stayed up until nine and I finally went out to my sleeping bag on the tarp.

I could see some stars, but it looked like it was clouding up.

In the morning the sky was overcast and the wind had come up. I packed up my saddlebags and packs and tied the mules across the road so they could get their fill of the luscious pasture. Edie had invited me for breakfast and I wasn't about to pass that up. I walked in and there was Sam, sitting at the table, his steaming coffee cup in the middle of the Forest Service map. He and Edie had been discussing the best way for me to go.

I hated to leave because the cabin was warm with a big wood stove. Aside from that, it looked like rain.

I was only an hour or so down the dirt road and it started to pour. I listened as the rain fell on the giant white pines. It was nice at first and the mules didn't seem to mind, until my saddle blanket started getting wet. I could feel the moisture seeping from the saddle blanket into my pants, from the knee down. I pulled my poncho out of my saddlebag and crawled into it while Mavis and Sarah walked on. Mavis didn't mind the sound of the poncho but I think she hated the feel of it, dripping cold rain down her sides. She whipped her ears around when they got too wet, and then she'd stop in the middle of the road and shake all over to get the water off her coat. Sarah would often follow suit.

I looked back to see how the pack looked. Under the orange tarp, everything would stay dry, even most of Sarah's saddle blanket.

"I'll sleep on Sarah's blanket tonight," I said aloud. I listened to the sound of the mules' hooves on the hard dirt road and the sound of the rain pounding through the sweet smelling forest.

I thought about how ridiculous it was that I still was carrying the guitar. I had hardly played it; usually, by the time the mules were set for the night and I had made dinner, I was ready to crawl into my down bag and go to sleep. The cheap cardboard guitar case was disintegrating.

The rain started to come down in big sheets.

The mountain road was steep and slippery. Mavis was hurrying down the mountain, anxious to escape the rain. Sarah was getting tired and was more than ready to have her pack taken off for the night. They grunted and carried on while they walked.

Then Sarah stumbled.

"Easy, girl," I said.

We hit Highway 95. The rain continued to come down hard and

steady. I rode down the highway, along a fence line. I was riding with my eyes closed. There was no longer any part of me that was dry. The mules were slowing down, looking for a place to stop, and Sarah tugged on the rope.

My tennis shoes were swimming. My hat dripped a ring of water onto my shoulders, then trickled down my arms. I was soaked.

"Let's stop," I yelled over the downpour.

I spotted a farmhouse and made a quick turn up the driveway. After tying the mules up under some huge pines, I knocked on the door in the carport.

"Nobody's home," I said sadly. I walked over and sat under the big pines with the mules. It felt good to be out of the rain. I was relieved and heaved a sigh.

"Might as well get this pack off your back, Sarah," I said. "You must be tired of carrying all this stuff for me."

Sarah butted me with her nose to wipe the droplets of rain off her face. The big pines along the driveway were sheltering her and Mave. They seemed as happy as I was to be out of the rain.

After a few minutes, nine cats surrounded us. They came over to say hello and welcome us to their yard. Two Australian Shepherd dogs sat quietly under the eaves of the shed and watched us with interest. I heard a car in the driveway.

When the older couple got out of their car, they looked surprised to find they had unexpected company. The dogs ran up to them, wagging their whole bodies. I must have looked a little strange, like I'd fallen in a lake or something.

"Oh, good grief, you must be frozen," the white-haired woman said to me. Come on in and get warmed up." Her husband Harvey had gone into the house for a towel.

"I'm Ethel. Who are you?" she said, looking at me with worry and pity. I thought to myself, so typical of the Idaho people I knew, to say "Come on in" before "Who are you?"

"I'm Jody, and these are my mules, Mavis and Sarah. I feel so funny, just dropping in on you like this. I guess I just couldn't take another second of that storm," I said, apologetically. My teeth were chattering and it was difficult to speak.

"Don't say another word about it. We were just surprised, that's all. Come in and have some lunch with us!"

I followed her into the house like a puppy. It was warm and cozy, a comfortable ranch house with electric heat. Everything was white and clean. I peeled off my tennis shoes at the back door. My socks were a disgusting color between gray and black, and everywhere I walked I left a trail of muddy water. I could feel my face redden. Ethel followed me with the mop, and I sat down at their table on a towel Harvey had placed on the chair.

"Not much of a lunch, just simple food," Ethel said to me, smiling.

She brought out the ham, then the potatoes, then the pasta salad. A little green salad, some Jell-O squares and some cookies.

"You know, we've been married for fifty-four years," Ethel said proudly. "You don't see that much anymore." I knew what she meant. My relationships seemed to last about fifty-four days.

"Have you lived here long?" I asked.

"Pretty much our whole lives. Never strayed too far from this county," Harvey said proudly.

Sometime between lunch and dessert the wind came up and the storm moved on. Sun poured through the mist and made a huge rainbow on the lawn. Logging trucks on the highway looked as if they were driving under the rainbow. Harvey and Ethel were as amazed as I was. They told me, in all those years, they had never tired of the scenery.

I took some carrots out to Mavis and Sarah. They were starting to dry out a little. When Sarah moved towards me to get the carrot, I noticed she was limping. I looked down and could see that her right ankle was noticeably swollen.

"Oh no, Sarah girl, you can't be lame," I said to her. I could feel a lump in my throat. Tears poured down my face. She nudged me with her nose, softly.

"It must've happened when you tripped. Poor Sarah, girl."

I went back in the house with Ethel to call the vet in Potlatch. Harvey called a friend who had a horse trailer to haul me down to town so I didn't make Sarah's ankle any worse. I felt sick, not knowing if this was the end of our trip, if it would end in a rainstorm off Highway 95, halfway between St. Maries and Moscow. I anxiously waited for the truck and horse trailer to arrive.

"Thank you, Harvey and Ethel," I said to them as I jumped into the pickup truck. Their friend was an elderly man with a kind face and a shy manner and we spoke only a few words on the way to Potlatch. Mavis and Sarah had not hesitated; they had hopped right in the trailer.

Sarah Metcalf, the veterinarian, was a tall, thin girl about my age. She took a look at Sarah's ankle. She watched her trot with a slight limp.

"You know, it's a sprain, but it's a real slight one. I sure would like to see you be able to continue on," she said as she rubbed Sarah on the shoulder.

"I bet the mule doesn't want to quit either," she continued. "Let's just give her a few days. You can use the corral behind my office, and there's a good place to camp right there next to the corral. Feel free to come on in and use my hot water in the house. Just keep soaking her foot and ankle in Epsom salts. I'll be gone most of the time, but just go ahead and let's try to make the mule better that way!"

I took her word for it and filled up the bucket. Sarah stuck her foot willingly into the warm water and sighed.

"You take it easy and get better, Sarah," I said to my mule. "We've got a long road to Newport." I wasn't sure what would happen, if I would be able to go on or not.

Sarah and Mavis enjoyed the good hay that I bought from the vet. I made myself comfortable out next to the corral. This was the first time I really played the guitar. No one was around except for the two mules and I played for two days, every song I knew and some I didn't know.

Sarah willingly kept her foot in the warm salt water for the better part of two days. I watched her move around the corral on the third morning and she didn't seem to be limping. The vet took a look at Sarah's ankle.

"Well, Jody, I think you did it. Must've been all that guitar playing," she joked. "I'd say you can start heading for Moscow. Just keep a close eye on her. Rest a lot and don't overdo it. Don't do more

64

than three miles today, if you can help it. I can't feel any heat in it and she seems to trot evenly. I wish I could take off and go with you!"

I waved goodbye. She sent us on our way with a box of Epsom salts and her best wishes for a safe trip.

"From the Y, take Flanigan Crick on up and over Moscow Mountain. You'll drop right down into Moscow," the waitress said as she refilled my coffee cup and looked out at the mules tied up in front of the tiny coffee shop. "Sure is a slow way to travel, but it must be fun."

I watched Sarah's walk, with great concern, all the way to Moscow. Following the doctor's orders, I barely made it out of Potlach before camping under some huge pines.

I cooked up some soup, then heated up some water in my coffeepot so I could soak Sarah's foot in the water bucket. I hadn't noticed her favoring it, but I still wanted to make sure the injury had healed. Feeling around for heat, I was relieved to find it was the same temperature as her other ankles.

I slept under the big trees with my tarp pulled over my sleeping bag. The two mules were picketed to a fence and the pasture was rich and delicious. They were glad to be back on the road again, and out of the tiny corral in Potlatch.

I followed Flanigan Creek across Moscow Mountain. The land was changing. I stood at the edge of the forest that covers most of Idaho, and could see, on the horizon, the yellow wheat fields to the west.

Before too long I came to a house with a beautiful little orchard, chickens, goats, dogs, cats and kids. I had reached the outskirts of Moscow. I rode down this road towards the town as the blackest thunderheads filled the sky. They were moving rapidly toward us.

All of a sudden the sky opened up and it poured rain. I looked back at Sarah as she dropped her ears down to keep the rain from getting in them. Mavis hurried toward town, the sound of the rain on the road making her a little jumpy. I reached down and grabbed my poncho out of the saddlebag, and pulled it on. Mavis took a few steps at a trot.

"Easy, Mavis, easy girl," I said in a low tone. Thunder cracked. Boom! I waited. Then, right in front of us, only twenty feet away,

bolts of lightning hit the electric line.

It made a sound something like the sky was falling, and Mavis was sure it was. She laid her ears down flat and took off running down the road.

"Whoa, Mavis!" I yelled at the top of my lungs. I was about to jump out of my skin. It was raining so hard I couldn't hear myself think. All I could see was the lightning bolt that luckily had hit the wire and not the long ears below it.

I was anxious to get inside but, instead, settled Mavis down and sat with the mules under a big white pine by the side of the road. All three of us were miserable and shivering. Then all of a sudden, the rain stopped.

The thunderstorm left us drenched. The mules shook off as much of the water as they could and we walked on towards Moscow, trying to regain our composure.

My friends Mike and Dede, from Clark Fork, had given me the telephone number of friends of theirs who lived in Moscow.

"I'll call Beth and let her know you may be riding through Moscow," Mike had told me before I left home. "I'm sure they wouldn't care if you stopped in for a night or two."

The phone number was soggy because it had been in my pocket since I left home. I strained to read the numbers and guessed at the last two. My guess was right. A cheerful voice answered the phone.

"This is Beth. Who's this?"

"This is Jody, with the mules. I almost got struck by lightning just a few moments ago," I blubbered. My voice was trembling, and it was good to share the news about my close call, even with a stranger. I looked out of the glass phone booth. The clouds were backed with the golden light of the afternoon sun and the whole sky lit up.

"Come on over and get dried out," Beth said without hesitation. "Mike said you might be coming through. There's plenty of room for the mules to graze in our back yard and out in the alley. They can do some weeding for me. How many are there?" she asked.

"Only two. I'll be right over, but how do I find you guys?" I asked.

Before long I was sitting by the wood stove in the tiny library with Beth. She was a round girl with black hair, dark eyes and a dry humor. Her husband, Jim, was tall and wore glasses and had a beard. Beth brought me a cup of tea with milk and sugar in it and put a box of cookies in front of me. I dug in, eating about four cookies with my tea. I didn't hesitate to stay a second night when they asked me to.

It was so nice to be inside next to the wood stove, looking out as the rain poured down continuously for hours. I watched out the window as the mules both lay down on the soft lawn once they had eaten their fill.

Beth, Jim and I fed the mules carrots and celery and carried water to them. I think they were beginning to wonder if I was going to stay for good by the second evening when another storm came through. I knew if I stayed a third night in Moscow, Beth and Jim might start to think I was moving in. The mules had done all the weeding and cleaning up around the yard that Beth could possibly want. In fact, Mavis started to chew on some fence posts that were stacked in the alley. I knew if I stayed another night, I would have over stayed my welcome.

"I guess I'd better get back on the road, Beth," I said to her after breakfast on the third morning. The sun was shining brightly and the town looked clean and fresh. "I think I'll make a visit down to the Rest Home and see if I can find an old timer to tell me a story or two."

Beth gave me directions to the Latah Care Center.

I parked the mules out on the side of the building where they busied themselves with grazing down the long grass that was in need of a trim, filled up the water bucket and gave them each a long drink.

I walked down the hall to the front desk and asked a heavy-set nurse with a big smile if I could visit with an old timer.

"How about Eddie Byseger! He'd love to have a visitor!" she suggested. "You'll find him looking out the window, Room 13."

I thanked her and walked down the hall to Eddie's room. There were people in wheelchairs and beds and some walked slowly down the hall. I couldn't help but think how they were all young once.

The place was small and only about twenty people lived there. I stopped and looked into Room 13. There sat a man in a plaid flannel shirt looking out the window.

"Mr. Byseger? May I come in?"

He turned slowly around and his face lit up when he saw me.

"Please do! No one mentioned a pretty girl was coming by today," he said in the soft voice of an old man.

I laughed. "Well, I actually rode my mules all the way down here from Clark Fork. I wonder if I could stay around and talk with you for a little while? My mules are tied to the trees over there. Can you see them?"

He slowly lifted himself out of his chair and took measured steps toward the window, leaning over to see out.

"Well, I say! There are two mules in our yard! It's been a long time since I've seen such pretty mules. One black and one white! Look at the white one! What a pretty little thing. I can see you have a packsaddle on her. Is it a sawbuck or a decker? Boxes or bags?" he asked.

"Bags. My sister made them for a big long trip we took back in '76," I told Eddie. "Sarah's saddle is a sawbuck, but I hear the deckers are better. Someday I'll have one," I said excitedly. "I took off the pack bags and wrapped them up in the tarp. Thought I'd give her a break since she was lame only five days ago. The vet up in Potlatch fixed her up for me."

"Where you headed?" Eddie asked.

"From here, I'm going out towards Lower Granite Dam. Then I'll be heading across Oregon to the coast."

"That is a long ride. Do you plan on a couple of months so you can take your time?" he asked.

"I hope to get there by Halloween. It's a long way and everyone keeps telling me that October in the coastal range can get pretty wet," I said pensively. I shuddered at the thought. I had had my fill of rain already.

Eddie patted my hand and invited me to sit by him. He moved another chair next to his, by the window.

"Seeing your mules reminds me of that old fellow who used to ride around the countryside. He used to ride by and we would see him when we'd be fishing, out by our old place. He'd be out on one of his tours. The old gentleman died last winter. I just learned that.

Chet Henning was his name."

"And he rode for years," I added. "I think he was eighty-eight on his last ride."

"Oh, so you knew him."

"No, just heard of him. He's pretty well known around the Spokane area," I said.

"He used to have a white mule too, just like you," Eddie said with a smile.

"Could you tell me a little bit about your life in Idaho, Eddie?" I asked.

"Sure, I can. But I hate to admit it, a lot of it's left me," he said, sounding a little surprised.

"Well, a lot's happened," I responded. "It's hard to remember everything."

"I'm ashamed to admit that," he said, "but I can tell you where I was born. On the old homestead place that my parents homesteaded in eighteen eighty-nine, on the East Fork of Deep Crick, north of Potlatch."

"I just spent four days up at Potlatch."

"You did? Well you are probably pretty well acquainted with a lot of it, then. Our place was on East Deep Crick," he said again.

"Well, I came over from Potlatch, up Flanigan Creek and over Moscow Mountain."

"Oh, yeah, I've never been over that road, but I know what you're talking about. There are several cricks up there. The whole country is full of cricks and they all feed into the Palouse River, you know."

"So you grew up farming?" I asked him.

"Yes, I grew up, well, see in this picture? There's a picture of the valley, there, and the first house, atop the orchard trees, is the house where I was born."

"How many other kids did you have in your family?" I asked.

"There were five girls and five boys. Ten altogether," he said, shaking his head.

"And where did you sit in the family? Were you in the middle, or. . ."

Eddie smiled. "I was at the tail end. I was the baby of the family."

"Me too," I said, smiling. "Did you like being the youngest?"

"No, because they always called me the baby and I didn't like that." Eddie looked out at the mules again.

"Did you ever work with mules?" I asked.

"I never did use mules." He thought for a second or two. "I don't have anything against mules, but I always worked with horses."

"What kind of horses did you have?" I asked him.

"Well, I would say that the best horses I had were a cross breed with the Clydesdales and the Percherons. And we also had Shires. They were good."

"So when you grew up, how old were you when you left home, or did you stay on the same farm?" I asked.

"I didn't leave home," Eddie answered without hesitation. "I stayed on the same place all my life. My youngest sister and I stayed at home and took care of my parents until their death. And I didn't marry until after that. And I can say, well, once in awhile I would work out in the little sawmills but people would say, 'Oh, I bet you worked out at the big Potlatch sawmill.' And I would say, no I never did. I never did work there. Never worked there a day in my life. You might say I was self-employed all my life."

"Doing different things, doing whatever you could to. . .," my voice drifted off.

"Yes, I would work harvesting. My dad would let me take a team of horses and go out and haul bundles, threshing you see, if you know what I mean."

"Bundle? What's a bundle?" I asked.

"Shocks. Shocks of wheat," he explained. "I hauled bundles."

"Did you hunt and fish a lot in your life?"

He laughed. "As much as I could. I used to say I'd work like a good boy all summer so I could go hunting in the fall."

"Did you take mules with you?"

"Oh, as I said before, I never had much to do with mules. But I'll tell you a little story about this mule that a friend of mine leased one trip. He rented a horse and a little mule. Now this little mule, it fell to me to ride him out up the trail and my friend was riding the horse. Now this little mule had the pack saddle on him and as we were going along, he saw a leaning tree, what they call a widow maker, hanging out over the trail. This little mule darted out and ran under that low tree, trying to pull me off! He had the pack saddle on so I was able to hold him back. But that little mule, he knew what he was doing!"

"They usually know what they're doing," I said. "I learn more from them than they learn from me."

"Yeah, you've heard the question, 'After a mule kicks a guy, was it an accident?' And the other guy answers, 'No, it was no accident. That mule kicked me on purpose.' Have you heard that one?" he laughed.

Eddie pulled out his photo album. He and his second wife had traveled over to London several years before.

"Don't you feel lucky you got to fly over there?" I asked.

"Very lucky," he answered. "I never expected that that would happen to me, but it happened. And I'll tell you how it did. You see, my second wife had traveled a lot and she said to me, 'Eddie, how would you like to go to Hawaya?' I said, no, I don't really care about going to Hawaya. So she asked me, 'Well if you could go anywhere in the world, where would it be?' I stopped and thought about it, and told her I would probably go to my father's country—to Switzerland. So, then, she didn't say any more about it, but she went to see her travel agent in Spokane and they laid out the whole thing, from start to finish. And she presented it to me and she and I went on a trip."

"How wonderful!"

"And I was glad that we knew just how many days we were going to be gone and, you might say, made the count down of when we were going to get back on the plane to come home again."

"It's a good feeling to get home again," I said with a little laugh.

"Oh, you bet!" Eddie said.

"This Latah Care center seems like a good place," I said, after looking through his pictures.

"Oh it is. It's too bad that we have to have these places. But it's human nature. We get old. You hear a lot these days about oh, you don't need to get old, you make yourself what you are, you know." Eddie smiled.

"But it's a fact. There's no getting around it!" I added.

"Well, you've heard that too, that if you don't want to get old, why, keep yourself young!" Eddie said.

"I just turned thirty," I told him.

"Why, sure," he said. "I never dreamed, or I should say, thought, as I was growing up, I would ever live life as an old person, although I lived with my parents and saw them live to their last breath. It comes. You can't help it. And I've seen that here, too. I've had several different roommates here and they are on their last journey. It's sad."

"That's why it's important to live each day to the fullest if you can," I said.

"That's right," Eddie said quietly.

"What's your helmet for?" I asked.

"That is why I am here," Eddie told me. "Something happened to me. I knew I was failing. Not in health, but in strength. I would fall. I could be walking along in the house or outdoors, mowing the lawn, say, and it was like a light switch was turned off and I would just keel over backwards. Always go over backwards. No warning whatsoever."

"So you wear your helmet," I added.

"I'm supposed to."

"I bet you feel kind of silly wearing it."

"Sometimes. Little kids look at me like there's something funny."

"Where's your motorcycle, Ed?" I laughed.

"You know, there's those cute Candy Striper girls in the nursing homes and I asked one of them, where do you tell your mother you're going when you come to see me?" Eddie laughed. "And she said, 'I'm going to see Ed with the hole in his head!' You see I fell and had surgery and they removed a blood clot from my head. So that's the hole in my head!"

"Boy, I bet that wasn't too fun," I said.

"No, it wasn't fun a bit." Ed said. "What happened to me, I was living alone. I've had three wives and they are all buried side by side in the cemetery. But this day I was batching, living alone. And walking bothered me, and going up and down stairs. I knew it did, but I was still getting along all right. I would leave my car near the house and I'd drive down to the mailbox to get the mail. But this day, I don't

73

remember much, but I found myself on the ground. The first thing I remembered was seeing my glasses lying on the ground beside me and then I knew. I had fallen, you see, not knowing when I fell or anything about it. But I was right there on US 95. Lots of traffic. And I thought, if I could get back in the car, as much traffic as there was, I could wave somebody down and honk my horn. Well, I did that. I got back in the car and did that! But people would wave back and keep on going! Well, then I thought that's not going to work!" Eddie stopped for a moment to catch his breath, shaking his head.

"Well, I made it back up to the house, and I called my nephew and his wife to tell them I needed help. I dialed that telephone number and the lady answered, and they came down and found me with a big knot on the back of my head. They took me right into the hospital in Potlatch. They saw me there and said you'd better go to Spokane. They did lots of tests and to this day they don't know what caused me to fall. That's how I ended up here. Otherwise, I would still be driving to the mailbox everyday at one in the afternoon. I'm afraid those days are over."

We sat quietly for a moment. Eddie pulled out a book from underneath the photo album of his European trip. "I have some verses I wrote. This first one is a tribute to the nurses:

A pretty little nurse, all dressed in white, she has to work all through the night. And then in the morning, when the sky is blue, she will say, here I am, may I help you?"'

Chapter Six

Runaway Mule

I needed a new salt lick. The five-pound salt lick was easy to carry in the pack, but the mules quickly destroyed it in a few days. On the way out of Moscow I stopped at the feed store and picked up a new one. "If you want to, you can let the mules have a little bit of that grain over there," a young blond man on the loading dock told me. "They dropped a pile off the truck when we unloaded."

"Thank you," I said to him. "They will sure love that." Mavis and Sarah opened their mouths wide, picking up as much as they could in each bite. We stayed there about fifteen minutes before we headed out of town for Pullman. I was becoming accustomed to small miracles. The Palouse stretched out in its yellow grandeur and I could see wheat fields forever.

Once I got back on the road toward Pullman, I felt relieved. I was back on the trail again. A little bit too much coffee shop food and a little bit too much warmth in the storm had taken me away from the ride. In town I felt relieved that it was still raining, giving me a valid excuse to remain under the roof of people I hardly knew. Once the rain quit and I was riding on the side of a wide dirt road headed west, I started to feel happy to be out there again. The late summer sun warmed my skin and comforted me as the land became quieter with every step we took. I felt stiff in the saddle, a little fatter and a little bit lazy.

On the way into Pullman a reporter, Peter Harriman, who saw me as a story for the Moscow Pullman Daily News, flagged me down. Chris Pietsch, the photographer, got a picture of Mavis, Sarah and me as we headed down the road. In the picture I smiled, with my reins held too high, in my warm wool sweater from South America. Sarah's pack looked so even under the tarp. Young Mavis walked proudly with a light step.

I camped out on Airport Road at the Hilltop stables. The mules had a soft dirt paddock all to themselves on the edge of an ocean of wheat fields that sang me to sleep. I found that the music of the fields and the trees always made me feel safe. And so did the Big Dipper. I would look up at it and know I had nothing to fear.

The rolling wheat fields were easy riding. Most were harvested or burned already and the mules found easy footing. Up and down the hills I rode without stopping for three or four miles. I found one lone tree along the road. I stopped under it and tied up the mules so they could eat the grass in the shade. It felt good to get out of the saddle and down onto the ground again.

My stomach growled and I reached into my saddlebag and pulled out an apple that was a gift from a lady way up Paradise Creek, east of Moscow. Slowly chewing the delicious, sweet fruit, I looked out across the hilly wheat lands. I could see forever in every direction. When it was time to stop for the night, I found a Quonset hut at the edge of the road, a place for cattle to get out of the storm. I was so pleased with my luxurious accommodations. I built a small fire and played my guitar to the yellow moon and then curled up in my down bag, resting comfortably on the saddle blankets. No one ever came by on the road and the silence of that place was haunting. I couldn't help but wonder if the rancher might come by, but he never did.

The hut was so nice I bet the cows really liked it on a stormy winter night. My voice, when I was singing, echoed off the galvanized metal walls and filled the whole hut with song. It was almost too beautiful to be alone that night and I found myself longing for a sweetheart to curl up with.

In the morning I packed up early, after two cups of coffee and an apple. I climbed back on Mavis, grabbed Sarah's thick cotton lead rope and headed back down the edge of the wheat field. No trucks or cars came by for at least two hours and the road was incredibly quiet. The sun came out from behind a cloud and threw light beams down on the field ahead of us. And still the rancher who owned the Quonset hut never came by.

It had been awhile since I left Clark Fork and I was just starting to feel at home on this wild and unknown road I was on. Once the sun came out, I took off my sweater and rode along in my sleeveless tee-shirt. The warmth of the sun heated up the ground as we left our prints in a straight line up one field and down the next.

I heard a truck on the road and looked over to see an old Dodge pickup.

"Headed towards the Snake?" the driver yelled from the window. He looked to be about forty or so. He had a round clean-shaven face and a very friendly voice, a stocky man in a bowling shirt. I could tell he was asking me anything, just to start a conversation.

"Yep. Down to the Lower Granite Dam. Everyone tells me that's the place to cross," I answered. There were only a few places to cross the Snake River. Mavis was anxious to keep going. I patted her softly on the neck so she would stand still. She spotted a little patch of wheat that had not been harvested and she and Sarah started devouring it.

"Well, the grade down to the river is steep and dangerous," he continued. I sure don't think I'd want to ride down that part of the road. I can send you another way."

"Okay."

"My name's Charlie. Got a little place up here I call Hole in the Wall. It's not too far up the road here. How about if you follow me up there and I can show you a better way to get to the river."

"Sounds good," I answered.

I followed Charlie over the next hump of the road. We climbed a steep grade. He was driving the pickup as slow as possible to keep from getting too far ahead, watching us in his rear view mirror.

The view from the top of that rise was one I will never forget. To the east, the Moscow Range looked far behind us. Behind them, the higher mountains could be seen, each ridge another color of gray and shade of purple. In front of the mountains, across Garfield County to the north, I could see nothing but wheat land with a grove of trees marking the towns of Colfax and Dusty. South, off in the distance, I could see Oregon Butte and Diamond Peak. To the west, the Snake River cut its way through the deep, brown canyons.

"What a perfect old pickup truck," I thought to myself. It hummed along at a slow speed like he had just tuned it that day. Charlie seemed like a nice enough guy to follow home.

He drove slowly up the road, obviously trying to go a speed the mules could keep up with. I looked around me. There was a small draw across the wheat field and then nothing as far as the eye could see but wheat. I followed Charlie off the road and up a small, dirt driveway full of potholes. In the middle of a grove of trees, sat Charlie's cabin, his Hole in the Wall. Most anyone on the road would never notice the little driveway or the grove of trees.

"What a place to live," I found myself thinking, "out in the middle of all this wheat."

Charlie showed me where to tie up Mavis and Sarah. I took off Mavis' bridle and tied them both with their long picket lines so they could eat the grass that grew in the big shady yard.

I quickly untied the diamond hitch and the orange tarp slid off Sarah's back. I removed her packs. They were feeling lighter and I was getting stronger. I took Sarah's saddle off, too, and the blanket which was soaked with sweat. I leaned it up against one of the big trees so it could air out and then propped the packsaddle up against the tree. Sarah immediately located a small sandy area within her rope's reach and she rolled all the way over, which each time added a hundred dollars to the worth of the mule, legend has it.

"Sarah must be worth a million bucks by now," I said to Charlie. I was flirting.

He laughed. "Come on in and have some lemonade."

"Sounds good," I said. Getting my walking legs back, I headed for the wooden door leading into the old house.

The house looked ancient. The narrow brick chimney had been repaired with patches of cement. Cedar shakes, which covered the house, were painted white and it was roofed with asbestos shingles. There were two big windows on each side of the door. It wasn't a big place, just a modest house that looked like it had been hiding under the shade trees for a century, its own island of shade in a sea of wheat.

"It was built in 1850," Charlie said proudly. "By a fellow named Cofman who was wounded in the Civil War. Later on, after he raised his family here, he sold out to the Hickmans."

He got two glasses out of the old china cabinet and filled them with ice and lemonade. It looked so cool and delicious. I drank mine slowly, relishing each sip of the tangy, sweet drink, and sighed.

"That must taste pretty good to you, after riding all morning," he said, filling my glass to the brim with more lemonade. He was so handsome in that bowling shirt with "Charlie" scrawled over the pocket in shiny purple thread.

"It sure does, Charlie," I answered. "You'll never know. Thanks!"

We talked for a little while. Charlie was a professional bowler from Tumwater who disappeared out to Hole in the Wall whenever he had the chance.

"Let's go outside and I'll show you around," he said.

I carried my lemonade glass with me as we walked out into the shady yard. Mavis and Sarah had fallen asleep, side by side. Mavis jumped a little when the screen door slammed behind us. I followed Charlie.

"Two of the Hickman women were accidentally killed, right here in the yard," Charlie said. "Mr. Hickman ran over his wife with the combine."

A chill went up my back and I wasn't sure if it was too much of the cold drink or the image of the woman, lying there, in the yard. He led me to the exact spot. We stood there for a minute. There was nothing good to say and it was quiet for an uncomfortable period of time.

He took me out back to see the root cellar, a damp, cool place down some steep stairs and through a heavy wooden door. He showed me every tree, the black walnuts, the golden delicious apples and the sugar maples that had graced the yard of this hidden homestead for a century. We walked out across the dry grass in the back to the old barn that was faded from the sun, built of big planks, with an old shake roof that looked like the thin wing of a seagull it was so bleached out in the sun. The '53 Dodge pickup had a special place in the yard marked by an oily spot in the dirt.

"I can send you down to the river on an old stage road," Charlie suggested. "Otherwise, you'll have to go right along the highway."

"Will I be able to take it without getting lost?" I asked, while putting on Mave's bridle.

"Should be able to make it. You'll have to hold onto your hat the first little bit, though, and be sure to wear long sleeves so you don't get too scratched up," he added.

He showed me how to find the old road, directly below his place towards the river. The folds of the land were filled with brush and scrub and, from what I could see, the old stage road ran right down the middle of one of those canyons. I searched the bushes next to the apple tree just as Charlie had told me to do and sure enough, I could see what looked like an old road beyond the brushy opening.

I held onto my hat and started to ride Mavis through the bushes. They were too thick and in a minute I realized I would have to walk. I tied Sarah's rope back onto the diamond hitch so she could walk on her own, put my head down and started charging through the underbrush. The mules put their heads down, closed their eyes and pushed. There was only one way to go and that was down the hill through the thick brush. There was no turning around. We had to keep going.

Mavis and Sarah were staying close behind me. They were thinking only of getting out of that thick brush that rubbed against their faces and necks and legs. A thorny branch reached out and grabbed my shirt ripping a big hole in the sleeve. Blood soaked through the pink fabric and I stopped it with the shirtsleeve and kept moving.

There was really no point in stopping in that steep, narrow gulch that I hoped would eventually drop me down to the road above the dam. I closed my eyes and kept going. The mules were nervous and were ready to run. It took everything I had to stay in front of them. Sarah's diamond hitch caught on a tree branch that Mavis and I had barely cleared. She stopped and looked at me. I didn't want to cut the rope and wasn't sure my dull little knife would cut it if I wanted to. The branch was not easily broken. After pulling it back and forth for several minutes, finally, it snapped off and we continued. The tarp was ripped and the new sound of the flapping ends made Mavis more than a little jumpy. Her beautiful dark eyes looked at me with question. Wasn't there a better way?

"Why did I listen to Charlie?" I asked myself angrily. I should have just stayed on the highway and gone down to the Snake that way, though I would've risked death by motorhome.

The old road hadn't been used for years, I told myself. It might have been a road at one time, but not anymore. And still, even though I found myself heading down a steep grade through a narrow channel of berry bushes, I felt honored to be the first pack train through there in quite a while. Most folks would have followed the highway. The blood dried on the sleeve of my last good shirt.

It must have been two miles of that, tumbling down the hill on the old stage road. I passed an old apple tree, lost from the past, and stopped only long enough to fill my red saddlebag with apples for later. I gave Mavis and Sarah each one. The apple tree was a comfort to me, reminding me that long ago this was probably a well used road. But was it as steep back then? Years of erosion and cascading water from storms had chiseled the center of the road into a big ditch. I kept my eyes on that crevice to keep from falling in.

Finally, the thick brush started to thin out and the enclosed tunnel opened up a little. Sagebrush started to replace the brambles, although the road was still washed out and rocky.

The mules both stopped at once, turning their frozen attention to a large coyote. We looked down the ravine and we saw three does. The coyote was the color of the light rocks dotting the hillsides. Until he looked our way, he was practically invisible.

The magnificent animal stared at us. The mules were frozen in their tracks and didn't make a sound. The coyote turned and ran effortlessly down the ravine after the three deer. I could see the deer jumping high over any obstacle in their path. Only an occasional sound could be heard of a hoof or paw hitting the ground, but for the most part it was silent.

It took a minute to convince Mave to keep going. The coyote had upset her and she wanted Sarah to lead. I put Mave's reins over the saddle horn and led Sarah for awhile, letting Mavis follow behind. I walked all the way down until we literally popped out on a big, black, newly paved road.

It was almost six o'clock and, to say the least, we were all tired of traveling. The trip through the bushes took a lot out of all three of us but it was most worrisome for Mavis. We walked hurriedly down the side of the new pavement towards the dam.

"Thank you, Charlie," I said aloud. The brown and gray hills were steep and dry. The Snake River was a ribbon of deep blue in the ravine. It made me thirsty. I emptied my canteen, drinking it all the way to the bottom. That was the last of the delicious spring water Charlie had given me.

The mules and I were surprised when we came upon two cowboys trying to catch a little black mule. They had one mule caught, a dead-ringer to the one that was racing around kicking up dust, avoiding the two cowboys with mule-like dexterity.

"Now where the heck did you come from?" the one large cowboy asked me.

"Out of the bushes, literally," I laughed.

"I guess so because we sure didn't see you coming. Name's Doc Holliday. What do ya think of these two little black mules? Bought 'em yesterday at the Colfax fair! I have some Shetland ponies that pull and drive, but the little buggers don't like to get caught. And now it looks like I got more of the same."

He removed his white straw cowboy hat and scratched his balding head with his thick, rugged fingers, watching the little black mule trot to the far corner of the barbed wire paddock. He had a black case for glasses in the bulging pocket of his blue and white checked cowboy shirt. The shirt's pearly white snaps struggled to hold back the big belly that hung over his black work jeans. His

cowboy boots were old and he wasn't the kind of man who could run after and catch a small, agile mule with a mind of its own.

When the little mule saw Mavis and Sarah, he trotted over and stood next to them. I grabbed his neck and slipped a halter on him. Doc had handed it to me, looking hopeful.

Once the little mule was caught, he stood there in a trance, a look of total resolve on his face. Then all of a sudden he reared up and took off again. I didn't hold on. After what had happened with Nina, I knew better.

Finally, the younger, thinner cowboy managed to coax the little black mule with a bag of pretzels. He snapped the cotton lead rope onto the halter and held on. The stocky little mule ran off as fast as he could and the skinny cowboy held on this time. Doc Holliday and I stood there and watched his shoulders tighten when he reached the very end of the rope. Just then, the little mule stopped and turned around, heading for the trailer and his identical counterpart. The only problem was Doc Holliday who had walked into the trailer in front of the little mule and tied him up. He climbed halfway out of the escape door and got stuck.

"This is one heck of a spot for a big fella to be!" he said as he struggled to get his whole self back outside and on the ground again. His hat fell to the ground and so did the glasses case from his pocket. His face was red as a beet and his toothpick dropped out of his mouth. But he still kept his composure. The skinny man looked at me sideways and shook his head. We didn't know whether to push or pull.

Finally, Doc was out of the trailer and back on the ground, panting for air. He pulled up his big work pants, adjusted his thick black suspenders and pulled a beer out of a cooler in the back of the pickup. He offered me one, threw another to the skinny cowboy and we toasted to the new mules. He told me about his miniature wagon and harness he used with the ponies and named all the parades and fairs they had been in. Finally, we said goodbye and I continued on towards Lower Granite Dam, walking at a fast pace towards the Snake River.

I dreaded the dam crossing and looked down on it with doubt. Then we saw it. The Corps of Army Engineers had built a beautiful park with a green, mowed lawn. It must have been the only green grass for miles around. The mules spotted the perfectly groomed park and picked up the pace after shaking off little bits and pieces of the old stage road that were left hanging across the saddles and the pack.

We walked down the steep road into Boyer Park. The sprinklers were on and the newly cut lawn looked so tempting to the mules who had seen the grass get drier and drier since we left the mountains. I noticed some uncut grass on the side of the park and tied the mules over there so they could eat. They were both hungry after the long descent through the bushes. I didn't unpack Sarah. I lay down on my back and took a little nap next to the them, with my head on my saddlebag. Falling asleep for an hour or so, I listened to the sound of the sprinklers. Mavis and Sarah finished their meal and stood quietly with their eyes closed and their heads down.

"O.K., you guys, it's time to cross the dam," I said, a little loudly. I'm sure they both could tell I was nervous by the strain in my voice. A Corps of Engineer worker drove by in his pickup and waved. I jumped back in the saddle and headed up to the dam.

"This isn't going to go away," I said under my breath. I had no idea how the mules would react to the metal grates beneath us. After all, they'd never cross a cattle guard. It was one hundred feet down to the river.

"Here we go," I said to Mavis once we got up to the bridge over the dam. There were six or seven huge turbines humming loudly.

Sarah looked down and sniffed the metal grate suspiciously. She pulled her nose away and snorted. This didn't make the young mule feel any more confident. She swished her long black tail and stomped her hooves on the pavement in defiance. I comforted them and got out of the saddle and started out over the grating, thinking good thoughts. At first they wouldn't go. They pulled back against the ropes, with their ears down, which means 'no!' in mule language.

I didn't force them. They were staring at me. Mave's eyes were getting bigger and bigger.

"Easy, Mavis. Easy, Sarah. It won't last forever. It's going to be alright," I said to myself more than to them.

The mules started following me across the grates. The holes were small enough that they couldn't get a hoof stuck, but big enough to leave a clear view down below to the river.

"Don't look down, mules." Mavis was dancing. Every other step, she was trying her best to not put her hooves down. Sarah was calmer. She put her head down, her ears forward, and stared through the grates to the Snake River far below. The huge turbines came on again for some reason when we were almost across and both mules trotted the rest of the way over the dam and onto the good solid earth on the other side. We'd done it! It just took some coaxing.

"Good, good mules," I said to them, patting Mavis gently on the nose to calm her down. They were as happy as I was to be across.

A Corps worker drove up in a white Chevy pickup and said, "Hey, why don't you put the mules in this fenced-in area for the night."

It was after six and the light had already left the steep canyon. I could feel a chill in the air as the last light disappeared. Overlooking the mighty Snake, I threw out my saddle blankets and sleeping bag. The mules grazed the grassy edges of the gravel yard surrounded by a chain link fence. I fed them some grain, piling it in the middle of the enclosure.

It was an incredibly beautiful night next to that big river. I watched what looked like a thousand birds fly in a wave down to the water's surface and then sail off over the steep cliffs. The moon was full and when it came up, the golden and brown hills glowed in the light. I could hardly stand to go to sleep, even though I got pretty tired after my coffee wore off. I didn't want to close my eyes for fear of missing that magic night. How quiet and bright it was! The Snake River was glistening like a ribbon of a billion stars far below me in the canyon.

When I awoke, the sun was already coming over the edge of the canyon, lighting up the river. I didn't even comb my hair or get dressed. I had my long underwear on and my hair was tangled and sticking out in every direction. I didn't make coffee first. I just walked up the steep gravel hill to where the mules had spent the night.

I couldn't believe my eyes! I blinked. It was true. My Mavis and Sarah were gone! I took a deep breath and felt a little sick. I ran down the hill and out to the road. One of the Corps of Engineer guys was driving slowly towards me. I could see a big smile on his face which made me remember I was in my union suit. I smiled back, but I'm sure I still looked worried.

"My mules. . ."

"Don't worry. They're back over the river in Boyer Park!" he said, laughing.

"No way!" I said. "You mean they went back across the dam?" I couldn't believe it.

"This morning at six, when the gates opened, the watchman said they were waiting there at the gate to go back across. He went ahead and opened the gate and there they went, the little white mule in the lead, trotting all the way across the grates to the other side. I guess they like Boyer Park!" he laughed.

He waited for me while I ran back to my pile of belongings and put on my jeans. As I ran away from his truck, I grabbed the back opening of my union suit because I could feel a breeze back there and I didn't want to embarrass myself any further. I slid into my jeans, grabbed my baseball cap and the two halters and ropes and raced back up to the truck. The Corps guy was still laughing and shaking his head, trying to figure me out. I smiled wide as I approached the truck and jumped up into the front seat.

"Haven't even had my coffee yet," I told him. "I just jumped out of the sack and went to go see the mules and they were gone! I couldn't believe my eyes!"

"We couldn't either. There we were, drinking coffee and hanging around the park before work and here comes the black mule and the white mule trotting across the dam. The sound of their hooves on the grate was echoing off the canyon. I'm surprised you didn't hear us laughing. We couldn't quit! Then the mules parked themselves in the middle of the greenest part of the lawn and started having breakfast. We moved them over to the wild part of the lawn so they wouldn't eat the mowed part because that could get somebody in trouble."

"Thanks so much," I said, smiling when I could see Mavis and Sarah Jane again, grazing happily and as fast as they could. I'm sure they had been expecting me.

"Hey girls!" I shouted to them. They both looked up when they heard my voice.

We loaded the mules in the back of the white pickup by backing it up to a hill and walking them right in. We had a parade of Corps trucks escorting us back across the dam. It was our third time across the dam, only this time we had wheels under us. The mules looked so funny standing at attention in the back of the Corps pickup, ears forward and eyes wide.

Everyone had a good time that morning. The Corps guys even filled my coffee cup when I got back to my camp.

Chapter Seven

Chuck and Snake River Lou

After I packed up, the Corps workers carried us in their pickup to the top of the first big hill up Almota Road. They hadn't had so much fun around there for awhile and I don't think they wanted to see me go.

It was a hot day and I stripped down to my tee-shirt by the second ridge. Mavis and Sarah walked fast all morning. They knew there was no real good place to stop, so they might as well keep moving.

As the hours passed, we walked along the side of the gravel road and didn't see a soul all day. It was so quiet and hot. I pictured in my mind what I would eat and drink when I got to Central Ferry, spending the afternoon obsessing on the thought. The Corps workers had told me about Chuck and Lou who owned the Central Ferry Store.

"Lou's been cooking for crews for over fifty years, or something like that. Everybody knows her as Snake River Lou. She's a gem," Dennis told me when he unloaded the mules at the top of the first hill out of the Snake River canyon. "They've been living there for a long, long time. They'll take you in before you can get down out of your saddle. It's about eighteen miles from here."

I made up a song to pass the time and sang it twenty times or more to Mavis and Sarah on the way to the Central Ferry Store. It went like this:

Chickens check the parking lot for wheat
A neighbor stops in for some coffee
Lou and Chuck are people to meet
At the Central Ferry Store

It's just up the canyon from the mighty Snake
In the middle of nowhere it seems to me
A mule man and a famous cook they say
For more than fifty years
Have made their way

I'm riding down the road
Ready for a Coke
I'm hungry and I'm sore
And then there's the Central Ferry Store!
The mules will eat
I'll rest my seat
Down at the Central Ferry Store.

The wheat fields rolled on and on. About seven miles or so from Central Ferry, we climbed a steep dirt road up through the wheat stubble. The wind was blowing wheat remnants and dirt into the air.

"Look, Mavis," I said, "look at that big barn."

It felt nice to sit in the old barn, to get out of the wind. It was good to take a break. I tied the mules to the thresher sitting silent until the next harvest. The mules fell asleep right away. I sat and listened to the wind howl loudly through the high roof of the barn. I watched their eyes widen when a huge gust came over the hill and through the drafty walls. Then they'd fall asleep again. Sarah was sleeping with her head up, her soft white eyelashes closed and her back foot up in a relaxed position. I thought about her load and how much heavier it was with all the new grain. I'd have to feed it to them when we got to Central Ferry.

There were at least twenty buckets full to the brim with seed and grain. Three old sinks lay on the floor of the barn next to a pile of rusty metal and baling wire. A few tires were stacked in the corner, in a stack that curved towards the top, the top tire about to fall to the floor. I sat on an eight-by-twelve board and practically fell asleep myself, listening to the wind howl over the wheat fields and through the boards of the barn.

After an hour or so, we headed for Central Ferry and I sang at the top of my lungs as we followed the dirt road to the store. Mavis and Sarah were tired that afternoon but kept walking. Eighteen miles is a long day and I could feel it in my behind as I rode towards our goal. Chuck and Lou's store was the only place for miles and miles.

I could feel my stomach turn. I was so hungry. I pictured the hamburger I would order at the Central Ferry Store, flipped by the best cook in the region, Snake River Lou.

And then I saw it, off over a rise or two. It was the Central Ferry Store! It was almost six, the sun was going down, and we hurried towards the mirage of a store on the horizon. The closer we got, the more real it became. Having a destination such as the Central Ferry Store, a place that was described to me in great detail, made the day eternally long.

We arrived about ten minutes later. I tied the mules up under a tree to the side of the store. It was white clapboard and galvanized tin and had brown window frames and a metal roof. A little yellow and black sign read "Central Ferry Store" above the brown door beckoning me to enter. An old gasoline pump stood crookedly next to the door. In the window was a welcome sign advertising Kool cigarettes. "Come In! We're Air Conditioned!" it read. There was a welcoming lace curtain in the window and I could see a chair and an old red linoleum table next to a big wood stove.

The screen door slammed and there was Lou and Chuck.

"Glad you made it! Come in and have something to drink," said Lou. She had on a purple and orange floral polyester shirt over brown polyester pants. Big round glasses stood out on her friendly face. Her gray hair was in soft curls on top of her head. She had on big white pearl earrings and cowgirl boots. The boots were so worn she stood crookedly on the cement next to the old gas pump.

"Get in here! We heard you were coming!" she yelled in a loud voice full of humor and authority. "You can sleep out in the dry shack and Chuck will put the mules down in the lower corral." Lou was smiling at me. I must have been a real sight. She was glad to have me there, I could tell. So was Chuck.

Chuck was frail and thin and much smaller than Lou and looked out at me from under his old stained Resistol hat. A band of sweat was this cowboy's hatband. He wore a blue cowboy shirt with a pack of smokes showing through the pocket. With a cigarette in one hand and both of his thumbs hooked on the pockets of his old jeans, his pants hung down low on his old hips and under a little bit of a belly. His frayed jeans were long and hung down over his boots and dragged on the dirt.

"I know mules," he said to me, "I've had over a hundred of 'em."

I walked down to the barn, following close behind Chuck. I had to slow down my steps because he walked real slowly. Lou went back in the store. I could hear the laughter inside as we walked away with the mules. Chuck led Sarah.

"What a pretty little white mule. You know, I must admit I've never seen one just like her. She's the perfect compact size for packing because you can reach her back. I'm a short feller, you know," Chuck said. "It looks like you've got the diamond hitch down, all right! We used to have room out here for twenty-nine trailers and, hell, we sold a lot of beer. Lou has cooked for every dam or road crew that was ever out here. That woman can cook for a whole room of people at once and never bat an eyelash!" he bragged.

"You'll be sleeping out in the dry shack so let's unpack the mules down there," Chuck suggested.

"Okay," I answered, leading Mavis by the reins towards the shack. Chuck helped me to untie the diamond hitch and he slowly coiled the rope up next to the tarp and the packs.

"Sure do got a light load there," he said.

"Except for the guitar. It sure takes up a lot of room." I unsaddled Mavis and put the saddle and the blanket down on the porch of the dry shack. We led the mules slowly down to the barn. Chuck looked around for a brush which he found in a little dusty room full of old saddles, bridles, and blankets. There was fifty years worth of tack in there. He dusted off the brush and gave Sarah a good grooming. He found some ointment to put on her where the hair was getting too short under the butt breeching. That steep stage road had been a little tough on Sarah and her hair was dangerously short from the constant rubbing of the breeching when we practically slid down that steep hill east of the dam.

We let the mules go in a corral made of thick planks, the edges of the boards softened through the years by the teeth of various mules and horses that had stayed there.

"There's salt," he pointed to a big white salt block in the middle of the corral. The mules went to it instantly and started to slowly lick it. The big chunk of salt was rounded and smooth and they stood there for at least five minutes getting their fill.

Chuck carefully measured two piles of grain in two rubber buckets and put them down in front of the mules.

"I used to have a string of buckin' horses. Had over twenty-eight at one time. Boy, those horses could buck! But the mules have always been my favorite. Now I have a thirty-two year old mare. That's it. I bought her in '53 down in Gila, Arizona. Went down there to Arizona and I bought myself a string of horses. They were mighty fine horses, too. All real strong and pretty. Good for cattle work and rodeo!"

He found a brand new chinstrap for Mavis' bridle in the little tack room and handed it to me without saying a word. He had noticed when he helped me unsaddle that mine was makeshift. I had long ago broken the old and rotten one I started out with.

"Thanks, Chuck! The mules look happy there," I said.

"It don't take much to keep a mule happy," he answered.

On the way back to the store we stopped and looked at the old mare. She was glad to see Chuck and nuzzled his hand for a treat. He pulled some grain out of his pocket and gave it to her. She was a white dapple mare with a long flowing mane.

"Let's get back up to the store before Lou has my head. She's probably cooking you dinner right now!" Chuck said, laughing and shaking his head. He pulled out a cigarette and lit it. We walked slowly up to the store.

"Where you been?" Lou yelled as we entered the store. She was back behind the counter flipping an egg. "I thought you rode off!"

There was another lady in the store, a thin middle-aged woman in tight plaid polyester pants with a shirt to match and a tall blond wig that was off balance on her head. No one seemed to notice, but I did see her reach up to adjust it once while she was talking to Lou. She lived in a fancy house trailer out in the back. Her trailer had wall to wall carpet and a dishwasher and the whole place sparkled, even the Astroturf which she had looking like a real lawn complete with a wide variety of colorful plastic flowers.

Lou sat me down at the red linoleum table. She put a cup of coffee in front of me and I added milk and sugar. Minutes later the bacon and egg sandwich arrived with home fries, more toast and thick slices of homegrown tomatoes. I had some garlic in my pocket. I sliced some into the sandwich as Lou and the trailer lady watched in surprise.

"My only weapon since I sent the 22 home with a friend," I told them.

I looked around the store. The wood stove was a miniature locomotive engine with a big bell. It was on tiny tracks complete with wheels, number 97, and with "Chuck and Lou" written out in welded metal letters.

There were pictures of old cowboys, of wheat harvesting and of the building of the Lower Granite Dam. There were pictures of men sitting proudly next to dead deer, with the deer heads propped up on their laps. A pool table filled up the area next to the table.

Chuck sat and smoked a cigarette, cleaning the glass top of the table with his sleeve. Lou had wildflowers on the table in a little vase. There were piles and piles of old newspapers, ashtrays and coffee cups, a jar of homemade jam, a bowl of sugar and a copper napkin holder.

A man came in and bought a can of chili and some glove liners. Lou rang them up. She held up the glove liners.

"How much did I charge before for these?" she asked herself loudly. The cash register opened with a friendly ring. "How much was these, Chuck?" She held the gloves up so Chuck could see them. "A buck fifty, wasn't they, Chuck?" Lou yelled.

"A dollar fifty," Chuck answered. "They're made to be used with the chain saw, so you don't get no sawdust down your gloves," Chuck told the man.

"Here's a nice mop," said the woman who lived in the fancy trailer next to the store.

Lou rang him up. "Sixteen-fifty. Thank you, now."

Everybody was talking at once. The store was so warm with the locomotive wood stove going full blast. They kept it lit even in the summer because the nights were cold.

"How long do you think it will take you to get to Newport?" Chuck asked. The other man looked my direction.

"Oh, I figure at the rate I'm going, it will take me another month from right now," I said enthusiastically.

The other man asked, "Do you know which way you are gonna go?"

"Sort of," I answered, hesitantly.

"Pendleton? You gonna head down to Pendleton?" he continued. "Are you going to go through Ukiah?"

"Yeah. Do you know that country real well down that way?" I asked him. "Which way would you ride, if you were riding a horse?"

95

"Well, you'd never find me riding a horse! But I used to have a cabin down by Pendleton."

"Ukiah's where they started on that wagon train!" Chuck said.

"You bet! That sure is, Chuck!" the other man answered. "It took them three days to get down to Pendleton, and that was with the mules and wagons and all."

"Did you do that, Chuck?" I asked.

"No, I didn't go. Dick Dern and Mary went, and Thomas and his wife."

"That was over the Fourth, wasn't it?" the other man asked Chuck. Chuck nodded. Lou poured me some more coffee.

"How long have you lived here?" I asked Chuck.

"Pert near seventy-five years."

"Right here on this spot?"

"Well, just four miles over the hill from here. Never did get enough money to get off the patch!" Chuck said with a chuckle.

"We'll see ya," the man with the gloves said to Chuck as he headed for the door. The bell on it jingled when he started to open it. Nobody was ever in a hurry to leave because there was absolutely nothing else around for miles and miles but hills and hills of endless wheat stubble. It was a little lonely for anyone who drove or rode away from that place.

"So you probably know everybody from here to Oregon!" I said to Chuck.

"No, I don't know too many people anymore. They all died off!" he answered, laughing softly.

"Chuck outlived 'em!" the other man said, laughing.

"Yep, I'm the last one left here that was born here," Chuck said thoughtfully.

"Is that right?" the other man said.

"Fred Yates was still alive, but he died about three years ago. I'm just awaiting my turn," Chuck said. "Down in that marble orchard, that's where I'll stay!"

"You know where the school house sits down here, there used to be thirty-five, forty kids going to school down there when I was a kid. Now there ain't that many in the whole country," Chuck said.

"Is that right?" the other man said.

"Now there ain't that many in the whole neck of the woods, out here," Chuck repeated.

"They've all moved to the cities!" the other man said.

"No!" Chuck said loudly. "People bought 'em off! There was about fifty families that used to live out here."

"So there used to be a lot of little farms?" I asked Chuck.

"Well there were some that were four hundred acres, but they were a hundred and sixty, most of 'em. And the families all raised six, seven, eight kids."

"Did you use to farm with mules?" I asked him. Lou filled my coffee cup and picked up the old newspapers from the table and stacked them next to the locomotive wood stove.

Chuck thought for a minute. "Yep. I had mules all my life."

"What was your favorite mule, that Beauty?" I asked.

"Oh, I don't know. I've had a lot of good ones and I've had a lot of bad ones. Most of the bad mules were bad because of people and the way they were treated." Chuck lit another cigarette.

Lou yelled from behind the counter, "We sent that dog back out there, that dog was out there killing chickens!"

"He didn't get any killed, but he sure did his best," Chuck said.

"He had that old rooster cornered out there," Lou screeched.

"Does he have a taste for chicken?" I asked with my mouth full of potato chips. I planned to eat the whole time I was there. I figured I'd lost weight on that eighty degree, eighteen-mile day. No one answered me.

The other man said, "Chuck, what about growin' banana squash? When do you know it's ripe?"

"Any time you wanna pick 'em," Chuck laughed.

"Well, I picked my squash the other day and it was nice around the center. But it was green around the shell," said the woman in the crooked wig.

"Well, we got a squash that's that long," the man bragged.

"Well, I got one that's forty inches long and thirty-two inches around." Chuck said.

"Stop bragging now, Chuck, and come eat your dinner," Lou

97

yelled from the kitchen.

"Well, I admired your squash out there today, Chuck, when you were watering," the woman said.

"I swear," Chuck said, "I swear those squash were shaking and vibrating because they were growing so fast!"

"This girl rode down the road with her mules," Lou said to the woman. "Did you see her out there on the road?"

"Uh-huh," the woman answered.

"Every once in awhile I stick my thumb out when a horse trailer goes by," I told her. She was adjusting her wig in the big mirror behind the counter.

I looked at Lou expectantly.

"What do you want now?" she asked me.

"Can I have a pop?" I asked her in a high, quiet voice.

"You ride your mules down the highway?" the woman asked.

"Sometimes. But I try to stay off the highway," I answered.

"She's going to Newport!" Lou yelled. "Oregon!"

"Oh," the other lady answered and gave me a funny look.

Lou asked me to get my guitar out and play a song or two for them. The man with the mop and the gloves decided not to leave and they sat around and listened to me play all three of the songs I knew well. We sang together, out there in the middle of nowhere: *From this valley they say you are going, we will miss your bright eyes and sweet smile, for they say you are taking the sunshine, that has brightened our pathways awhile...*

The hungry stomach I had walked in with was long gone and I sat there for over two hours listening to Chuck. Lou stayed busy cleaning the grill and closing up for the night. It was time to go to bed.

The dry shack was so comfortable. I fell asleep to the sound of the wind whipping down the dirt road, past the Central Ferry Store. I hid my head under my sleeping bag and slept like a baby. It felt so good to be inside on a real bed.

Chapter Eight

Bread Basket

I woke up and propped my head on my jacket. The sun was streaming through the small, dirty window in the dry shack. Chuck shuffled by the door.

"Fed your mules," he said and kept on walking.

I guess he figured eight o'clock in the morning was too late to be sleeping. I rolled out of my down bag and stuffed it into its nylon sack, found my hairbrush and tried to work the tangles out of my hair. I knew Lou would be cooking me breakfast. Life on the trail made me hungry, but it didn't take too much to fill me up and one of Lou's meals would certainly do the trick. I changed into my other shirt, changed my socks, tied my shoelaces and stumbled out of the dry shack into morning at the Central Ferry Store.

"How'd ya sleep?" Chuck asked me. He had a small sack of grain in his hand which he placed on the top of my gear. "This should get you to Dayton. Sure wish I could ride out with you, but I don't think Lou would let me," he said, jokingly.

I could smell the bacon as I opened the door of the store and walked in headed straight towards the steaming cup of coffee that sat on the glass tabletop. I added a little bit of milk and sugar and took a sip. It was really hot and delicious.

"Now this is the life," I said to Lou.

"How'd ya sleep in the dry shack? How's that old mattress out there?" she asked as she put in front of me a big white breakfast plate stacked with potatoes, four pieces of perfectly cooked bacon, three eggs over easy and three pieces of dark rye toast with homemade jam on the side.

"Perfect," I answered.

I watched Lou as she walked out the door wearing another colorful polyester print shirt.

"Chuck!" she yelled. Her voice echoed off the far away Snake River canyon. "Chuck!" she yelled again. "Come on in when you're done with feedin' and have some of this fresh cornbread!"

She put a steaming piece of the freshly baked cornbread on the middle of my now empty plate. She scooped a big spoonful of butter on the top and walked back in the kitchen without saying a word. I looked out the window and saw Chuck heading slowly towards the corrals with a pitchfork of hay.

I packed up Sarah Jane in front of the dry shack. Chuck helped me throw the diamond hitch and helped me pull the rope tight. The diamond hitch was more perfect than it had ever been. He went into the store and came out with his Polaroid to take some pictures.

Lou walked out to say goodbye. She handed me a giant size Butterfingers candy bar.

"Thanks, Lou," I said to her.

Chuck lit up a smoke and rested his thumbs in his front pockets after taking a drag. He smiled and said, "Have a good ride, lady." I could tell he wanted to ride out with me on that big dappled horse of his. The mare ran along the fence, showing off for us as we rode towards Dodge Junction. She reached the end of her pasture, spun on her heels and raced back the other way, her long white tail blowing in the wind as she ran.

I could see Chuck and Lou standing in the road in front of the Central Ferry Store, waving. They grew so small I could hardly make them out. They stopped waving and walked slowly back into the store.

I rode across the hills in the wheat stubble and hit Highway 127. At Dodge Junction, after a hamburger, I headed down the Pomeroy Highway. The waitress didn't tell me about the dirt road straight over the hill that would have saved me over fifteen miles. I guess she didn't think I'd want to go that way.

I rode most of the afternoon, stopping at a big ranch along the highway, the home of John Herres and his daughter, Joan Kay. Without question and within minutes, they put the mules in the corral next to the calf pen.

Tiny calves looked out at the two mules with big, curious eyes. I put my gear in the barn and came into the house. I thought about Nina and how much she would have loved these people. They took me in like they were expecting me.

The kitchen was so clean and homey and smelled of some wonderful baked apple cake. Joan Kay was busy with crafts; the fair was starting that next day in Pomeroy.

There were homemade wooden boxes on the table. There were wooden cows waiting to be painted and dried flowers in a bag on one of the chairs. A boy about two and a little girl around the same age sat on chairs at the big, roomy table. Joan Kay was busy with three things at once. She was a beautiful, energetic woman who helped run the ranch. Her dad was in his late seventies. He and his brother had farmed and ranched together for fifty years in Colombia and Garfield Counties.

"Do you babysit a lot?" I asked her.

"Well, I do," she said. "I used to have kids all week, but I would tell the mothers when I was going to be gone. It worked out pretty well. I had these two all last summer!"

"Did you make those boxes? They're beautiful," I said as I started to eat the apple cake she had given to me when I came in.

"My dad did," she said proudly. "I've got a salad bar coming up, where we decorate the tables for one of our local organizations. And I thought, why not use 'em and fill 'em with weeds, basically. Cheap, anything cheap!" Joan Kay laughed. "We fill them with witches' hair. I'm sure you've seen it going down the highway. It's a fuzzy green thing and it fills in real good. I grew some baby's breath last year, so I'll put some of that in, too."

"What's this salad bar thing?" I asked her. I was thinking about food again.

"Oh, it's an Election Day salad bar that one of the organizations has. Anyone in the town can come on in and have a salad."

"Sounds like fun."

"It's a lot of work."

"Is it one of those kind of salad bars that has everything on it?" I asked.

"Oh, it has the most delicious salads, everything you can think of. I don't think I've ever eaten there!" She laughed. "I've worked the last four years and I don't think I've ever had a chance to eat!"

I noticed she was doing some stenciling on another table in the dining room.

"Oh, you're stenciling. Those are beautiful. A purple cow!" I said to her. She was stenciling on boxes.

"Oh, he's my experiment. He's the first wood stencil I've done. We did stenciling before, though. At 4H camp," she said.

"And then, what? You're going to let all the ladies take one?"

"No, we sell 'em. We have no trouble getting rid of decorations!"

"Do you want one of these?" I said to John who sat quietly at the table. I offered him one of the cookies that I had bought at the Central Ferry Store. He was busy watching the action and didn't hear me.

"Papa?" Joan Kay said to him. He took one of the cookies. He handed it to the young boy who dropped it on the floor.

"Better watch him. He'll eat one bite and B.J. will get the rest of it," Joan Kay said. I could already hear the nails of the tiny dog on the floor under the table.

I looked behind John at the big pile of books. "Looks like you read a lot," I said to the old farmer.

"I do. The older I get, the easier it is to find time to read," he laughed and looked off, smiling.

"Boy, ranching and wheat farming must keep you busy," I said, shaking my head.

"Yep, keeps us out of mischief most of the time," he chuckled. "We changed to raising calves three or four years ago. If you would have come yesterday, that whole green field would have been full of calves."

"Good timing," I laughed. "I'm glad I'm finding good pasture this way. My mules need it."

"Well, it's quite a ways between people, if you went the other way. There's only a few farms out there," John said as he picked up a piece of cookie and tossed it to the dog.

The timer was buzzing on the stove in the kitchen. I looked at John. "Does she have something in the oven?" I asked hopefully.

"No, she turned that on so she'd remember to shut the water trough off," John said.

"She's amazing," I said to him.

"She's my girl! You know, I swear she's the Mother Confessor to half of the women in this valley! She hears it all!" He laughed and looked fondly in the direction of Joan Kay who was running in to turn the buzzer off. Then she ran out the back door, out to the water trough.

"Yeah," I told John, "I came all the way over from Clark Fork, over the mountains and down to St. Maries, over to Sanders, stayed in Potlach, Moscow and Pullman and then on down to Lower Granite."

"Oh?" he said, interested.

"We crossed the dam. That was a big accomplishment. But the guy who let me put the mules in a corral by the river didn't close the gate tight and the mules ran all the way back over the dam to Boyer Park, back to the green grass!"

"Whoa!" John said, laughing.

"I couldn't believe it," I said.

Joan Kay came in just as the little boy grabbed one of the freshly painted boxes.

"These are for our fair. It's starting up tomorrow," she said excitedly.

"In Pomeroy?" I asked.

"Yep."

"And down in Waitsburg they're having that salmon deal," I said to her. "Is that coming up, or is that over?"

"I can't remember," she said.

"And the Pendleton Round-Up is coming up, too!"

"That's this weekend," Joan Kay said.

"I'm missing all of them!" I said to her.

"Oh, well. You'll have to come back this way in a car sometime and hit 'em all!" Joan Kay squinted at the cow she was painting.

"I'm putting purple on one side and blue on the other side. We try to stay comical so we don't offend anyone!"

"What do you mean?" I laughed.

"Well," John said, "if you make it look like a Hereford, the Semintal people get upset."

"Oh, I see," I said.

"This one is going to be a black cow with kinda spots and a white stripe down her back. That way nobody will get offended because if I put Hereford, Semintal or Angus on it, the Charolet people are going to get upset," Joan Kay said, as she painted.

"Kind of a generic cow," I added, laughing. "What kind are yours?" I asked John.

"His are just like this," Joan Kay said, holding up the inoffensive cow. We laughed.

"A little bit of everything, huh?" I asked.

"We've got some Herefords and some Angus. But mostly, right now, we have Semintals. We've got some Angus-Charolet cross and some Angus-Hereford cross. See, most of the guys who run cow and calf pairs buy them in the spring, run them all summer and sell them in the fall! That way you don't have to feed 'em all winter," John said.

"That gets expensive!"

"Well, if you got to buy feed. But we raise all our own. We have a ranch over by Starbuck, down by the Snake. It don't get too much snow, so we winter them down there. I usually just winter the calves up here."

"And you have another place down by Dayton?" I asked.

"Yeah, it's about nine miles out of Dayton, up in the timber. We run most of the cattle there in the summer, down in the Blue Mountains."

"Do you use it as a hunting cabin?" I asked.

"No, I don't hunt down there," John said.

"Papa doesn't hunt down there because everybody else does!" Joan Kay yelled from the kitchen.

Later that evening, Joan Kay showed me to the shower and I soaked off the dirt and dust I was carrying with me in my hair. I relished the hot, steamy water and let it run a long time on the back of my head. It was good to get out of my hat and jeans and dirty

shirt. She did my laundry for me while I slept outside, next to the calf pen.

In the morning it was cloudy and windy. Joan Kay and John were off to the fair in Pomeroy.

"Goodbye!" they yelled and waved from the car as they headed down the road.

I thought about going to the fair. They had invited me, but I decided to make miles for Dayton. I packed up Sarah and saddled Mavis.

The barnyard was quiet as we rode out of the gate and up the road towards the Marengo Grade. Mavis and Sarah were feeling really good that morning as we headed out from the ranch.

"It must be the grain that Chuck gave them," I thought aloud. They were both walking with a quick step down through the wheat stubble. Joan Kay figured it was about twenty-two miles down to Dayton, a full day on the mules.

I felt comfortable in the saddle and we rode over the Marengo Grade and across the Tucannon River. This was the old migration route for the Nez Perce Indians. They lived in this abundant land part of the year. They could find flint in the river bottom and camas root along its edges. At high water, in the spring, boats could make it beyond Lewiston.

I arrived at Covello, now just a few fir trees and a cemetery. Years ago it was a town of seventy people. I sat below an old, unkempt apple tree and enjoyed a piece of its delicious fruit. Mavis and Sarah Jane ate the weeds around the tree.

I sat there and looked out at the country around me. Hills and hills of rough grassy wheat land. I could imagine the pack trains going by on their way from the gold fields of Idaho. I could see them pulling into the tiny town of Covello for supplies and a good night's rest. This was the old route from Walla Walla and Lewiston to Spokane. It was a place where trails met. Indians, settlers, miners, trappers and travelers all passed through Covello.

I looked at the tombstones, some not attended to, some buried under a mound of grass. Many of the graves were those of children.

The wind came up and the clouds, huge and white, were blowing across the sky faster than I could ever remember.

When the mules were rested, I rode on, leaving behind that eerie place that seemed to haunt me until I could see the well-developed trees of Dayton. Mavis and Sarah came to a fast stop at a huge pile of wheat that lay on the edge of the road. After they had eaten as much as they possibly could, I sat still in the saddle for a few minutes and looked around me. The already harvested wheat fields were the warmest color of gold. The blue sky came right down to their golden edge. All I could see were wheat fields, hill after hill of them all the way to the Blue Mountains.

The wind blew like crazy all the way into Dayton. As the trees got closer and larger, I started thinking about where I would sleep that night. I was almost to town when a brown pickup stopped and a nice looking man in work clothes got out.

"Hi, I'm Bob," he said. "I work out here in hydraulics. Where are you planning to put your animals tonight?" he asked.

"I'm not sure. Is there a fairgrounds?" I asked in a hopeful tone.

"Sure. Keep them there. It's right on the edge of town."

Bob directed me to the fairgrounds where the manager set me up with a place for the mules in a sawdust-filled barn with alfalfa in the feed box and a little grain on the side. I put my gear under the tarp next to the barn where I planned to sleep and accepted Bob's invitation to go out to dinner with him in Dayton. We had fun that night looking over the map. He knew the country well since his job kept him on the back roads.

It had been a long day in the saddle. I kept thinking about the graves in Covello. I had visited a place from the past, had crossed over the land where so many other travelers had crossed before me. I knew many had stopped to rest there under the apple tree, as I had, some staying long enough to be buried there.

It was a clear, starry night. Quietly I found my way back to my pile of gear next to the mules' corral. Mavis and Sarah were both lying down in the sawdust, breathing softly.

In the morning, I fed the mules some breakfast and walked downtown. It was a gorgeous, sunny September day and I had slept soundly next to the mule corral.

I went into a store called Dingle's. It was originally a brick hotel built in 1885. I found Mrs. Dingle in the back carrying a box of shirts. She was a little woman with a wide, friendly smile and white hair. Her lacy white blouse was tucked neatly into her red and blue plaid skirt.

"Hello there," she said. I think I surprised her.

"Are you Mrs. Dingle?" I asked.

"Yes, I'm Cletys Dingle," she responded in a friendly voice. "Can I help you find something? A new shirt perhaps?" I saw her glance at my road-worn shirt. I wished I had worn my nice one.

"I heard from old Bill at the fairgrounds about you and your store. What a great place!" I said to her. She put down the box of shirts and walked with me to the front of the store, her pumps making a hollow sound on the old wooden floor.

"The store has been Dingle's since 1920. My husband's father went into business here with his two sons, Bert and Hedley, right after World War One. We've been here ever since. I'm eighty-four and I still enjoy working," she said enthusiastically. "I must say, there are some things in the basement that have been there since we first opened. It's like a museum down there."

We stood silently for a moment while she refolded some blouses and colorful scarves. "What is it?" she asked.

"Oh, I was just thinking about how much I would love to see the basement. Is that a strange request?"

"Well, usually only my son Bertram and our clerks go down there. But if you'd like..."

She smiled and turned away, motioning to me with her hand. She walked down an aisle stocked with red metal lanterns and oil lamps, flashlights, blankets, tarps and rain boots. It seemed to me that Dingle's had a little bit of everything.

I looked down at my tennis shoes and wiped at my blouse again, feeling dirtier than usual under the florescent lights of the store.

Mrs. Dingle carefully descended the creaky wooden stairs into the basement and flipped on the light. I stood silently next to her at the base of the stairs. She turned and smiled at me like a young girl sharing a secret.

"We were proud to be the first distributors of Caterpillar tractors in Dayton, in the whole county, for that matter. See those bins? They were full to the brim with everything the farmer needed to get his tractor going again."

I peered over her shoulder as she pointed to some shelves stacked high with old dishes and glassware. Beyond, I could see some old wooden display cases full of old tools. I gazed longingly at the furthest reaches of the big basement. If Mrs. Dingle had given me the go ahead, I might have stayed there all afternoon running my fingers over the remnants of sixty years of hardware.

"My husband loved this store. You see, he had graduated from the University of Idaho and was admitted to the bar. But he never practiced law. Once his father presented the idea of the hardware store, his life took a different course. He was always a big football fan and coached the Dayton football team for quite awhile, until they finally hired someone else. And he loved boxing! In fact, he was quite a fighter himself. He trained boxers right here in this basement and in the hallway upstairs."

I could practically see the smoke in the air and the young, robust wheat farmers boxing their way around an invisible circle.

I followed Mrs. Dingle back upstairs.

"What advice would you give a young person about how to live life?" I asked her out of the blue.

"Eat right, get lots of rest and remember you are the only one writing the story that is your life," she said as if she kept that bit of wisdom on the tip of her tongue. She walked to the register and started folding shirts.

I did my laundry in the warm, clean laundromat. It felt good to have a clean shirt on. I only wished I had done my laundry before meeting Mrs. Dingle.

Before I left Dayton, an old timer came down to the fairgrounds in an old Chevy pickup truck. He got out and sat on the sideboard. His overalls were ironed with a crease down each leg and he wore a piece of polished stone as a bolo tie pulled snug up to his collar. He told me he wanted to meet me before I left and to tell me something about the town.

"You know," he said, "bands of Cayuse and Nez Perce had long used Dayton's main street as a racetrack. And right downtown there were close to a hundred teepees! In 1848, The Oregon Volunteers fought over four hundred Cayuse for thirty hours and the Indians unhappily retreated. The racetrack became Main Street with wooden boardwalks and hitching posts right out in front of the buildings. The farmers built beautifully crafted homes here in town, in all different styles, according to where they came from in Europe! Have you seen the old Depot and the Courthouse? You really must ride your mules around town and take a look."

I had the mules saddled and packed and we were ready to go. Every time I rode away from a town, I knew I was going too soon.

Mrs. Dingle came out of the store and admired the mules as I passed by. I waved to the gentlemen in the barbershop as I rode down the street and headed out towards Waitsburg. It was early afternoon. I took another look behind me at the tall, beautiful shade trees that spread their arms across the town. The well-kept lawns with the flower-lined sidewalks disappeared behind a wheat field as I rode into the unending contours of the hills along the Touchet River.

Chapter Nine

Pure Luck

On the road to Waitsburg, we rode from silo to silo. The mules knew the silos were full of grain and they always walked towards the shiny silver columns with great enthusiasm. I hated to pass up any such treat as the grain kept them fueled on the long road to Oregon. It seemed there was always a big pile of spilled grain in the vicinity of each and every silo we passed.

I rode along with my feet out of the stirrups for a few miles to stretch my legs. It felt so good to let them dangle free and I worked out the cramp in my leg. "Mave's gait is so smooth," I thought to myself. "I could paint my nails if I wanted to."

"Whoa, Mavis," I said. She came to a stop. I jumped out of the saddle and decided to walk. I swung my legs out in front of me in an exaggerated walk until I found a pace that suited the fast paced mules. Sitting in the saddle was good for so many muscles, but walking worked out the kinks in my legs. I was soon comfortable with the pace and my body felt strong and as pliable as a rubber band.

I thought about my home up in Idaho. The old homestead was far away now. My friends in the valley probably only thought about me once in awhile. What had happened to Nina made me want to stay away from people who would shake their heads and say, "I told you so."

Even though I was away, the ranch remained a grassy canvas for my imagination.

I had jumped right in. My ability as a carpenter was lacking and so I came to depend on my neighbors' expertise as I dished up the hashbrowns from potatoes I grew in my garden. I cooked eggs I had thankfully gathered from the hens that seemed to lay them with ease in the warmth of the chicken coop with the outside strolling area. I baked bread and made huge pots of beans. I traded eggs for fresh milk and cream.

Living there could be like heaven or hell, depending if I had money and company. When it got too cold and the wind started blowing the old lacy underwear pieces out of the log cabin's hand hewn walls, I would run away to Mexico. This caused problems because it wasn't fair to everyone else, my friends who had suffered through a long and wet and snowy winter. For me, it was the best thing, just to leave. And then in the spring, when the streams thawed and the river was full and flowing, I would come back and plant my garden. I knew I had probably bitten off a little more than I might be able to chew, but I'd die chewing. It was a dream place as long as there was money in the mailbox, the kind no one seemed to have.

With the help of my neighbors, Dave and Alirene, Mike and Dede, Bev and Stan, we replaced old leaky pipes, built a porch and rebuilt the bathroom. We fixed up the kitchen, tearing out the ugly ceiling tile to find a tongue and groove white pine ceiling beneath it. We laid a new wood floor and refinished the old wood floors until the homesteader's cabin shined. There was the pink and blue tulip wallpaper in the kitchen and the huge yellow logs that were hand hewn to perfection.

And I cooked. No one went away hungry. It was a wonderful, warm time. We always had plenty of apples and potatoes.

The coffeepot was always on, Willie Nelson's album played on a stereo in need of a new needle. I slept upstairs in an old room with a dormer that was too dark in the winter and heavenly in the summer. And then, in the late afternoons, I'd ride Cowboy through the woods at a lope or a run, with Sarah close behind, following us.

The store in Clark Fork had everything. It was the center of the town and if you sat on the stoop in front of the store, you could get your fill of conversation. It was called the Clark Fork Mercantile and was run by a big woman named Etta who was tough but kind.

Etta wore old-fashioned floral print dresses and shoes that must have dated back to the '40's. She would walk back to the little fountain to talk to Emma, a short woman with gray hair who served up a great egg and sausage breakfast and the biggest and best pancakes around. The little coffee shop was in the back of the store beyond the rows and rows of canned goods, the insect sprays and the glove rack. Then she'd walk back up to the front counter and sell someone a fishing license.

The Merc was as much museum as general store. There were fabrics and sunglasses that had been there since the '50's. Etta had a complete line of fishing and hunting gear and everything a person needed to catch a fish or kill a deer. The wool socks were 100% and the huckleberries, which never stayed in the vegetable bin for long, were picked every morning in the summer in the woods by retirees with enough self control to not eat too many of them. Everyone else got a purple face and, eventually, a stomach ache.

I loved the sound of my boots on the wooden front porch of the old store. The old screen door had an authoritative slam that announced each and every shopper. When my parents came to town, they would gleefully drive the seven miles to the old store to buy whatever I needed. Etta would watch them out of the corner of her eye as they filled an old shopping cart with mops, mop replacement pads, scrubbies for dishes, dish soap, ammonia, paint, paint brushes, blankets, brooms, drinking glasses and mouse traps.

When I turned on the water at the ranch and nothing came out, I'd throw on my boots and walk a quarter of a mile to the pump house. It was down a steep hill on railroad land, which was part of a grandfather water clause. That pump would quit every time it was freezing, which was often, regardless of the light bulb and insulation.

The pump men, there were two or more kindly old men in Clark Fork who were willing to come out, would arrive in the middle of the storm. But there was a cut off point when no one would dare drive the road as the snow came flowing down in such abundance and with such quiet grace, the whole place would be frozen solid.

It was so silent after a big snowfall. Once the snowplow quit plowing, if the storm came too fast and too deep, there was no pump man, or anyone for that matter, who would head out to Cabinet.

The Clark Fork Merc would usually have anything we needed to fix my pump and soon the water would be flowing again.

People had depended on the store for pipes and wrenches, clothes and grain for almost a century and Etta reigned as queen. I loved thinking about home, knowing everything was pretty much the same. When I got lonely, I would remember the sound of that door slamming at the old Clark Fork Merc.

Walking all the way into Waitsburg felt good and gave Mavis a break. She was a young mule and although she didn't seem to mind the long miles, I didn't want to overdo it. Anytime I felt like walking was fine with her, but she nudged me with her nose if I slowed down. It was nine miles to Waitsburg and the sky was as blue as it could be that day with unthreatening clouds way off in the distance, towards the Blue Mountains.

Sarah's pack was light; it was a pleasure to travel that way. I only had about half the pack I had left home with. I had no need to carry much besides my clothes, the guitar, coffee and popcorn. There were canned beans and powdered milk, too, and a little bit of the grain that Chuck had given me in Central Ferry. I had tossed the travel iron back in Dayton.

I walked along in front of the two mules on the edge of the wheat field, along the side of the small highway. We were in a rhythm, lost in our own separate worlds while occupying the same world. Only a few cars went by and huge combines that were being moved to the next field on big trucks. Mavis looked at the huge machines with fear in her eyes as they passed. She flipped her ears back and forth and was annoyed she had to share the road with such big monster rigs.

Soon it was quiet again. I got back in the saddle and rode the last three miles or so into Waitsburg.

Riding into the fairgrounds, I saw a big sign over the gate that read,

"Days of Real Sport Ground." Farther in, I found a nice big corral where the mules could roll and run without their halters on. There were lines of stalls and corrals, a track and spectator stands. There were no fairs going on, no horse races, so I had the place to myself.

Some cowboys brought their horses down in trailers and practiced team penning in the covered arena. They gave me the name of a local horseshoer to call. It was time to get the mules shod since their shoes had worn thin on the roads from Idaho.

I noticed a pickup driving slowly up to the stalls. I was sitting in the stands watching the cowboys practice in the arena. Their brown and white Blue Heeler sat at my feet, his eyes following every move the horses made. He was a pudgy little dog with even spots and intelligent eyes. He looked up at me but only as a quick thank you for petting his head. He couldn't look away from the action in the arena.

"Hello there, mule skinner," said a tall man in a white straw cowboy hat. I couldn't help but notice his firm grip as he shook my hand. "Don Thomas is my name. You might say I'm the Ambassador of Waitsburg," he laughed. His smile was contagious. He was in his early seventies and was a tall and good-looking man.

He sat down next to me to watch the cowboys work their horses in the arena.

"Glad to meet you," I said, smiling.

The little brown and white dog thumped his tail twice, looked up and then looked back at the cowboys. He probably knew Don. Everybody did.

"I saw that nice looking little white mule of yours out there in the pen. What a pretty little mule. She looks strong, not for driving, but for riding and packing. And the gray! She looks young in the face! How old is she?" Don asked, smiling wide.

"She's only three. Her name is Mavis. She was never ridden much before this trip," I told him. "Only three or four times."

"Well, I'll be. The guys told me you rode all the way down from Sandpoint or up that way. That's quite a ride for a gal all alone with two mules! You know we've had a few people come through here. Once a man and two thin looking donkeys pulling a little cart; another time two men on Appaloosas going south to Mexico, or so they said. Wondered often if they ever made it. You know, I'm a mule man myself," Don continued. "Ever go to the Draft Horse International Show in Sandpoint?"

I laughed. "Oh yes, I showed Sarah, that's the white mule, one year in a halter class. She looked beautiful and I washed her with a little bleach. Her coat was as clean and white as a rabbit's. But we were up against some real pretty, tall and dark mules from Washington. Those mules were professional and stood still as statues as the judge circled them, silently. But poor Sarah thought the judge was a vet! She practically jumped out of her skin when he turned his attention her way. I think she expected him to stick her with a needle! She trotted out of that arena, with me trotting along next to her, as fast as my legs would carry me. It was a little embarrassing, but there was no way I could stop her, once she started moving for the door."

"I remember that! Those were my mules! I remember you and that little white mule, now that you say something! Everybody clapped!" Don was laughing and slapping his knee. "So, I'll be, we've met before."

"That was our one show," I laughed. "But this little mule has carried my gear a lot of miles. Eight years ago we rode all the way from Utah to Spokane. It took us three months. That was quite a trip."

"It sounds like it. Ninety days in the saddle. I'll be!" Don said.

"Then, a few years back, we went up into British Colombia, Canada, and followed the Sourdough trail. We camped in an old log cabin that still had a jar of sourdough starter on the shelf. It was all dried up and must've been fifty or sixty years old. There was a grave in the front yard with a little wooden cross made out of a board from the old cabin. Sarah's seen a lot."

"Well, she could live to be forty, you know, as long as you take care of her," Don said. "Mules can live a long time. Why, I figure some of my mules are gonna out-live me!" He laughed so loud the cowboy looked up from the arena.

"Hey, Don, how ya doin'?" the cowboy yelled.

"Not bad at all, Johnny. Not bad at all. Met a mule lady."

"Yeah, we've had a great time with our mules," Don continued.

"We attend as many shows and parades as we can, all over Washington, all over the west! In fact, tomorrow I'll have my Belgium mule team, Bert and Bell, downtown for the Bruce Memorial Mansion Buffalo Feed! We'll be there with the team giving rides in the wagon all day long. There'll be music and square dancing and some of the best barbecue you've ever had. I sure hope you'll lay over a day and join us!" Don said with a big smile.

I had to stay. I'd never in my life been to a buffalo feed. The idea of eating buffalo repulsed me when I thought about their big noses and those hairdos. I kept missing the fairs and the mules could use a day off. Aside from that, Don's smile was not one you could say no to.

"Sure, I'll stay," I said to him.

"Glad to hear it. It's getting pretty close to five. Want to join me for a coffee or a coke up at Ginny's Grill?" he asked me. "I'll drive you back out here afterwards," he offered.

"Let's go," I said happily. Sarah and Mavis were satisfied and had plenty of hay and room to lounge around.

Don yelled goodbye to the two cowboys and we walked from the arena out to his truck. It was a big comfortable pickup that was neat as a pin and even smelled good with one of those pine scented cardboard trees hanging from the rear view mirror. He drove slowly towards town, heading for Ginny's Grill.

"You should see my mules when they're all hitched, eight up. Beautiful dark Quarter Horse mules and they sure can pull a wagon. We've worked with them for a long time now and boy, do they go. You should see them this year up at the Draft Horse Show!"

"I'll miss it this year," I said. "I'll still be on the trail then!"

"You will be?" Don said with concern. "It's gonna be frost on the saddle by about the beginning of October, you know. Sure hope you've got some long underwear 'cause you'll need it."

He drove slowly towards town. "The mules will be pulling a beautiful wagon. We're always working on the wagons, painting and polishing, trying to keep 'em shiny."

"What are your mules called?" I asked Don as we drove slowly on the quiet Main Street of Waitsburg. The houses were all nicely painted with picture perfect lawns. I could tell the wheat farmers

117

had no problem with their lawns, a piece of cake after farming hundreds of acres of wheat. The front porches looked inviting, most with big chairs on them.

"Well, there's Beck and Kate, Mabel and Jib, Sally and Kit, Molly and Ruby. They're big dark Quarter Horse mules. Sometimes we hitch 'em two or four or eight, depending on the event. To haul people in town, I like to use Judy and Sue or Bert and Bell. They're all fine looking Belgium mules. Can't be beat. Some of the prettiest mules in this whole country!" Don said loudly, with his usual smile. I felt at home with the old mule man.

We parked in front of Ginny's Grill. Parking was not a problem in tiny Waitsburg. Don knew everybody and a bunch of his old friends, mostly wheat farmers, sat at a table next to the window. It must have been their special booth.

"Hey, Don, where'd ya find the younger gal?" one of the men yelled from the booth. They all had overalls on.

"Well, I'll tell you, this gal rode all the way from Sandpoint, Idaho," Don said, "on mules."

"Well, then," the man teased, "I guess you two have a lot in common!"

Don and I grabbed a booth near his friends. The waitress, a tall redheaded woman about my age, brought us both coffees. Ginny's was the hub of the town. Don ordered peach pie as the waitress suggested because it was straight out of the oven. I ordered a dinner salad with Thousand Island dressing and a slew of saltines. The waitress smiled when she returned with a big basket of crackers: Rye Crisp, saltines, Melba toast, my choice. And then to top it all off, she brought a cold silver bowl of butter pats.

"That's dinner," I said to myself.

"Been around mules my whole life, one way or another," Don said to me while I tried not to smile with a mouth full of saltines. I drank some coffee and listened, nodding.

"Came out with my family from Missouri when I was five years old. It was the kind of land my father was looking for and we settled in Patahah, then moved over to a place in Prescott, then to Waitsburg and then, in 1945, to the ranch we have now. We've always been wheat farming. You know, this is some of the best wheat land in the west!"

118

I smiled and nodded, my face still stuffed with crackers.

"You see," he continued, "the wheat that's grown here provides the world. They take the grain in trucks from the inland elevators out to Lyon's Ferry terminal on the Snake River. They put it on barges for the trip down the Snake and the Colombia to Portland, Oregon. And from there, it goes everywhere!" Don laughed, making a big gesture with his arms. He didn't see the waitress and smacked her with the back of his hand. She dropped a tray of tall ice teas, but the glasses were plastic and bounced on the hard linoleum floor of Ginny's. There was ice tea everywhere, in the booths and underneath our shoes. Two old ranchers in overalls jumped up and skated across the floor to the back and came out with big mops on long handles. Before long, everyone was seated again, and the waitress brought more ice tea.

After an hour or so, Don and I left Ginny's and he dropped me off at the Days of Real Sport Grounds. The horseshoer I had called from Ginny's was already half way finished shoeing Sarah Jane. The mules stood so still for him. He had no trouble at all with either of them. I paid him thirty dollars, fifteen for each mule.

I felt safe there that night under the stars in the quiet rodeo grounds as I fell asleep on my saddle blankets in the big barn. I could hear Mavis and Sarah eating their hay and breathing softly.

I fell asleep wondering what it would have been like if Nina were still on the trip with me. I thought about the long hard miles I had ridden to get where I was. I figured I was half way to Newport, Oregon. The snow on the Blue Mountains didn't make me feel very confident. I knew I was pushing it, trying to make it before the serious snows hit the country.

I pictured Nina in her home in Seattle making some wonderful meringue or cookies. I pictured her with her cat on her lap and I thought to myself that she must have been thinking about us, too. She had told me on the telephone when I called from Cataldo that she had a picture of Sarah Jane and herself, as we were leaving the ranch, on her refrigerator. That day seemed so long ago.

I walked to Waitsburg in the morning and found Don and his beautiful team of mules. He was looking good in his special white

cowboy shirt, perfectly ironed, tucked into his new Wrangler jeans. He had on the same white straw hat with the brown hatband and shiny black cowboy boots.

People of all ages were piling into the wagon and enjoying a walk around the block. This went on for hours. I got to sit in the wagon next to Don and drive the team. That was a first for me.

The whole town of Waitsburg was on the lawn in front of the Bruce Memorial Mansion. The buffalo was roasting away in big giant barbecue pits. Ladies in pink quilted square dance skirts rustled past. The dancing took place in the middle of the street and old farmers and their wives made each turn with ease, never missing a beat.

I joined right in on the dancing and swung with the best of them, men with narrow waists and perfect cowboy shirts tucked neatly into pressed jeans. It was the special event that brought out the good clothes, free of stains from work.

Don took a break from giving rides for awhile and joined me at one of the long tables the ladies had decorated with red checkered tablecloths and wagon wheels. I had never eaten buffalo before. The ladies of Waitsburg had made every salad imaginable.

The fiddle music from the stage drifted through the town and the square dancers continued on into the late afternoon, until the tables were cleared and the extra food was loaded up in station wagons and pickup trucks. The sun set behind the grain elevator on the edge of town and I knew that tomorrow I'd be back on the road again. Dropping into Waitsburg, just in time for the buffalo feed, was pure luck.

I packed up in the morning and got an early start, for a change. I grabbed a cup of coffee at Ginny's and hoped to run into Don, but he wasn't there.

It was another bright, sunny day as I rode south along the highway towards Walla Walla. I figured it was a good fifteen miles into town. A truck had dropped onions, Walla Walla sweets, along the road for the first five miles as I rode out of Waitsburg. I picked up a few and put them in the red saddlebag. I tried to feed one to Mave and Sarah but they both snorted, insulted.

I followed a road paved with yellow onions halfway to Walla Walla.

There was a lot more traffic on the road which made riding dangerous. I camped on the edge of Walla Walla behind an abandoned house. It seemed safer to me than to camp along the road where anyone driving by could see me, a situation to be avoided.

It was an old, dried up homestead. The windows didn't have glass in them anymore and thin white curtains blew in and out. I looked away from the curtains because they gave me the creeps, the way they were blowing in the wind. The back porch was broken down. The stairs were collapsed. There was, as there always seemed to be, an old apple tree but its fruit was tart and wormy. The mules were up to their knees in deep grass.

I fell asleep listening to traffic on the highway, hoping no one would see me, and felt relieved when I woke up to a new day.

I rode into Walla Walla, waving to the cars as they passed. Childrens' faces in the back windows cheered me as I rode along.

The fairgrounds in Walla Walla were nothing like they were in Waitsburg. I had called the caretaker and had permission to stay there, but I didn't feel at ease.

After I had settled in Stall Number Four, I crossed a tall fence to attend a Gene Wilder movie at the local theater. It was a funny movie about a woman in a red dress. I laughed and felt incredibly lonely walking out of the theater, filled with sadness. I fought back my tears. Of course, once I crossed back into the fairgrounds and buried my head in Sarah's thick mane, I started to come to, but I barely slept all night in the thick sawdust of a stall.

Large shadows loomed on the walls and then would disappear. The sound of heavy feet in the dirt outside the stall had me terrified. Was it the wind or the big door latch? For some reason, I convinced myself that someone was going to sneak in there and murder me. It was so far away from where anyone could hear me if I screamed.

I didn't sleep a wink, tossing and turning in the sawdust, listening for footsteps. I was overcome with a fear that tormented me from the time I first closed my eyes until I finally fell asleep out of pure exhaustion.

The morning came and I said a prayer of thanks when I opened my eyes to the day. I went out to the track where Mavis and Sarah

Jane had spent the night. When they saw me, they came racing across the track, kicking up their heels. I was so glad to see my two mules after my sleepless night in the stall.

"Should've stayed out here with the mules under the stars," I thought to myself.

Mavis raced up to me with her silky ears forward. Her beautiful big eyes looked right through me. I reached out and touched her soft muzzle, grabbing her halter. Sarah stood with her nose nudging my pocket for grain. When she didn't find anything, she turned on her heels and raced off across the track. Mavis pulled away and ran off after her before I could say, "Whoa."

They chased each other for a few minutes. Mave caught up with Sarah and then they ran back to me. I could tell they had no problem with their accommodations. They had enjoyed the thick grass and had rolled in the soft earth right in the middle of the track.

I couldn't believe it. I was almost to Oregon! The snow on the mountains worried me. Every day as the mountains got closer, the more snow I could see.

After riding through Whitman College and giving Sarah a drink from the fountain on the edge of campus, I rode on through town to the Odd Fellows Home.

I tied up the mules in front of the stately mansion with a perfect lawn and giant sycamore trees. I hoped to talk to an old timer there about the old days, maybe find another mule skinner.

The head nurse, a pretty, quiet woman, introduced me to Wayne Fry who lived there with his wife. He had been having a little trouble with his pacemaker, but he was up for a visit.

I entered his room but he didn't see me at first. He was looking out the window of his second story room at the mules tied out in front on the grass.

"Nice looking animals. Where you headed?" he asked as he walked slowly towards me. He was at least ninety, I guessed. He invited me to sit and he pulled out some old, framed photographs of what must have been forty horses and mules, all hitched to a combine. He pointed to himself, a young man of no more than fifteen standing with his hands on his hips.

"I've plowed such steep slopes, out by Dayton, that the lead mules' feet were at the same level as the second pair's backs. Here, look at this picture. It's our barley Holt combine used for the harvest of 1911. That's me on the seat. I was sack jig and sewer. My brother was a driver at only fourteen. We were paid three dollars a day and the harvest lasted about forty-two days. So when it was all over, well, heck, we were rich!" he told me.

"See, in the early years, before the combine, the grain was cut with a turkey wing cradle and bound and shocked. Then they'd haul it from the fields and the team of oxen would tramp it out. A shovel was used to throw the grain up in the air so the wind would blow out the chaff. It wasn't until later they brought in the big teams. Now they're all machines." He stared at the picture for a moment. "I remember those long ago farming days like they was yesterday."

We sat quietly and looked out at the mules. Mavis had wrapped her rope around the tree.

"So, Wayne, what advice would you give a young person?" I asked.

He replied, after some thought, "Well, always treat another person the way you would like to be treated. And tell the truth. If you don't, it will backfire on you. I'm ninety years old now and I still have my wife. We live together here in the Odd Fellows Home. And we're still going strong."

As I was leaving his room, he pointed to a plaque on the wall next to the door:

> *Let me swing from a walker, a crutch or a cane, and to make it right now understandably plain, that my spirit still sings and I'm up and about. Oh it's much too soon to count this bird out.*

His wife walked me slowly to the elevator. "You know," she said, "he makes such awful sounds in his sleep, I always think it's his last breath. I never stop worrying about him, never will. We've been married seventy-five years."

"You stay healthy, Mrs. Fry. He needs you," I said as the

elevator door opened. She grabbed my hand, patting it. "We need each other," she said, with tears welling up in her eyes as she waved goodbye.

The attendant told me they were paving the parking lot and I had to move the mules or stay for three days until it dried.

Perry Baker, a very short old man with a harmonica, played me a song as I left the Odd Fellows Home. I untied the mules and walked off as the music grew fainter and fainter and the old mansion faded from view.

Chapter Ten

Breakfast with the Beamers

"I can't believe it!" I said to Mavis and Sarah as we headed out of Walla Walla on the shoulder of the highway. "Look at all those onions! Look, girls. Big yellow onions, as far as the eye can see." I laughed a little. I was following a path of yellow onions to the Oregon line. Then a big pile of apples came into view, and Mavis walked decidedly faster until she reached the pile that spilled out into the middle of the highway.

"Easy, Mave. Don't slip, girl," I said to her, pulling back hard on the reins.

I got off and picked up as many apples as I could fit in my red saddlebag, which was already full to the brim. I didn't want to get it too heavy. The zipper would rip out or Mave would be off balance. Before we moved on down the road, they each ate about ten apples.

I crossed the line and smiled and waved to the "Welcome to Oregon" sign on the side of the highway.

"Yippee!" I yelled to the mules. "We made it!"

People drove by slowly and waved. As the sky turned orange, I rode on towards Weston. I could see it off in the distance, just a few houses surrounded by large trees. A huge silver grain elevator stood tall on the edge of town.

"Only about five more miles," I promised the mules.

We reached the tiny town and rode down Main Street. Everyone must have been inside eating already, because the town was deserted and quiet. The click of the mule shoes on the pavement was the only sound I could hear.

I caught a glimpse of us in a shop window. Sarah saw the reflection also, and she brayed loudly. Mavis twitched her ears and looked over at the window. She looked surprised to see mules and brayed. It didn't really come out right and sounded more like a squeal. Sarah had perfected her bray over the years. A young mule like Mavis was just getting the hang of it. It would take years for her to develop a bray like Sarah's, one that could be heard for miles and miles.

It was getting dark. I stopped at a well-kept house on the edge of a big, fenced pasture. I knocked on the newly painted door of the tidy farmhouse and stood there on the shadowed porch. An old, white-haired man wearing faded blue overalls opened the door. Behind him I could see his wife standing next to the table serving dinner. Steam rose from the platter.

"Sorry to bother you folks, just as you are sitting down to eat." I stammered. My stomach growled and I hoped he didn't hear it. He was standing there, smiling a little, wondering what I wanted. "I rode down from Idaho, and I was wondering if I could tie my mules up next to your pasture for the night?" I asked. My voice was high and thin. Once the old man spoke, all doubt left me.

"You can put them in the pasture if you'd like. There's lots of good grass in there and I don't have any cows to put on it right now," he said in a shaky, barely audible voice. "Where'd you ride from? Idaho? And where are you headed?" he asked. His wife walked up to the door. She was tall and stately and looked a little younger than he. She wiped her hands on her apron.

"I'm riding down to Newport, on the coast," I answered. "My name is Jody and those are my two mules, Mavis and Sarah Jane, tied out there on the fence," I added.

"I'm Roscoe and this is Winnie. We're the Beamers. Now go out and put those mules in the pasture. There's no need to leave them tied to the fence. Then join us for dinner, if you'd like," Mr. Beamer said.

"That's sweet of you, thanks. You go ahead and eat, though. It will take me awhile to get the mules unpacked," I said to them. "I'll just sleep next to the pasture, if you don't mind."

"Don't mind our old Collie. She may come up and give you a kiss while you're asleep. She does that!" Winnie Beamer told me.

"I'll make sure to sleep with my head under my jacket," I laughed.

I had seen the Burnt Toast Cafe as I rode into town and figured on going down there for some coffee and a salad. It had been a long twenty-mile day and the mules raced gleefully away with a buck and a bolt when I set them free in Roscoe Beamer's pasture. I could see the old couple through the window, sitting down at the dining room table.

The Burnt Toast Cafe was open until ten. Diane, a fiery woman with blazing red hair, ran the place and ruled her kingdom with cheerful confidence. The Burnt Toast had a little counter that sparkled, small tables set up for future customers, and fake pieces of pie in a glass display case on the counter. Diane collected cookie jars and fifty or so graced a shelf about a foot below the ceiling.

She even had lobster on the menu, but I ordered a cinnamon roll and coffee and settled for my usual dinner salad with Thousand Island dressing. I stayed there until it closed. The company was good, and we had a lot of laughs before the night was over and Diane had the last dish washed. There I was, a total stranger, treated like an old friend.

Diane said good night and locked up. She handed me a sandwich wrapped in wax paper with "roast beef" scribbled in marking pen on the outside.

"No mustard," she said as she stepped into her big pickup truck. "Spoils the bread." She started up her engine. "You ought to get yourself one of these and a horse trailer," she said with a laugh as she revved up the engine. "Good luck and be careful. I hope you have a good trip," she waved and drove off.

I walked down the quiet street. A thin black dog followed me. I stopped and opened the sandwich. He approached less warily when he smelled the roast beef.

"No mustard," I said to him in a whisper. The sandwich was gone in two gulps and he ran off.

The wind had died down and the air was so still. I felt as if I had

129

to tiptoe down the deserted street. I wasn't at all tired, not after all the coffee I drank at the Burnt Toast.

I decided to take a walk. Before long I was out of the tiny town and on the black highway, walking down the centerline. I could only hear the sound of my footsteps as I walked on the farm road towards Helix.

I heard an echo to my step and I turned around to find the skinny black dog by my side. He wagged his long silky tail as if to say: "We are the only two awake, so let's stay together." He was looking for another sandwich and a little company. It was good to have a buddy to walk with and we walked together about a mile before we turned around and headed back for town, the streetlights misty globes in the distance.

Suddenly, the dog yelped and ran off towards Athena. He blended in with the road and I could no longer see him. I looked behind me. A large coyote stood in the middle of the road, his round, bright eyes staring at me with interest. I stood perfectly still as he walked slowly towards me, not moving a muscle. I didn't speak to him. His paws didn't make a sound on the blacktop. He was much bigger than the skinny black dog and was not afraid of me. He was looking for the roast beef sandwich. All I had was the wax paper with "roast beef" written on it. I offered it to him. He turned and trotted off into the wheat field. The wheat rustled under his feet and then it was silent again.

I looked over my shoulder every minute or so, all the way back down the road to Weston.

The town might have been asleep, but Mavis and Sarah weren't. Sarah brayed so loudly the Beamers' bedroom light came on. Mavis made a high pitched hee-haw that had a laughable tone to it. I sneaked quietly on tiptoes to my sleeping bag which was already unrolled by the mule corral. I fell asleep in the quietest town on earth.

Winnie Beamer came out in the morning at seven and said loudly, "Well, you won't turn me down for breakfast."

"Oh, I'd love breakfast. I wouldn't miss it." I got up and slipped my tennis shoes on. I was already dressed, one convenient thing about sleeping in your clothes.

I walked in the back door and through the mudroom with Winnie. She moved slowly and deliberately. I sat down at the dining room table in front of a big breakfast of eggs and toast. Winnie looked at me and smiled.

"Coffee?" she asked.

"Love some," I answered.

She sat down next to me at the table. "Where do you camp usually, at night?" she asked, concerned, her brow furrowed.

"Well, I always try to make sure my camp is concealed. That makes me feel safe."

"Yeah, its kind of scary isn't it, camping out just anywhere, anymore? And all alone."

"Well, in the mountains, I never once felt afraid," I answered. "But then I wasn't afraid of anything. But once I get near the big city and the highway, I just don't know who could be going by."

"Well, Missy, I'd be careful. There's so many things going on anymore, oh dear." Winnie shook her head slowly, comforting herself with a piece of toast.

I changed the subject. "Have you seen a lot of changes around here?" I asked.

"No, not too many."

"This town has always had the cannery?" I asked her.

"No, not always. I don't know how long it has been here. Maybe twenty years or so. But it's supposed to be the biggest cannery in the world!" Winnie said.

"Hmm," I answered, with my mouth full. I was devouring a piece of toast covered with thick homemade jam.

"Yep. It's a pretty good size!" she continued. "They say they're going to build another freezing unit up there. Yep! They'll be cannin' and freezin' both!" She laughed. "They started in with peas and then corn, then lima beans. They employ quite a few people over there. I'm not sure how many. But they got three shifts, so they hire quite a few."

"What did your husband do for work?" I asked, between bites.

"He worked at the Grain Growers wheat elevator over here, across the road, behind us up here. Yep, they've got a big grain elevator there. He took in wheat, treated wheat. You know, all this area around here is all wheat. They raise peas, too. But he didn't have anything to do with the peas. All wheat!" Winnie Beamer got up and went in the kitchen for more toast.

"So isn't the Oregon Trail right around here?" I asked.

"Yeah, somewhere right around here close. But I don't know which way it goes!" She laughed. "Once in awhile some folks come through, riding the Oregon Trail, over by La Grande, and out that way," Winnie said.

"How many kids did you raise?" I asked.

"Three."

"I don't have to ask you what you've done in your life!" I joked.

"Yeah, back then they didn't have all the conveniences like they do now."

"No Pampers!" I added.

"They got so many things now, geez, it would be fun to raise a family now! If you had money! It's awful expensive, but with all the new things they've got, why, it would really be a lot of fun. I've got nine great-grand children. Had a new one just the day before yesterday. My grandson's got his hands full. He's got four now. Two boys and two girls."

We sat quietly for a moment.

"I sure appreciate breakfast," I said to Winnie.

She laughed. "Oh, it's fine. Got some more toast there, better eat that piece of toast right there."

"O.K., you talked me into it."

"Might be a long time until you get a home-cooked breakfast!" She smiled and shook her head.

"I don't know how far I'll get today. There's an old timer in Athena I want to talk to. And it looks like it might rain," I said.

"Yeah, it looks a little cloudy," Winnie said. "The paper yesterday said showers. But that's better than it being too hot!" She laughed. "Yeah, it was pretty warm there for a few days."

"It was ninety-six when I rode into Walla Walla," I added.

"I know it," Winnie said. "Want some more coffee?"

"Sure, I'll go for some." She filled my coffee cup from her old ceramic coffeepot.

"That's a nice pot," I said, looking up at her.

"Yeah, it's the first one we ever had! It's kind of an oldie! I don't know, I just don't like the new ones. Seems like the coffee never gets as hot."

"Is this town mainly older people, Winnie?"

"Yeah, it is. People that have been here a lot of years. Don't know just how old the town is, but it was here long before my time."

"I saw some pictures in the Burnt Toast, of the old dirt streets."

"Yeah, it's a real old town," Winnie said. "There's a few real old places up here they're trying to restore."

"I went to the Bruce Mansion up in Waitsburg," I told her. "Have you been there?"

"Nope, I haven't been to Waitsburg for a long time. Not since I was a little girl."

"Did you read in the paper about the buffalo feed?"

"No, I didn't read about that. I don't read much." She laughed.

"You probably stay busy, taking care of your garden and your husband."

"And my chickens," she said. "Don't forget my chickens!"

"How many chickens do you have?"

"Oh, I got three different stages out there. I've got fifteen or sixteen pullets I'm moving down to the chicken house, to the laying pen for this winter. Then I got twenty-five of the white ones. I haven't turned them out yet this morning. I raised them by hand and we'll kill them about November. They're around here. And then an old hen set her nest down there at the neighbors! I was there the other day and she come in with six baby ones." She laughed heartily.

"Six babies of yours?" I asked.

"Yep!" She was really having a good laugh.

"So the neighbor came over and said congratulations!" I said, laughing.

"Yep," Winnie said. "That's right. So I got three different outfits of 'em."

"Ever had a horse?" I asked.

"Well, our grandson had one down here. But the horses and the

134

cows don't mix. Oh, yeah, and our son had a horse when we first moved to this house. My dad gave him one, but it was too wild. It never had been broke. So he sold it and bought himself a bicycle!"

"What did your dad do?" I asked.

"Farmed. Wheat farmed."

"Where'd he come from?"

"North Carolina. He came on a train."

"And that was 1880, or something?"

"Oh yeah, because he was born in 1865 and he was just twenty-one when he came out here. My husband's dad and my dad and one other man all came out here at the same time. And they worked in the brickyard. There was a brickyard right over here. And they worked on that for years. And then finally they got into homesteading a little place and started raising wheat and just stayed on," her voice drifted off. "We went back east two years ago. First time we've ever been back. We flew back and saw the old home place. It sure was interesting, but I wouldn't want to live back there," she said.

"Who lives at the home place now?" I asked.

"Oh nobody lives on it because they tore it all down. I don't know. Probably raised tobacco. Probably plowed it all out. They farmed it and years ago tore all the buildings down. I don't know. I wouldn't live back there. Too darn hot!"

"Too muggy!" I added.

"Oh, you better believe it. But not when we were there. It was March, and winter back there. Oh I tell you, I've never been so cold in all my life!"

"Because it's a damp cold."

"All ice," she continued. "The runways were all iced up, oh my gosh! We couldn't even land. We had to land someplace else and stay over night because the plane couldn't land in North Carolina! And then when we did land, and we got a little shuttle bus to take us to where we were going. And we got in, slammed the door and that window just shattered in a million pieces, it was so cold."

"How awful!" I said.

"Yeah. And the driver tried to put a bath towel over the hole but the wind came in there and, oh my land, was it ever cold! No matter what we did, we just couldn't keep the ice out!"

"How far did you have to go like that?" I asked.

"Oh, I don't know. Far enough. Ten or fifteen miles or something like that. Oh, boy, were we ever cold." Winnie laughed. I looked out at the gathering rain clouds and shivered. The big old Collie dog had his paws up on the window directly next to the dining room table. He stared at the toast I was eating and looked hopefully at me through the glass.

"I don't like airplanes at all," Winnie admitted. "I'd rather go in a car."

"Some people are just like that," I said.

"I'd rather go on a plane than a boat. I don't like a boat at all. But I don't like a plane either! Too noisy. And you're up so far. And you're up so high you can't see anything. You're just out in space. Have you ever flown?" she asked.

"Yep."

"You can't see anything. And you don't know where you are. And, oh it gives me a funny feeling. I just don't care about it." She slid the window up enough to get a piece of toast out to the Collie.

"Was that the first time you've ever flown?" I asked.

"Yep. And as far as I know, it's gonna be the last time!" Winnie laughed. "I don't like the darn things."

"It sounds like you've stayed pretty close to home."

"Yep. Never went anywhere. We never went anywhere until we went east three years ago. I'm not crazy about it. I just like to stay home."

"Well, you raised your family here. You probably have lots of family right around."

"Oh yes, we got our son living outside of Athena about a quarter mile. He raises Quarter Horses. Oh, he's got some beautiful ones over there. And he farms wheat, too. He and his wife's family, two or three of them went in together, and they farm. He raises the horses for a hobby!" She brought out a framed picture of one of the horses. It was a gorgeous, regal animal.

"He wants more toast," I said as we watched the Collie beg

determinedly. He looked directly at Winnie and wagged his tail, giving her his best smile.

"How old is he?" I asked.

"He's about seven," Winnie said.

"Can I clear this?" I asked her, as I started to pick up my plate.

"Oh, no, don't worry about it. When my son was home he always had some different kind of pup. He was always bringing dogs home!" Winnie said, shaking her head and smiling. "Always did like Collies, though."

Roscoe Beamer closed the gate behind me. He raised his old, tired arm up and slowly waved as I rode off towards Athena. The wind picked up and wouldn't quit as I rode away from that warm place, with Winnie filling my coffee cup and bringing me toast and jam.

These people had never budged from their spot.

I watched my shadow moving along the road beside me.

Chapter Eleven

Robbers, Gypsies, and Wait a Minute Red

The days were getting shorter. I knew I had to keep moving. It was not always easy to leave camp before ten or eleven. This wouldn't have happened if Nina had been with me. She would have had me up at dawn, riding four miles or so before breakfast. We would have stopped for tea every afternoon at three, as she had planned, riding a few more miles before we stopped to camp.

It was only three miles to Athena but it took all afternoon in the forty mile an hour wind. I squinted out from underneath the bill of my hat only occasionally to keep the trees of Athena in view. As long as my eyes were shut, I could keep the dirt out of them. Sometimes the wind would moan and then gust down the road at breakneck speed, swirling into a wind devil in the wheat field. Mavis and Sarah kept their eyes closed as much as possible, their thick, white eyelashes protecting their eyes from debris as they walked toward Athena with their heads down. A couple of cars came by, slowing to a crawl as they passed. No one in his right mind was out in this wind. But I knew that. Still, I found it invigorating and scary. The wind took the form of a big dancing dust storm. Some of the little devils were just a few yards away and they dropped rocks as they rolled past. It was best to be inside somewhere, looking out. I pulled down my hat and we pressed on.

To the south, the Blue Mountains were no longer purple shadows in a far off landscape; they were right in front of us, covered with snow. Wildhorse Mountain had a light snow covering that looked like a sprinkling of powdered sugar. I would like to ride through the Blues if it wasn't so late in the year, I thought to myself. They looked inviting. Canyons of white led up into the high valleys and lakes.

Mavis and Sarah were as tired of the wind as I was by the time we got into the tiny spot of a town called Athena. The screen door of the Country Bumpkin Cafe almost ripped out of my hand as I entered the cheery place on the corner. It was warm and full of laughter. A tall woman with a big smile and a thunderous laugh ran the place. Her name was Mary Pat. She took one look at me when I walked in, red in the face, hunched against the wind, and said, "For God's sake, why on earth are you out riding a mule on a day like today?" and poured me a cup of coffee. I just laughed and tried to straighten up, once the last cold gust of wind started to lose its hold on me.

I took a deep breath and a big sip of the hot coffee with real cream in it. I looked out to where the mules were tied to see an old chubby farmer with a Scottie dog, walking from an old Ford pickup towards Mavis and Sarah. He was carrying a grain sack and dumped a pile of oats in front of the two hungry mules. Without a thank you, they lowered their heads and started eating.

The man in the overalls came in the Country Bumpkin, barely grabbing the screen door before it slammed into the Scottie, who wanted to come inside and warm up. The small dog walked slowly back to the pickup and sat down, watching the mules' every move.

The man walked up to the counter and sat down next to me.

"Brought out a little grain for the mules. Thought they'd like that. I saw you leaving Weston this afternoon. Drove by you on the farm road. Sure took you a long time to get here. Must've been that wind. They say part of a silo blew apart up by Milton!"

"Thanks for the grain. It's just what they wanted," I told him. I didn't want to dwell on the fact that we were more than a little lucky to have arrived in one piece. We sat and drank coffee and I told them about my trip so far, the way I had started out with Nina and continued down from Idaho on my own. Each time I told the story, it got a little longer.

Mary Pat told me how to find Bud Miller who was the Sheriff for thirty-nine years in the tiny town. If I wanted to know about Athena, Bud could tell me.

I left the Country Bumpkin warmed up, inside and out. The wind had died down enough and huge, billowy clouds filled the sky. In the distance, the horizon was layered with big thunderheads racing our direction. A storm was coming, no doubt about it.

Three little girls showed up and escorted me down the streets of Athena, past the park, the well-kept yards, the white painted farm style houses of the early 1900's with sculptured bushes and perfect lawns.

I put two little girls on Mavis and they rode double down the street, their own parade. The third little girl held Sarah's rope carefully in her left hand and carried her mom and dad's mail in the other. She led Sarah down the middle of the street. There was no traffic in Athena, and no stoplights.

"Hi Ray!" one of the little girls yelled out to a man in a yard. "I'm riding a horse!"

"It's a mule!" the other girl yelled.

The little girl leading Sarah wore a red skirt and a white blouse. Her knee socks were slipping, but she didn't dare stop to pull them up. Mavis followed Sarah and the two girls, who both fit in the saddle, were having a ball. Up and down the empty streets of town we marched, finally landing at Norma and Bill Thompson's. Norma was working in her yard when the little girls jumped off the mule and ran excitedly up to her, circling her in anticipation. They knew she was the one to ask. She looked up at me and smiled. Her eyes were the kind that danced when she laughed. She wasn't much older than I and she rolled out the red carpet in a moment's notice.

"I'd give anything to saddle up and take off on a trip like yours," Norma said to me with a look of delight in her eyes.

Norma said her husband Bill wouldn't mind. He was always bringing home strays, she told us, laughing. "But never mules, never yet," she said.

They had just arrived from Fairbanks and had only lived in Oregon for ten weeks. She said she had never seen the wind blow like it blew that day, not even in Alaska.

We put Mavis and Sarah in the back yard, hauling out a big bucket of water for them and then she showed me the way down to the Miller's.

Helen and Bud Miller came out the front door onto the porch as I walked toward the house. Word had already reached them, in the few minutes since I had left the cafe, that the lady with the mules wanted to talk to them about the town.

Family pictures and old Sheriff badges lined the shelves and the walls were covered with more pictures. They were glad to have me in. Bud was a large man with a friendly face. Helen, who was several years younger than Bud, had strawberry blond hair and a firm grip when she squeezed my hand. She was neat as a pin and I felt so road worn and dirty standing on their porch. I looked down at my dirty tennis shoes and slipped them off, leaving them by the door as we walked into their cozy living room. Bud walked slowly towards his favorite recliner chair and sat down. Helen offered me a chair.

"Did you see the mules downtown when they were packed up?" I asked. "I think I saw you drive by real slowly."

"Yes," Helen said. "We were downtown and we saw them eating that pile of grain. And I said to Bud, those are mules aren't they? Because I don't know a mule from a horse from a jackass from a zebra, except one has stripes." We laughed. It felt so good to be inside, out of the wind. "Everything's closed downtown and I bet you haven't eaten. Let me make you a hamburger," Helen said as she disappeared into the kitchen. Within minutes, I could hear the hamburger sizzle and the clattering of plates.

"When I was a boy," Bud said, "I lived with my grandparents and my Grandfather Payne had a saddle mule. And that was my saddle horse, that saddle mule. She was a red mule named Becky. There was a team of mules, Becky and Blootch. They were both good riding mules. But Blootch, if you didn't watch him, he'd dump you off when he got a chance! But Becky, I could out-run most of the saddle horses in Athena on that red mule! She was a good saddle mule and a pretty good size one, too. What's the name of that black saddle mule you've got?" Bud asked.

"Mavis," I answered.

Helen laughed. "Don't tell Mavis Shields that!"

Bud and his wife Helen knew everyone in Athena. "Has to do with the fact that we delivered the water bills by hand," they told me.

"How long have you lived here?" I asked Bud.

"Oh, I've lived here all my life. I was born just a block up the street. I'm what you call a native son, I guess. After serving in the Sea-Bees in the South Pacific, I came home and took back my job with the city. It used to be real busy back then. Now, everyone drives out of town for work. Out to the cannery or to Milton-Freewater and up to Walla Walla. It's a ghost town compared to what it was then!" he said.

Helen brought me a delicious hamburger with a salad on the side. I looked down at it and smiled.

"Go on, enjoy it. We've already eaten."

Helen came from New York in 1946 to visit her mother and new stepfather. She first saw Bud on the street in overalls, sweeping up in front of the Sheriff's Office and Jail.

"I thought he was Lil' Abner!" Helen said, affectionately. "Back in New York, they didn't wear overalls. Girls were just starting to wear jeans back there. But I wasn't allowed to because ladies didn't wear pants. We were married in '47," she continued. "I was nineteen, he was thirty-two. And they said it wouldn't last. We've got five kids and six grandchildren now."

"I had pneumonia when I proposed marriage. She got me when I was down," Bud joked.

Helen got him back. "I always say, we only had one argument our whole marriage. It's just lasted forty years!"

Bud never packed a gun in all his years of service. "Never wanted to kill a man," he told me. He depended on hand cuffs and common sense. He remembered the bank robbery, back in February 1948. The fellow took a sledgehammer and busted a hole in the brick wall of the bank vault.

"Did they ever catch the guy?" I asked.

"Yeah, Blackie Odett was his name. He robbed banks clear up into Canada. I remember when the gypsies used to come into town here. They used to park right down here by the railroad tracks," Bud said, shaking his head slowly.

"Did they wear real bright colors?" I asked.

"Oh yeah."

"What else did they do, dance and sing?"

"Oh yeah, they'd dance, and carry on. They wasn't too bad. In later years, when they got so they traveled in cars, why it was worse when they traveled in cars than before when they traveled with horse and buggy."

"Because they were going faster?" I asked.

"Oh, I don't know. Probably," Bud laughed. "They all had big Cadillacs. Big enough to hold the whole family."

"Down here," Helen continued, "where the trailer court is now, they used to have a little restaurant there and they had cabins and so forth. And they'd stay down there. And once they had a baptism at the Catholic Church. And Father Beard was here at the time. And then they had a big meal afterwards. And they roasted lamb and what not. They'd invite different fathers down, but Father Beard said he

144

didn't have the nerve to go down there." Bud smiled and looked affectionately at his wife.

"But Ed Murray, who used to run the court at the time, used to go down to their big feasts. The gypsies used to run him ragged, because those little kids would run in and out, you know. He wasn't used to little kids. That was the problem. But I don't remember them causing any problems around here. They were just transient labor, you know. They just went around to the harvests. They'd do odd jobs and they'd travel. But they never hurt anybody."

"It must have been colorful around here back then," I added.

"This town was wide open twenty-four hours a day during the harvest," Helen continued, pulling a box of candies off the shelf. "Because they had the night crew and the day crew. And they were always going. It was kind of exciting. The hotel and the restaurants were all open twenty-four hours."

"Really?" I asked. She nodded.

"You had guys like Wait a Minute Red and there was another guy they called Cabbage," Helen said. "They had some of the weirdest names, some of those guys that worked the harvest."

"Gypsies?" I asked.

"No, just men. Men that worked the harvest."

"Turn Around Murphy, you know, you'd go down the street and you'd holler at him, Murph! And he'd spin around so darn quick they called him Turn Around Murphy," Bud laughed.

"Who was that one, Bud? Oh yes, it was Jim Clayton. He'd hit who ever was in front of him. He put his hand right through a glass window downtown. Somebody hollered at him," Helen said.

"Is this lately?" I asked.

"No, this was during the harvest. It was up to 1966. That's when it was really bad with all the transient workers. Then, after that, they changed over to the big combines in the fields. Our son Raymond worked out in the fields during harvest when he was thirteen, pitching peas into the viners, because he was over six feet tall when he was thirteen," Helen said. "And then they said no, because he was too young to be around the machinery. He was supposed to be sixteen. But we used to say that at least Raymond was sober because a lot of those other guys weren't. It was a wonder they didn't get gobbled up in the big pea viners!" Helen laughed. "Some of them would work a shift just long enough to get some money and they'd drink it all up. But some of them were well-educated men. Lawyers and teachers and what not. But they became drunks and transients."

"I picked up a guy for drunk driving, one time. He used to be an insurance salesman in Pendleton for awhile," Bud said, shaking his head. "He was driving down the street and he was just froze to the steering wheel, just staring straight ahead. I had a heck of a time getting him stopped up there by the High School, but I finally did. And the next morning when he was sober, I told him that he was accused of drunken driving. And he said, 'No way it could be me, drunken driving. I don't even know how to drive!' And he wasn't kidding." We all laughed.

"You know, I would feel so much better if I could just wash my hair in a tub," I said to them out of the blue. I think Helen was looking at my face closely, and I started to realize I might have dirt all over it. "You know, just run it under the water, even with just dish soap. I'm getting kind of grubby, and if you wouldn't mind, it would only take me about five seconds to do that."

"You can take a shower if you want!" Bud said immediately.

"Can I just jump in there real fast?" I said.

"Step in gradually," Helen said, laughing. "If you jump in, you might fall and bust your butt!"

In the morning I got an early start. I had slept comfortably near the mules until I heard the rain on my sleeping bag, about seven o'clock. I packed up as fast as I could, and rode across the tracks, thinking about the colorful gypsies, in their old Cadillacs full of kids. It was raining steadily as I headed out of Athena, the snow on the mountains a not-so-subtle reminder to keep moving.

A lady named Sophie at the Country Bumpkin told me about a runaway mule she saw down at Mule Days in Joseph. The rider reached down and grabbed his mule's ear, and twisted it so hard, the mule finally stopped. I thought about it and right then and there decided I would never do that to my Mavis, even if she did run away with me.

146

In the wheat stubble, we rode along Wildhorse Creek as it followed the highway towards Pendleton.

I saw the big rig coming up from a long way off. How could I miss it? There was the most gigantic tarp, billowing like a giant parachute above the truck. As it approached, I hunkered down in the saddle and hoped for the best. I wasn't sure what would happen when Mavis first saw the tarp flying towards us at seventy miles an hour down the wet highway.

She saw it, and so did Sarah. They both took off at the same exact moment, racing through the wheat stubble. They took me by surprise, and I found my feet up above my head for a minute until I got my bearings. I leaned forward and held on tight. Sarah was keeping up with Mavis. They were neck in neck and they weren't stopping. Only for a moment I thought of grabbing Mave's silky black ear.

"Easy, girls," I said to them as we slowed to a walk. I'd make Pendleton in no time. It was a sixteen-mile ride; I had seen the mileage on a sign just out of Athena.

I rode in the rain towards town. The mules had calmed down right away and acted like nothing had happened. We kept walking and the rain didn't quit. My heart jumped when I heard the train as we approached the old station at Blakeley. A long freight train heading for Washington flew by us. I lost count at fifty cars.

We rode into Pendleton, a city of rivers. Riding into town, I could see the old routes of the Cayuse and the Nez Perce. My map was full of names that sounded like poetry: Patawa, Tutuilla, and Buckaroo. There was Birch Creek and Wildhorse Creek, Moonshine, Coonskin and Greasewood. There were so many tempting trails to take. I searched the map at night, sometimes making up routes and following trails with my flashlight until the bulb dimmed.

The Round-Up Grounds seemed like the logical place to stay. It had been the site of the famous rodeo since 1909 when an attorney named Roy Raley decided to have a rodeo after the harvest. It began as a small bronc riding contest held on the baseball field.

The names of famous riders like Yakima Canutt, Jackson Sundown and Prairie Rose Henderson are spoken over and over

147

again in Pendleton. People never tire of the stories and legends of one of the west's most popular rodeos.

I paid eighteen dollars, nine dollars for each mule, for two stalls and a place to put my bag down. It was like a night at the Mule Hilton. Beautiful hay was served with a side of grain and a lick of salt.

Mavis was uncomfortable without Sarah, but the stalls weren't big enough for the two of them. Mavis looked through a hole in the wooden wall between them and didn't settle down for an hour. Sarah seemed to appreciate the break and rolled almost immediately in the shavings provided by the Round-Up Grounds. The accommodations were deluxe.

I put on my down parka and a warmer hat and walked downtown to the Rainbow Tavern, one of those old western bars. Pictures of old Round-Up heroes graced every inch of the smoke stained walls. The old pictures pulled me in and I couldn't stop looking until I had looked at them all. Bars in Pendleton like the Silver Saddle, the Frontier Tavern and the Rainbow Tavern are museums full of old memorabilia from many of the Round-Up shows.

Old cowboys smoking cigarettes sat at the bar hunched over their beers. I sat with a draft beer next to the jukebox and listened to Willie Nelson. It was a quiet fall night in Pendleton.

The pink and green neon lit up the street as I walked back to the Round-Up Grounds and slipped in the gate.

Mavis and Sarah were glad to see me but had settled into the soft shavings of the stalls. They both woke up and nickered to me as I grabbed my sleeping bag and threw it down on the saddle blanket which was wet and cold. I tossed and turned and then fell asleep, dreaming of the Happy Canyon Pageant and Barbecue.

Chapter Twelve

Don't Knock, Just Come In

About five miles out of Pendleton, it started to rain. At first just a sprinkle, a steady one that fell from a sky that was only half-cloudy. The sun's light made a double rainbow that had one end in Pendleton and the other in Pilot Rock. Pilot Rock and the buttes to the south, surrounded by thunderheads, stood out on the horizon. This was a fast changing sky. The week before had felt like summer. Then fall came one night when I was asleep.

Every truck that passed was loaded to the gills with firewood, Mom and Pop in the cab with a dog in between them. It was a little ironic, being out on the road with the snow so close on the mountains. The season approached with the speed of a gazelle while I walked on across the land at three miles an hour.

Pilot Rock was fifteen miles from Pendleton. I rode at a good pace in the rain, my big blue poncho keeping me dry. I had on five layers underneath it and I was still cold. It couldn't have been much more than forty degrees.

"What is it Mavis?" I said to her as she came to an abrupt stop. I could see her ears, from underneath the poncho, following the sound of a car as it pulled up behind us, the sound of the wet gravel on the tires making a grating sound. I pulled off the hood of my poncho and smiled at an old woman in a flannel shirt and a bandanna. She had a Pekinese dog on her lap, one of those longhaired dogs with the funny expression on its face. The man at the wheel leaned over to get a better look at our caravan all covered in orange and blue tarps.

"Hi!" I said to her.

"How're ya doin'?" she said in a jarring voice, full of twang.

"How are you?" I answered.

"All right. How're ya doin'?" she asked me again.

"I'm doing great. A little wet! Whoa, Mavis!" I said. Mavis had decided to start walking again since the visitors in the station wagon weren't coming up with any treats for her. The rain was really coming down and if she kept moving it didn't drip in her ears.

"We saw ya this morning when you was just comin' out of Pendleton. So we figured you'd just be getting to Pilot Rock," the woman said. The dog jumped up and down on her lap. He was excited about the big animals with their giant heads practically in his window. His little eyes were just about ready to pop out of his head.

"How many miles an hour do you average?" the man asked me, leaning over the dog and his wife. She also had a big bag of Fritos on her lap. Mavis saw them too, and started to stick her head in the window. The little dog flew backwards, doing a back flip into the back seat of the car.

"About three or four, usually, unless it's a runaway," I answered as I pulled Mavis away from the bag of Fritos and the woman in the flannel shirt.

"Where am I here?" I laughed, trying to peel back some of my layers so I could see them better. "I feel like the Pillsbury Doughboy!"

"Well, by golly, you gotta dress against the weather," the woman answered.

"Where do you folks live?" I asked.

"Pilot Rock," the woman answered. Before the old man could speak, she went on, "We saw the picture of you in the paper and then we saw you this morning on your way out of Pendleton. And we was out driving so we said to each other, let's go down and see how far she got!" The woman held the Fritos out the window for me to have a few and Mavis grabbed the edge of the bag before I could stop her, shaking her head so that Fritos fell to the ground. She and Sarah busied themselves with picking up each and every one.

"Where ya gonna stay tonight?" the woman asked in a concerned tone.

"I don't know yet. I figured I'd head down to the fairgrounds, if there are fairgrounds, and look for hay and a place to keep the mules," I said.

"There ain't no fairgrounds in Pilot Rock, but I imagine you could stay down at the High School Park. They let that rendezvous outfit stay down there," the man suggested.

"Yeah, but would they have any hay?" the woman asked.

"You gotta have some hay, haven't you?" the man said.

"Well, I don't know, I think I'll just wait until I get there and then try to find a pasture," I said. "Sorry about your Fritos!"

"Well, good luck to you. Have a good ride!" the woman said. They waved as they drove slowly off the shoulder and picked up speed. The little dog stared at us out the back window. He looked relieved.

Mavis checked the gravel for Fritos one more time and started walking towards Pilot Rock. The foothills of the Blues were getting snow. I could see the white flurries leaving a blanket behind them as they raced across the mountains on the wind. The wind was really blowing hard. The rolling hills were getting drenched by the storm and the smell was so pleasant, a mixture of sage and wild grasses.

Soon I would reach the confluence of East and West Birch Creeks, two important tributaries of the Umatilla River. As I rode on, Pilot Rock became visible. The wide basalt rock with its sheer cliffs and rounded top could be seen from the Oregon Trail and was used as a point of context by wagon trains traveling over Emigrant Pass and Cabbage Hill.

Finding a place was not a problem in Pilot Rock, Oregon. I saw a bright green pasture with cows and sheep grazing and asked about it at the white house adjacent. Ed and his wife Doris, who looked to me to be in their mid-forties, welcomed me in and set me up in no time. Ed had a welcoming smile and neither one of them asked what I was doing or why. They just helped me get the mules unpacked.

Once in the gate, the mules ran off and kicked up their heels.

"That's their way of saying thank you," I said.

They found the greenest corner of the pasture and started in on their dinner.

Doris, a tall woman with a nice smile and big glasses, showed me to an empty trailer. "I'm afraid there's no heat in here," she said apologetically.

I walked up town and threw all the clothes that I wasn't wearing into a washing machine in the deserted laundromat. Then I walked up to the old tavern on the main street of the town, up a crooked sidewalk surrounded by brick buildings and old wooden stores, many of them boarded up.

I entered a tavern under a neon sign that said Samson's, except the 'm' was out. The wooden door slammed behind me. A couple of old gals were hitting the pool table pretty hard. I ordered a cup of coffee and sat on a tall stool, looking at myself in the big mirror behind the bar. My face was red from the wind and rain and I smiled, so glad to be out of the weather.

The bartender was happy to see a new face in the old bar. He attentively kept my coffee cup full with a strong brew that had undoubtedly been on the burner for several hours.

I had a beer and ordered some fried chicken, two pieces the bartender microwaved and set in front of me. It was steaming and smelled delicious. I looked again in the mirror behind the bar and saw a huge smile on my face, a hungry one. The chicken was too hot to eat so I sat there for a few minutes sipping my beer slowly, listening to the sound of the pool balls hitting the pocket.

The women playing were surely locals. They had that air about them, almost as if they spent more time in Samson's than they ever spent at home. The pool table was their playground and they knew the words to every Western song that played on that old jukebox.

I watched them play pool until the chicken cooled down. Smothering it in ranch dressing that the bartender had thoughtfully brought, after embarrassedly telling me they were out of ketchup. I dined in Pilot Rock as the older gals tied for another game.

"Did you make the Round-Up?" the bartender asked, smiling at me.

"Nope. I missed it. We did sleep at the Grounds, though. Paid nine bucks a mule!" I added.

"Well I'll be a son of a gun. I bet that surprised the heck outta ya!" he said, in a loud voice.

"It was real nice, though," I told him.

"Well, it had better be, for nine dollars a mule! Guess they gotta keep the lawn mowed!" He laughed, and brought me a slug of napkins. I think I had chicken drippings on my chin.

"Thank you," I said to the bartender. "I've got to run down to the laundromat. Save my place for me, will you please?"

"No problem, mule lady. We'll be waiting!" the bartender said, as I slipped out the door of Samson's into the rainy night. It will be nice to sleep inside in the trailer down at Doris and Ed's, I thought to myself, even without heat.

There was a cold forty-degree wind and the rain was blowing sideways as I walked into the warm laundromat. My clothes were ready for the dryer. I looked forward to clean, warm clothes to wear.

"I should have brought my sleeping bag down here to dry it out," I said aloud.

I went back up to Samson's. There was a new person sitting at the bar, next to my half-empty chicken basket. He was an old man, must have been in his eighties. He was hunched over a beer and his large rugged fingers were slowly rolling a cigarette. A brand new pack of "Roll Your Own" was on the bar. He had on an old plaid shirt, its pockets packed with Kleenex. He looked up and smiled at me, his thick black eyebrows arching in a friendly way. He had trouble breathing. I could tell by the way he took a big breath before he spoke.

When he was done rolling the smoke, he lit a match with a shaky hand and aimed for the cigarette. After three tries and two matches, the end of the hand-rolled smoke caught the flame and the old man was happy. When he smiled, his whole face lit up, his eyes and every part of it.

I was in no hurry to leave the warmth of Samson's. The rain beat hard on the window, with the wind blasting it against the glass and the Samson's sign with the missing 'm'. Western songs played on, smoke swirled, beer was poured and drunk, and the night outside was kept at a distance as we turned on our stools, which spun easily on their bases, to watch the older gals play another game of pool. No one was there to challenge them for the table, so they just kept playing each other, over and over again.

"What's your name, little lady?" the old man asked.

"Jody Foss. What's yours?" I asked.

"Breeze Looney," he said, taking a shaky sip of his beer. "Been here all my life, right here in Pilot Rock. My house is right up the street. But I spend most of my time sitting right here, listening to this guy's bull!" He pointed to the bartender and laughed a big laugh for such an old man.

"Oh, I got a story for her, Breeze. The one about my troubles up at Joseph," the bartender said.

"Oh, God, here we go," Breeze said to me, shaking his head.

"This is what happened," the bartender started in. "I was up at Joseph, at Joseph Days. My girlfriend and my daughter and I were out on the lake, taking it easy. I fell asleep and that was all it took for them to turn on me and have some fun at my expense. They took my clothes, since I was sleeping out there in my underwear, and swam to shore. They left me alone out there on the lake."

"Then what happened?" I asked.

"When I woke up, burned to a crisp, I rowed in to shore and took my buddy's pickup, even though I didn't see him anywhere around. I drove on in to Joseph to the Rainbow Room, and walked right in, with nothin' on but my skivvies! Everyone was laughing real hard as I walked up to the bar, looking for my girlfriend and my daughter, who were hiding in the bathroom laughing themselves to death. I went out to the parking lot and was about to put a rock through the window of my pickup so I could get to my clothes. Everybody and his mother came out of the Rainbow Room to get another good laugh at me in my near naked state. A cop showed up and grabbed the rock out of my hand. He didn't care that I was mostly naked. He just didn't want me getting glass on the street. Ever since that day, anyone can come in my bar without shoes or shirt or pants, for that matter, and get a beer!"

Breeze's shoulders shook with silent laughter.

"They're still laughin' about it, over in Joseph at Swede's and the Rainbow. Once in awhile they come over here to Pilot Rock and take off their shirt and shoes just to give me a hard time." We were all laughing, even the pool playing gals who must've heard the story a hundred times before.

"I just rode down here on my mules," I said to Breeze.

"On your mules?" Breeze asked, sounding surprised.

"Yep, from Sandpoint, Idaho."

"Oh," Breeze said. "From old Sandpoint, huh? Sandpoint used to be a pretty good loggin' town."

"Yep. It took me a whole month!"

"What the hell brought you down here?" Breeze asked.

"I wanted to see what the country was like. I wanted to take a trip all the way across Oregon," I answered. "So, you've been here your whole life!"

"Yeah, 'bout gol'damn eighty-four years," Breeze told me. "Yeah, I was born in this gol'damn country here. You're gonna go on a gol'damn mule all the way across Oregon, huh?"

"Do you want to come with me, Breeze?" I asked.

"Yeah, but I think that's too much of a trip for me," he answered, smiling, his eyes dancing. His thick dark eyebrows stood straight up adding an exclamation point to his expression.

"You've been around horses very much?" I asked.

"All my gol' damn life," he answered.

"Did you know Frank Burger? He used to cowboy down here. Once he rode all the way from Pilot Rock to Mexico City. Did you know him? I met him when I was lost up by St. Maries, Idaho." I took a sip of my beer. It was going flat in a hurry.

"No, can't say that I did," Breeze replied.

"Did you cowboy when you were younger?" I asked.

"Oh, yeah. I cowboyed all my damn life until I got so damn old I couldn't sit on a horse."

"Doing rodeo, or what?" I asked.

"No, I didn't fool around. Oh, I made all the little brush shows, but then I never did go for the big stuff," Breeze said as he rolled

another smoke.

"Has this town changed much?" I asked.

"Oh, yeah. There ain't nothing here now but a gol'damn trading post. That's about all that's left here. The damn mills are all shuttin' down. There ain't nothin' left. It never was anything but a farmin' country anyway. Just an old tradin' post. That's all that Pilot Rock ever was. And by God, it's not even that any more. So you rode from Sandpoint down this way!" Breeze said loudly with excitement in his voice.

"Yeah, I've got my mules over at Ed's place, right as you're coming into town. It's that old white house with the pasture, a couple of sheep and some Black Angus cows are in there," I told him. "What did you do for work in your life, Breeze?" I asked.

"I logged. I logged around here for, let's see, close to fifty years. Raised a family here. Damn! I've often thought, what did I stay in this gol' damn country for? Damn! But, I did!" He laughed.

"In the twenties we logged with mules. You better believe it. Those mules were hard workers. Model T trucks would carry the load out to Milton-Freewater where ol' Clyde Harrison had a box factory. Yeah, we used to skid out the logs with the mule teams. With a pulley, a cable and a team of mules, we rolled those logs up onto the bed of the Model T truck."

"Do you remember the Depression?" I asked.

"You're damn right I remember the Depression. You bet your life I remember it."

"What was it like?" I asked.

"By God, there was a lot of hungry people out there, I'll tell you that," Breeze said, quietly. "Oh, Geez, a lot of hungry people. But there's gol' damn near as many now as there were then, with the damn cut backs," he said. "You know, that last Depression, it started in '28. Then in '29 and '30, it was rough. I mean rough, girl. You couldn't sell a gol' damn thing. You could raise good crops, but you couldn't sell 'em. You couldn't get any money! All they did was trade among themselves."

"Barter system," I added. "Is that what you did, Breeze?"

"Nope. I managed. Don't know how, but I did. See, the loggers

157

were issued scrip instead of money, just a slip of paper that promised payment. The scrip could be sold at a loss for those needing cash. I saved mine. And sure enough, it added up. Man, back then it was pretty rough. But the people got where they learned to cook and can so they could save money. Darn well right they did. It didn't take an awful lot of money during the Depression. It wasn't that it took so much money, there just wasn't any! But the people who did have a little bit of money, they was holding on to it. They wasn't putting it out."

He stopped and caught his breath, then took a sip of his beer and rolled a smoke. "Weaner pigs and calves, you couldn't sell 'em. You couldn't give the damn things away. People didn't have anything to feed 'em, so they didn't want 'em. Yeah, it was sure rough."

"Did the animals get skinny?" I asked.

"You could tell they was damn hungry all right. Geez!" Breeze answered. We both sat at the bar, quietly. I thought about Mavis and Sarah in the good graze down at Ed and Doris' place. They hadn't been really hungry a day in their lives.

"I'm glad to meet you, Breeze," I said. "I've met some really interesting people on this trip."

"So where are you going to go next, now?" Breeze asked.

"I'm heading down towards Prineville. I'm going to Heppner," I added.

"That's a good little town, Heppner," Breeze said cheerfully.

"Is it?"

"Oh, yeah," he said.

"Is it bigger than Pilot Rock?" I asked him.

"Oh, hell yes. They could hide this whole gol' damn town on the main street of Heppner. Oh yeah," he answered.

"Then I'm going down to Spray, down to some of those ghost towns down there. Hardman and a couple of other ones," I said. Do you remember when that country down there was real busy?"

"Well," he said slowly, "it never has been too awful busy."

I laughed. "A lot of cowboys come through here? Is this part of the Oregon Trail?"

"Yeah. You left the old Oregon Trail when you left the main highway comin' from Pendleton. It goes on towards Emigrant Pass.

Highway 395 goes clear through to John Day. That's good country. They've got some good looking ranches down that way. I done all my work in the woods," he continued after we sat for several minutes in silence reading the jokes on the cocktail napkins.

"You've ridden a lot of horses, I bet," I said.

"Yeah, oh hell yeah. I'd break horses in the wintertime, when I wasn't logging. And I'd go out here and break a horse or two to ride. Some of these old boys didn't like to break 'em. But that used to be a lot of sport. Oh hell, it was a lot of fun," Breeze said, thoughtfully.

"Can you tell me about a certain horse you remember?" I asked him.

"That I remember? Yeah, I remember breaking the one they used to call Powder River, down here in Pendleton. It was finally sold to the Pendleton Round-Up deal. I broke that horse to ride!"

"Oh yeah? Was he a pretty hard horse?"

"Oh, he was a little bit salty all right, when I first started breakin' him. But as quick as he found out I wasn't going to hurt him in any way, he gentled down to where a kid coulda rode him! But you put him in the bucking shoot and turn him out of there, by God he went to work out there!"

It was getting pretty noisy in the old tavern. The smoke was thick and the jukebox was wailing another cowboy tune. I looked out and could see the rain had stopped.

"So what would be your advice to somebody fifty years younger than yourself?"

"What?" he looked at me, a little surprised. He was still back on old Powder River.

"What advice would you give someone fifty years younger than yourself?" I said again. "What would you tell 'em?"

Well, I'd say live life the way you see it, regardless of what the hell it is. You know, you only have got one life to live, and if you lived it, took somebody else's word for it, do this, or do that, you'd always think, why the heck did I take that advice? Why didn't I live it the way I wanted to!"

"Yeah." I answered.

"Yeah. That's the first gol' damn thing ya think about. Yeah! Just

159

set a certain way and a certain thing you're gonna do, and go ahead and do it that way."

"So, you're almost eighty?" I asked, being careful not to guess too high.

Breeze laughed and gave me a funny look. "I'll be eighty-four, next November," he said. "I was born in 1900. Yep."

"So this town was more active in the old days?" I asked, hopefully.

"Just damn near like it is right now. All it was, really all this damn place was was just a trading post. That was all. And farming around here. And just the trading post. And finally in later years, they got these two or three mills in town here. And that built the town up a little. But now, it's damn near back to what it used to be! Every other house you come to on these streets is for sale! That's how good things are around here! Yep! People trying to get enough so they can get the hell out of here. They're lookin' for work, just like they did in the Depression. People are going from one place to another, lookin' for work. And everywhere they go, it's the same damn way any place they go. They might as well just take what ever money they got and just sit on their butts as to go travelin' around, because they ain't gonna get anything. But they're tryin'. Yep! They're tryin'."

We sat quietly and watched as the older gals hung up their cue sticks and racked up the balls. They had played about three hours straight, bending over the table with concentrated precision in a series of motions they had performed a million times. Dropping coins in the jukebox, racking up balls, lighting cigarettes, dropping an eight ball and groaning, winning and losing, drinking and telling a joke. They said their good byes and strolled out into the now freezing night. It had started to rain again.

"Supposed to rain through tomorrow," Breeze said to me. "Do you think you'll hit the trail in the morning or wait out the barometer? Either way, come on up to my house for coffee."

"I think I'll wait and see what it looks like in the morning. But I sure don't feel like riding in the rain right now!"

I walked back to Doris and Ed's place with my head down to the rain. But I couldn't help but look up at the old streetlights in Pilot Rock, as the rain was making halos around them. Walking back to the little trailer, I said good night to the mules who were standing side by side with their heads down, trying to keep the rain out of their ears and get a little sleep. I was ready for some myself.

The trailer would have been perfect that night if my sleeping bag hadn't been so wet. I knew when I first crawled into it, on the old cot, that I had made a big mistake not taking it up to the laundromat. My cold, damp legs felt no warmth from the wet down bag and I shivered.

It was a long night. I decided to stay another day when I woke up to the sound of heavy rain. I sat up on the cot and looked out at the pasture, rubbing my eyes and yawning. Mavis and Sarah were busy enjoying the thick, green grass.

"Come in for breakfast," Doris yelled from the kitchen. I went straight over after putting on some dry, clean clothes. Sarah brayed at me when she saw me walking up the path towards the back door of the big white house.

"Good morning, girls!" I yelled to them. They started walking over towards me in the rain, as if to say: "Well, we've had breakfast, let's get walking."

Doris smiled at me and said, "Good morning. How did you sleep?"

"My bag was sopping wet. I think I will wait out the storm today and dry out that bag at the laundromat."

"The mules look like they don't mind the cows or the sheep," Doris said as she put a big two egg and potato breakfast in front of me and filled up a large coffee cup with steaming hot coffee she had just made. "I saw the black mule chasing the sheep around a little this morning for sport," Doris laughed. "She seems like she likes to play."

"She's still a kid," I told her with my mouth full. Everything in her house felt so cozy. The wood stove was putting out a lot of heat and it came rushing up underneath the table, warming my still half-frozen legs.

"Also, she went up and touched the electric fence with her nose. And oh my, you should have seen her jump backwards! She didn't like that," Doris said, laughing.

"Thanks so much for breakfast, Doris," I said when I had finished.

"Anytime," she said. "We're glad we had the pasture. Come back tomorrow morning for breakfast before you leave. The storm is

161

supposed to quit tonight. Ed had to go to town and he was going to pick up some grain."

I walked to Breeze Looney's, up the steep hill with the cracked sidewalk, past Samson's and the abandoned, boarded up buildings. I knocked on the old, torn screen door and Breeze yelled from inside: "Don't knock, just come in!"

I walked over the creaky wood floor in the living room. Breeze was sitting in the kitchen at an old table, rolling a cigarette.

"Come on in. Sit down. Have some coffee," Breeze said in a loud voice. He got up slowly and left the newly rolled cigarette in a big wagon wheel ashtray on the table.

His kitchen was painted white and was pretty clean for an old man living alone. He walked over to the cupboard and got a cup for me, then set it down slowly in front of me, turned and went to the wood stove to get the coffeepot. I could hear the coffee boiling away in the pot and I think it was a good thing he took it off the fire, because it was plenty strong enough and left grounds in my teeth.

"You know, I'm getting so old I shuffle around like an old Chinaman. But dammit, I used to run around these hills like a rat up a rafter!" he said as he walked over to his favorite chair and sat down again.

"I just couldn't ride today," I said to Breeze. "It was raining too hard."

"Yeah, it's too cold to be starting out today, anyway. And you don't want to end up out there stuck in the rain someplace all night," Breeze said.

"So, I decided to come back and bug you some more," I joked.

"You don't bug me any."

"I didn't know if you'd be here or not."

"Oh, hell, I go downtown ever once in awhile and have a few beers, but I ain't goin' down today. It's too damn cold to be goin' out!" Breeze said emphatically. "I said, to heck with that, I'll just stay in the house."

"So, there was a big flood here?"

"Oh hell, yeah, there was a big flood here in '34 or '36, and it covered this whole country down here. Geez! And there was another one in '64. Geezus! There was about four foot of snow out here and

162

we got this warm rain. And then a hot wind. Geez! There was water all over this darn place! All the stores were full of water out here. Yep, it was pretty wet."

"So what happened?" I asked.

"Well most everything was ruined in town here. There wasn't a hell of a lot left. It broke all the fish dams out, and fishing ain't been worth a damn in any of these cricks since then. It took all the fish dams out you know, the ones nature builds. It's just getting now where you can catch a few. But this used to be damn nice fishin' country. You could catch trout, ten to twelve inch trout."

"So that was a long time ago, now," I said.

"But it seems like yesterday," Breeze said. "The water down Main Street here was way up past your knees. It was a blanket of water. It sure made a heck of a mess. And it took a heck of a long time to get it all cleaned up. But the fishing has never been the same since. Breaks my heart because I used to love to catch a trout for my dinner!"

With that, Breeze got up again and shuffled over to the cupboard and opened it. The whole cupboard was filled with pork and beans, and nothing else but a can of Folger's Coffee. He pulled out his knife and opened a big can of pork and beans with ease and heated it up on the wood stove, still in the can.

"People in town worry about me too much," Breeze told me. "Always telling me to quit beer and smokes and to eat better. But heck, just look at all the good pork in them beans!" he laughed. "I don't cook fancy. Heck, I've been batchin' it here for sixteen years and I ain't dead yet."

"So do any Indians ever come in to town?"

"Oh, hell yeah. They come in from the reservation and around, you know. And I see them down here once in awhile at Samson's. They have a heck of a good time in town when they come in."

"Do you know any of them?"

"Oh, hell yeah. I know 'em all. There's one fella around here I'd like to have you meet while you're here. Maybe he'll be in town. If he is, by God you'll know it. His name is Charlie McKay. His mother is 103 and that old girl has got a good memory yet. A heck of a good memory. She still does most of her own work. I don't see how the old girl can do it, but she does."

"Where does he live?" I asked.

"Out here on Dry Crick. Old Charlie might be in after awhile, and I thought I might walk down there and by golly I'll introduce you. He's from the Yakima Tribe."

Breeze was quiet as he rolled another smoke.

"There's three or four different Indian nations out here on the reservation. Some of these Indians are darn smart and well educated. I get quite a kick out of them. I enjoy talking to them and by golly I sure hope we run into Charlie while you're here."

The rain continued to pour outside, and never quit until late afternoon.

"Breeze, do you know the story about the Black cowboy who won a bucking contest and about Jackson Sundown who competed up in Pendleton in 1911 or so?" I asked.

"Oh yeah, that was George Fletcher. He was a Black man. And old Jackson Sundown was the Indian. And this other guy was from Oklahoma. He was Indian all right. He was Cherokee. It was 1911 or 1912, somewhere along in there. It had to be around then, because after that Hoot Gibson, the cowboy, you know, from the movie pictures, named the Pendelton Round-Up. I'll have to ask old Charlie, I bet he remembers."

"So what was the story?"

"The Black guy won it, fair and square. But they wouldn't give it to him. So they gave it to Jackson Sundown, the Indian. But I can't remember the Cherokee Indian's name for some reason it just won't come to me."

"So what did the Black cowboy do when they wouldn't let him have the award?" I asked Breeze.

"He didn't do anything about it. There was nothin' he could do, you know. He was working for a rancher out here, breakin' horses. They had already awarded it to the other guy, so there was nothin' he could do. He just kept his head up and kept after it. They wouldn't give a black man a break on anything. It was the wrong thing for them to do, but they did it anyway! When I see Old Charlie, I'll ask him if he remembers. He probably even remembers the name of the rancher George Fletcher worked for. He remembers everything. And this Fletcher was married to an Apache woman. By God, when she bellered he listened!" Breeze laughed.

"But old Sundown, you know, he was a member of Chief Joseph's Wallowa band. His Indian name was Wetas-Tenia-Naka-Pykt. How's that for a name? And it meant Earth Left By The Setting Sun. He even fought in the Nez Perce War. And he was pretty old when he started bronc ridin'. He was fifty or so when he won that big World Championship," Breeze told me. "Yeah, that old Sundown, he was quite an Indian and quite a bronc rider."

Breeze and I walked down the deserted Main Street, carefully watching our step on the cracked sidewalk. We stopped on the little bridge overlooking the creek which rushed beneath the road, swollen and muddy from the rain.

We walked down to Samson's to look for Old Charlie but he wasn't around. My sleeping bag was dry and sat in the bottom of the dryer in the laundromat, light as a feather. I promised myself I'd ride out in the morning.

As I said goodbye to Breeze, he said: "If it was twenty years ago, I would have rode on out with you!" He grabbed my hand and held on.

Chapter Thirteen

The French Ranch

The storm had passed and the day broke crisp and clear. The sky didn't have a cloud in it and the sun felt warm on my face as I rode out of Pilot Rock. The huge, rounded rim rock stood out on the horizon, first in the foreground, looming like a huge trail beacon, and then later in the day I could no longer see it.

Passing a big windmill which stood still in the practically windless air, I rode up through Jack Canyon, along a tributary of Birch Creek. When I reached the spot in the road called Nye, I headed west on the Heppner Highway, riding once again in the sage on the edge of the road.

People told me it would be pretty desolate and lonely once I got on the Heppner Highway and, sure enough, I didn't see anyone all day. I did see a lot of deer, though, and they were all curious about the mule with the big pack. They followed us along the road, keeping their distance and running further away when I stared at them too long. There was a whole family of them and they seemed to be on the move. Hunting season was just a week away. I said a little prayer for the beautiful does and their fawns that they survive the coming months, that they find a hidden spot in one of those valleys, far from the hunters' scope.

The day could not have been more beautiful. Heavy growth of

thorny bushes and sagebrush stretched across the landscape. I was in awe of the lonesome, rugged hills and canyons in every direction as far as I could see. Mavis and Sarah stopped suddenly for what I thought was no reason, but I had dropped my knife while I was peeling an apple.

"Thanks, Mavis," I said to her. She had learned so much from Sarah Jane, every day a new lesson in life. This had to be the best way to train a mule, I thought to myself. Just get out on the road and ride. By watching Sarah, Mavis was learning things I would never have thought to teach her.

"Nothin' at Vinson, 'cept for some old ranches," Breeze had told me. I thought about Breeze, down at Samson's, wondering where I was going to camp. I could picture him sitting there talking to the bartender, rolling smokes.

The mules walked at a fast pace. They were feeling refreshed and ready to go. It was a perfect day for making miles.

I rode eight or nine miles before I knew it, stopping under some trees for a cup of coffee and a peanut butter sandwich. I had a brand new jar of peanut butter I had bought in Pilot Rock, along with wheat bread, coffee, popcorn, dried apricots and some apricot jam.

After building a small fire, I got some water boiling for coffee. The mules grazed, tied to fence posts, and then fell asleep while I looked at the map and followed Butter Creek to its beginning in the Blue Mountains. Looking at the names of the nearby canyons, I tried to figure out which folds in the hills they were. There was Coombs Canyon to the north and Willow Springs Canyon to the south. I could see by looking at the map that I would cross Butter Creek when I came to Vinson, so I could find water there.

The map also showed a water tank. Sometimes it was possible to get water out of the water tank directly from the pipe. Otherwise, the water was for stock only.

It was starting to get dark and I wanted to camp. I had seen an old water trough next to some ancient trees and had almost stopped there, but decided to ride on. It looked like a good camp, but there was nothing to tie the mules to. If I let them both go, they'd run sixteen miles back to Pilot Rock and the last green pasture.

It was one of those ranches that had been there so long it blended in with the landscape.

Built in the cleavage of a brown hill, tucked away at the bottom of a draw, it sat next to a runoff from Butter Creek. The sign on the gate said, "Beware: Biting Dog." There was an old white two-story farmhouse that had seen better days and cried out for a paint job. It, too, was beginning to look like the land around it.

I didn't dare go in the gate. The mules were happy to be tied up so they could have their dinner as it was that time of day. They always made sure I knew when it was time to eat and were never afraid to share that information with me. Sometimes they would shake their heads and snort if I didn't let them stop. Or they would simply walk off the road to the nearest patch of bunch grass and start eating before I knew what happened.

I knocked on the cold metal door of the old, weathered trailer next to the road. There were tire tracks in front of it, but no one answered the door. It definitely looked like a bunk house, but there were no cowboys in sight. I left them tied to some heavily built corrals right on the road.

I sat there on the ground next to them trying to decide what to do and finally started unpacking Sarah, putting the gear in a neat pile beside me. When the dog barked I was glad there was a fence between us. He sounded ferocious and upset that I had stayed so long on the lonely road to Heppner.

I unsaddled Mavis and then both mules rolled in the soft, dry sand next to the corral. They stood up at the same time and shook the dirt from their coats covering me with more dust. I closed my eyes and waited for it to settle, feeling it stick to my skin.

The sound of a car engine broke the silence. I listened as it got closer and closer and finally crested the hill and came into view. A woman about my age with a car full of kids pulled up and turned off the engine.

"Passing through?" she asked. "My husband's the foreman here on the French Ranch. No one is staying in the house right now and you are more than welcome to put your mules in the corrals and stay the night."

I felt a wave of relief as I watched the night come sooner than I had been expecting. The days were getting shorter and the temperature dropped ten degrees in ten minutes once the sun settled behind the hill to the west. The sky was on fire, full of oranges and reds of all hues, turning dark blue and then black. I made a quick wish on the evening star.

Mark showed up. He was a real good-looking cowboy and, for just a second, I felt a wave of envy towards the woman in the car. He was tall and handsome, with bright blue eyes and a big smile.

"Howdy. Where are you headed?" he asked. He looked like he was about to start laughing.

"Newport, Oregon," I told him. "We left Idaho about a month ago," I said, feeling my face flush. I hadn't seen a man so handsome in a long time.

"What an adventure. And no horses. Just mules! What do you know! We don't get too many girls traveling across this country on mules, that's for sure." He started laughing a little, shaking his head and looking at me. I'm not all that funny looking, I thought to myself.

"What?" I asked him. "What is it?" I laughed along with him even though I wasn't sure what the joke was.

"Come here." He led me over to the side mirror of his pickup and turned it out so I could see my face. When the mules had shaken off the sand after they rolled, most of it had settled on my face. I smiled in the mirror. My eyes were shining out of my dirt-covered face. I tried to brush off the dirt with the sleeve of my pink blouse. I had such a crush on this handsome cowboy I looked good to myself, regardless of the dirt on my face.

"Brought you some hay for the mules. It's oat and alfalfa. There's a big salt lick in the corrals, too, and water. They'll be fine in there," Mark said as he got back in the pickup. If he didn't have a wife waiting, I would've suggested he stay for dinner, to join me for a can of beans and a cup of coffee.

I let Mavis and Sarah out of their halters into the big, heavily built corrals. They went from one corral to the next with their ears cocked, listening. At that moment, a big snake slithered towards my pack bags and saddle. The mules were high stepping nervously through the grass, checking for snakes. But after a few minutes they were chewing the hay with delighted satisfaction.

"The house is open. There's everything you need. Hot water, stove. Feel free to go in and cook your dinner, fix coffee, what ever you need. Oh yeah. The dog's on a chain. His bark is worse than his bite anyway," he said with a laugh. Mark had been to Ukiah and was anxious to get home to dinner. He drove off in the pickup truck.

Rubbing my eyes to get the sand out, I listened as the treeless hill swallowed up the sound of his engine. Aside from an occasional warning bark from the dog, there was a great stillness.

I walked down to the old farmhouse, down the dirt road that eventually circled the house and disappeared across the back hill. The back door creaked as I went to open it and the dog growled in a low

171

tone. He sounded more scared than I was at first. Once I spoke, his growl changed to a softer, less worrisome tone, as if he knew I had permission to be there.

I had the shivers as I opened the old screen door of the porch and stepped into the mudroom. There were at least thirty pairs of boots on that back porch that smelled of manure and leather, rubber boots with dung caked to them, cowboy boots that had seen better days, some with toes that were twisted and warped from wear. There were corks for logging and every other kind imaginable. The boots told the story of a working ranch.

The dog finally stopped growling. Silence filled the house after the door slammed behind me and I marveled at my whereabouts and my luck.

Doris had given me a can of beans which I opened with my knife and then lit the old propane stove. I boiled some water for coffee and turned on the radio that sat on the scratched kitchen table. Mexican music filled the old house which made me feel more secure and lonely at the same time. It brought back wonderful, bittersweet memories of my dog Robin. I fought back the tears when the image of her became so clear in my mind I half expected her to be curled up under that kitchen table.

I changed the station, settling on a Western station from Boise, Idaho. They were playing two hours of uninterrupted Willie Nelson songs. Drinking my coffee, eating the beans and listening to the radio, I sat at the old kitchen table for hours.

My legs were getting stiff so I jumped up from the table and tuned the radio back to the Mexican station that was coming in loud and clear from Walla Walla, Washington. I started to dance around the kitchen, kicking up my heels when I reached the corner where the old empty refrigerator stood. Then I danced around some more, laughing at myself, wishing there were a cowboy to spin me around the cracked linoleum floor. Instead, I made my own fun and played in the ranch house for awhile with an old mop for a dance partner.

If anyone had been watching from outside and I'd known about it, I would have died from embarrassment. But I knew I was totally alone in that big old house with the Mexican music and Willie

Nelson echoing through the heartwood walls.

I decided I'd prowl around a little bit and see what the rest of the house was like. My fear had kept me from investigating any further than the old kitchen where I was keeping myself entertained.

The other rooms were dark and when I hit the light switch, nothing happened. My flashlight had burned out and I had forgotten to get batteries in Pilot Rock. I groped my way up the narrow, rickety stairway, my heart in my throat. The music in the kitchen was no comfort as I felt the peeling wallpaper on the stairwell which smelled like mold and old paper.

The stairs creaked beneath my step but I made myself keep going slowly up the stairs, one by one. Finally I reached the top and found a light switch on the wall. I switched it on and nothing happened. A shiver went up my spine.

At that moment I heard the beating of wings. A large bat came directly for me and I felt his wings touch my hair. That was enough to get me screaming. I flew down the stairs and back into the kitchen where it was safe and light, hitting my head with my hand to make sure the bat wasn't stuck in my hair.

I sat down at the table and tried to breathe. I heard something fall on the floor in the room directly above the kitchen, but I didn't have the nerve to investigate. My hands were shaking as I turned on the old propane stove to make a cup of tea. I had myself more than slightly terrified and decided, then and there, I would sleep outside next to the mules, as far away as possible from where the snake had run through the grass.

After my cup of tea, I started out through the mudroom and pushed on the rickety old screen. The dog was quiet. It was a dark night with no moon. There were more stars in the sky than I had ever seen. The hills were as black as the sky and they ran together. I stood for a moment by an old wooden gate and looked at the stars above me and felt hot air on the back of my neck. My blood ran cold as I spun around, preparing for a ghost or worse, and came face to face with a big black horse. He snorted, butted me with his nose, and then turned and ran away into the deep, dark night. I heard the sound of his hooves pounding the dirt as he raced up the hill. Finally, it was quiet again.

"I've had enough excitement for one night," I said aloud, once I caught my breath. The sound of my own voice comforted me a little as I gathered up my nerve to go back in the house and turn off the light in the kitchen.

Once the light was off, I ran for the back door, returning to the pitch-black night. Walking as fast as I could back up to the road, I climbed over the metal gate. My saddle pads made a soft bed and I lay on my back in my sleeping bag staring at the star-studded sky, until I finally fell asleep.

I woke up to the sound of the cowboys arriving in their trucks. I hid in my sleeping bag, knowing my hair would certainly scare them. Mark was the lucky one to see me just as I sat up in my old red bag. I immediately pulled on my hat and, once again, could feel my face blush. He was so handsome.

"Why didn't you sleep in the house?" he asked.

I just laughed a little and shook my head.

I went back in the house and made my coffee and some toast which I covered with apricot jam. It wasn't a bit scary in the light of day. I watched through the window as six or seven cowboys saddled up their horses and rode off up the trail behind the house. Mark turned in his saddle and waved to me as he rode off behind the others. I smiled and waved to him, turned away from the window to gather my saddlebags and headed off in the direction of Heppner.

The French Ranch

It's so quiet on the land
Where the French Ranch stands
Down in the gully,
This old white house
Whispers stories of another age
When its halls and walls
Echoed the sounds of children.
Now,
Only the foreman's boots stand on the porch,
Only the sound of a big horse
Galloping back and forth.
The wind blows.
The hay truck roars by.
The trees stand the same
As they always have,
The corrals stand crooked and empty.
It's quieter than quiet.
The ranch has suited her people fine.
The quiet sings a quiet song
Of another, long ago
Cowboy time.

Chapter Fourteen

Canteens of Gold

The road was quiet between the French Ranch and Heppner and we had it all to ourselves. Mark told me that it was a good thirty miles and I might not see a soul. We climbed slowly towards the sky on the first big grade. It was deep blue and the air was furnace warm, an Indian Summer day.

"Wish I could've brought Mark along to keep me company," I said aloud to the mules, squinting at the sage-dotted hillsides. I had to laugh at myself, always a sucker for a pretty face. It gave me something new to think about as I rode along but after about half the day, I gave it up.

Breeze told me the Oregon Trail was just a few miles north of the road to Heppner. I could see the Colombia River Gorge to the northwest. There was the Umatilla Forest and the Blue Mountains to the south.

Breeze had said the land was chock full of rivers and underground springs. During the Gold Rush, miners rode through there on their way to Idaho and Canyon City and Seneca. Some followed Willow Creek Valley, cutting off on Butter Creek and Dixie Creek and the forks of the John Day River. That was one thing nice about traveling down to the gold mines in Canyon City: there was plenty of water.

The Indians also followed this route to hunt deer, pick berries and camp in the Blue Mountains before returning to the salmon fishing at Celilo on the Colombia.

I sat in some bunch grass while the mules had a snack. I pictured the wagon trains and the people walking and riding towards their dream of the green richness of the Willamette. As they passed through that bench country, fording rivers, through sand and sage, I'm sure many of them wondered what the heck had been wrong with Philadelphia.

I crossed over the desolate, lonely hills and looked back up into the draws of Dixie Canyon and Matlock Canyon. I stopped at Dixie Creek and remembered the stories I had heard about the many pack trains that had come down that rugged, well-worn trail. The people who passed through there, heading for greener pastures, must have later thought back to the bunch grass and the abundant water and solitude. After a few wet winters in the Willamette, they'd remember that quiet land with fondness.

Mavis and Sarah walked with a steady pace towards Heppner. As we were coming down to Little Butter Creek, we saw a porcupine sitting by the side of the road basking in the warmth of the afternoon sun. We had interrupted his nap. He was upset by the mules and waddled off before I could get a real good picture of him. What a wild looking coat he had on! He bristled as he walked off as fast as he could and disappeared in the deep grass. Mavis and Sarah were not a bit afraid of him, but their eyes were wide and they kept their distance.

We saw about twenty or thirty hawks and about twenty game hens as they sped off through the sagebrush. Two huge pheasants crossed the road together, right in front of us, parading confidently in their bright feathers.

We had gone sixteen miles and the sun had turned the sky into a mix of orange and purple. I could hardly take my eyes off the brilliant masterpiece the sky had become. Just as quickly as it had arrived, the color disappeared as darkness came, blanketing the sky with a million stars.

I never felt at home until I lit a tiny fire and heated up some water in my little coffeepot. It was then that I would start to relax. Waiting for my coffee or tea, the mules fed, I'd listen to the night.

The mules were so happy when I turned them loose in the well-built corral by the side of the road. They pranced around, Sarah chasing Mave. Then, side by side simultaneously, narrowly missing each other's legs, they rolled all the way over from one side and back again. They clipped the grass as far as they could reach in a square around the wooden pen and then fell asleep standing up. Sarah finally went to the corner of the corral and lay down.

I built a small sage fire and made myself a cup of coffee with milk and sugar. I ate the rest of the beef jerky, rolled out my bag and fell asleep next to the corral. Before I knew it, the sun was urging me to rise. The sunrise was even more colorful than the sunset had been. Red and orange bands of light raced upward from the black, cold hills. I sat there in the silence watching the color fade as the sun crested and soaked us in warmth.

Making myself a cup of coffee on the tiny remnants of my fire from the night before, I sat on a log that was a perfect bench and listened to the sound of the grouse clucking and running through the sage, warning me not to stay. Hawks circled over me as the sun broke across my face and warmed me up. The whole landscape glowed with the muted green of sagebrush in the light of that morning sun. It was so beautiful it made me cry as I packed my household on Sarah and saddled Mave. I felt like the luckiest person alive.

Little Butter Creek made a comforting sound as it passed my camp by the corral. I walked around with my coffee cup and kicked the sagebrush with my tennis shoe. The smell of the sage was so sweet I could smell it all day as I rode on towards the town of Heppner and, after that, I started sticking a little piece in between my shoelaces.

I counted up the miles and it looked like a good fourteen across the sagebrush until I reached Heppner. Following Hinton Creek all the way into town, I looked north towards Sand Hollow and Black Horse Canyon into some bench country I wished I could ride into. The frost on my sleeping bag in the morning kept me from riding too far off a steady route to the west, across the mountains that would soon be deep in snow.

I had heard about the Doherty Family from an old skinny rancher in a 1948 Chevrolet pickup truck who stopped by to see what I was up to. He was the only person I saw on that road.

"James Doherty came from Ireland on the 'Encoria' which arrived in New York City in 1883," he told me as his old engine idled and finally sputtered and died. He didn't seem the least bit concerned. He just turned off the key. He was enthusiastic with his stories and had found an eager listener.

"He found his way west to Oregon to Butter Creek where he worked for a rancher named Cunningham. He worked and saved and bought his own sheep business. Then around 1890 he moved to a big ranch up Black Horse Canyon. He built up his ranch, starting with three hundred and twenty acres, and ending up with thousands."

"So this was big sheep country."

"No, they were average-sized sheep." This got the old man laughing. He was hitting the steering wheel with his bony hand and having a good belly laugh. He continued, still parked in the middle of the road, "A lot of those rugged Irish immigrants found their place down here in the hilly bench country south of the Colombia. Their ranches were huge, with range horses and cattle and sheep. But mostly sheep. The government passed laws that allowed the settlers to stay on the land, you know, prove up on it. And that's what they did. But no one asked the many tribes that had lived here for centuries. The laws were made back east and the Indians stood, as long as they could, in the way of the settlers who aimed to make it all theirs. There was very little regard for the tribes."

As he spoke from the cab of the old green truck, he made large hand gestures and pounded on the old metal dash. I noticed the radio, an old black and cream colored one with big black knobs. After another minute, he drove off and disappeared over the rise. Must have had to go feed since it was getting to be that time of day.

The conflict had been fought right beneath my feet. I drank from the streams, thinking of those who had quenched their thirst before me. It seemed their voices sang in the river, their histories and stories left untold.

180

There was the trail stop at Cecil and the old water well where everyone filled their canteens and jugs, Indians and pioneers alike.

"I would like to fill up my jug at the old water well," I said to the mules. The Oregon Trail could still be seen some places. Deep ruts in the sand and dirt heading off across a distant hill. By then the travelers heading for the Willamette must have been dreaming of that green country just over the mountains, and of the trees and crops they would plant in the fertile valleys west of the Cascades. Later on, when the Willamette was too crowded for cows, many of the cattlemen came back to the wide open land east of the mountains.

Riding along at a fast pace, before long I saw the big tall trees on the edge of town. I knew Mavis and Sarah were glad to be back in a town close to a feed store. We rode down the Main Street of Heppner and the sound of the mules' hooves on the pavement made quite a racket since people came to their doors to see who was riding down the street.

The fairgrounds were on the edge of town. I was told to put the mules in a series of pens directly behind the arena and the bleachers. I slammed the big metal gate and headed up to Heppner. The mules never looked up from the grass hay as I slipped away and headed for town with my red day pack slung over my shoulder.

It felt so strange to be walking again after riding so many miles without a break and I hobbled towards town, stiff from the day's ride.

I bought a bag of carrots at the store. Later I would split it evenly between the two mules. I looked forward to a dinner salad and maybe a sandwich and longed for a tall glass of ice tea. I stretched out my legs on the walk up to the coffee shop passing the neat houses and the old brick and stone buildings of downtown. I looked over and saw myself in the window of a store as I walked in long strides up the sidewalk. I couldn't help but smile when I saw my reflection, walking without a care in the world needing little more than pasture, water, and an occasional dinner salad with Thousand Island Dressing.

The Wagon Wheel Cafe looked inviting. I tugged on the big door and found a table by the counter. There were two waitresses.

The older one with a pink frilly hair net, a pink waitress blouse, pink earrings and a necklace approached me and wiped her hands on a fresh bar towel, which was also pink.

"So where the heck did you come from? You look like you've been out in the wind and the sun. What's the story?" she asked as she filled my coffee cup and slammed down a stainless steel pitcher of cream.

There was a big rooster clock on the wall and a sign that said "Good Morning." There was one of those milkshake machines next to the stainless steel sink. The pies smelled so good; they were being laid out on a shelf to cool.

Coffee cups remained full at the Wagon Wheel. Big luscious steaks and pancakes and pie and delicious salads were served to hungry ranchers and farmers and hunters and families. It was about the only place to eat in Heppner and was the most important place in town, besides the feed store, especially to me, living on popcorn and beef jerky.

"I rode down from Idaho on a mule," I answered the pink waitress.

She put down the coffeepot, put her hands on her ample hips and started laughing so hard she was shaking the counter. A pile of plastic menus fell on the floor.

"Now what would ever possess you to ride a mule from Idaho all the way to Heppner?" she asked. She looked at me hard with a funny grin on her face.

"I guess I just wanted to get out and look around," I answered, "see what's out there, you know."

"Well you couldn't get me to do something like that. I'd be cryin' like a baby that first night on the trail, wanting to be home in my bed. Oh, when I was younger, my husband talked me into camping once, but, by God, I swore never again," she laughed again. She shook her head, picked up the coffeepot and poured me another cup.

I ate about twelve saltines and smeared butter on each one, making little butter sandwiches. And I ordered a small dinner salad and ate it in seconds flat. It filled the hole in my stomach and I sighed to myself what a perfect day it had been. I listened to Willie Nelson's "Red Headed Stranger" album, which was being played on the radio in the kitchen. I planned to stay awhile, as long as I could without irritating the waitresses.

I looked up at the door to see an old man with a ruddy complexion limping slowly towards my table. He was obviously wishing he was younger just then. The mischievous look he gave me made me smile and remember that old men are still young men at heart. This old man in the blue plaid cowboy shirt sat down and ordered some coffee from the waitress with the pink hair net. The other waitress was organizing the pie case.

He sat down at my table without asking. He just smiled at me and nodded his head. He was pretty crippled and moved slowly. His hat was green and white and it said "Cutsforth Ranch, Lexington, Oregon" across the front.

"I'm Orville Cutsforth, glad to meet a lady who needs company," he said with a smile. The pink waitress laughed and shook her head. The older waitress at the pie case was giggling, too.

Orville looked out at me from behind big metal glasses. I noticed his hearing aid. He was perfectly dressed, neat as could be except for the worn hatband that hung down onto his forehead. His face lit up when he looked at me.

"Glad to meet you," I said, smiling at him. He grabbed my hand and shook it hard just as I was taking a sip of my coffee. It spilled down my shirt. The pink waitress loaned me her pink towel and I mopped at it half-heartedly.

He looked at my empty salad bowl. "Is that all you're gonna eat?"

"Yeah, for now."

"Well, why don't I feed ya?"

"Oh no, that's okay."

"I got a dollar and a half, two dollars," he said. He looked up at the pink waitress and winked. She winked back.

"I'm not real hungry right now," I said. "That's okay."

"It would tickle me to death to do it," Orville said.

The waitress asked Orville, "Are you gonna have anything?"

"No," he answered slowly, "I don't think I want a thing because I'll be having dinner pretty soon and that'll spoil it."

"I saw your mules when you were riding into town. They look

like they're out of Thoroughbreds," he continued.

"No, the white one is an Appaloosa mule and the black one is a Quarter-Arab mule," I told him. "Why did you think they were Thoroughbred mules?"

"Well, like I told Collins, I know more about mules than anybody in this country. I owned forty-two head. Worked 'em on the farm down here. I farmed twenty-four thousand acres."

"Twenty-four thousand acres?" I asked in astonishment.

"Um-hmm. Wheat land. Oh there's some pasture land, but mostly wheat land. And then there's six, seven hundred head of cattle," he added proudly. "And then I also told Collins I know more about women than anybody in this country, too." The pink waitress laughed. "I have forty-eight children and grandchildren here," he said, smiling.

"And how many wives?" I asked.

He shook his head. "Three of them."

"I believe you."

"So you're out seein' the country, huh?" he asked.

"Yep."

"So you want to hear something about Heppner?" he asked.

"Why not?"

"Well, we came here in 1906. And the Heppner flood was 1903, so you can tell I know all about the flood. Yep! But I got here three years late. Have you seen our dam?"

"No," I answered, taking a sip of my coffee.

"It's gonna control all the floods from now on. And it's leaking something terrible. I was just talking to my old friend about it. He called me and said, 'Orville, I hear the dam is leakin'.' It's runnin' through I told him. Then he asked, 'Well what's gonna happen when it freezes?' Why it's just gonna burst, I told him. You see, in 1919 it was forty degrees below zero for thirty days. Well, that dam will saturate with water and then when it freezes it will be saturated with ice. Look it up in the encyclopedia, how much it will expand when it freezes. It will expand eleven percent! Well, it's a hundred and sixty feet high, so it will expand another sixteen feet! And then next spring when it thaws out, it won't shrink. It'll be full of cracks."

"That doesn't sound good. What will happen then?" I asked Orville.

"The sad part of it is, there's no steel in that dam. The Army of Engineers is condemning dams all over the United States. And if that dam cracks, and there's no steel in it, it's gonna open up like a barn door, isn't it! And that'll be the biggest bulldozer to ever went through Heppner," Orville said, looking around for the waitress to fill my coffee cup. "And that's just my opinion," he added.

"Is your house high enough on a hill so you won't get wet?" I asked him jokingly.

"No, it isn't high enough. My house is about twenty feet higher, but it won't be high enough. See, that water would be sixty feet high. Now wouldn't that make one hell of a swipe comin' into Heppner?" he asked. "I used to love to ride to town on my horse to see the train come in once a week. Oh, I used to love to watch that train coming in. And people would ask me, why do you want to see the train come in? And I answered, oh, because someday it will come in sideways. And won't it cut one hell of a swipe?"

Orville laughed.

"They wanted to build the dam to spurt the economy. All they needed was to clean the channels going through town. They didn't need a dam. So you want me to tell you about the Heppner flood?"

"Yeah, tell me about the flood."

"See, I bought a seven thousand acre ranch from the Hynds brothers, old Scotsmen. They'd lived there fifty-four years and they told me many stories about this flood. To begin with, the road going into the mountains crosses a crick they call Balm Fork. And they built a trestle, out of poles, thirty feet high across that crick. Well these cloudbursts come from the west and they travel east. And this storm was about a mile wide. But it rained about fourteen inches of water in one afternoon. Fourteen inches!"

"Wow! That's a lot of rain," I said, my mouth full of saltines.

"Well, it came across Balm Fork and dropped its fourteen inches of water and everything loose on Balm Fork came down the crick. You know, hay racks, wagons, hog pens, cow corrals, everything piled against this trestle and made a dam across Balm Fork. Well, the cloudburst traveled across the ridge and put fourteen inches on

185

Willow Crick. And the same thing happened on Willow Crick. Logs and branches, oh anything, came down. And it arrived the same time as the trestle gave way at Balm Fork. So we had two floods hit the town at the same time. And if they hadn't had that trestle there, the Balm Fork flood would've been twenty miles down the crick. You see, that's the way nature does it. You've got three cricks comin' through here. You've got Shobe, Balm and Willow. See, the storm hit Shobe first, and it didn't have any obstructions in it. So it hit town and just went right on through. And then Balm Fork got stopped with this trestle, until Willow Crick got there. And then the two hit the town at once! That trestle caused the Heppner Flood. Man caused. It wasn't an act of God, it was man. With that trestle. These Army Engineers, they wanted to build this big dam to stop floods. No use tellin' them that. Because they didn't want to hear it. They wanted to build a dam."

"Did you try to tell them that?"

"Oh yes, yes, yes. I can take you a couple miles up Willow Crick or a couple of miles up Balm Fork and show you grooves. Yep, grooves as big as this room, comin' down the hills like that, where that water hit. Just washed the face of the hills full of grooves like that for about a mile. I tried to get those engineers to go with me and look at those grooves so they could see just how much water there was in that flood. But they weren't interested. Now that's my own opinion. But I'm old enough to get away with sayin' what I want. Nobody's gonna hang me!"

Orville looked a little worried. "I tell you what. Let's drive over to the fairgrounds so I can get a good look at those mules and I'll call my wife and let her know to keep my dinner hot."

"Sounds good. Let's go."

Orville slammed a five-dollar bill down on the counter and whistled at the pink waitress. "Here, honey. Here's your money," he said in a sing song voice. "The mule lady and I are going out for a tour of the town and to feed some mules," he said loudly. Everyone in the place knew Orville and they all sort of laughed and shrugged.

He slowly walked towards the door of the Wagon Wheel. I could feel my face redden as he held the big glass door open for me.

We walked out and stood next to his pickup. He leaned against it so he didn't fall over. He looked somber for a minute as he gazed up the wide main street of Heppner.

He sat on the back bumper and leaned on his cane. I looked inside the Wagon Wheel and a young red faced rancher was laughing and shaking his head. I guess everybody knew that Orville liked to talk and was good at it.

"Like I said earlier, I bought a ranch, seven thousand acres, from the Hynds Brothers, old Scotsmen, who lived there fifty-seven years. Those old timers told me many stories about the flood in Heppner. You see, there were three brothers, Dave and Will out on the ranch, and Jack, who ran a livery stable here in town. It was right over there." He pointed down the street.

"They were all friends of the Indians. Oh, they were fine people. I never knew them to carry a gun or anything. The Indians would come through in the spring, going to the mountains. And in the fall going back down to the Dalles because that's where a lot of them wintered. And they'd camp at Jack's corrals down there by the livery stable. And this day in early June, they came through and never stopped at his corrals. They camped up there on the hill where the school house is now."

Orville paused, looking down and shaking his head. "He wondered what he had done to offend these Indians. Then two young Indian squaws came down and told him, this was along about Sunday noon, that much much water was comin', that's just what they said, much much water was comin' and for him to get his family and move up on the hill with them."

"Did he do it?" I asked. "Did he take their advice?"

"The old sun was shinin' bright and the sky was blue, so he didn't do it. And this wall of water came through town and drowned his wife and three children and carried him on a bunch of railway ties halfway to Lexington. And he got out, down at Monahan's Ranch. And we lost about two hundred and sixty-seven settlers and about sixty Chinese. But not one Indian. Now those Indians knew," he paused, "six or seven hours before the water came."

He got up and walked to the door of the Jeep Cherokee and

187

opened it, holding his cane out of the way of the door. I didn't help him. I could tell he didn't want that. I was relieved when the heavy door swung open and didn't knock him over in the street. He slid into the seat and nodded at me to get in the other side.

"When I was up in Alaska, diggin' gold with my gold dredge, I found lots of gold."

"Oh yeah?"

"Oh yeah." Orville laughed. "I traded a fruit jar full of gold for this here Jeep Cherokee," he said, with a glint in his eye.

"You did?"

"I did, straight across," Orville said as he slammed the door and rolled down the window.

"Up Willow Crick, we've got a bunch of timberland. And we've got a cabin up there. It's a lodge. It's built of logs and it's round with double fireplaces in the middle. And it's the best mountain cabin in Oregon. We really like it. Well, my wife and my neighbor's family were up there and they got one of those cloudbursts. And they got afraid of the storm. And so they jumped in the rig. And my wife told about how the water poured on the road so deep the pickup could hardly make it through. And they got back down here where we live. And see, I have Tennessee Walking Horses.... Well, anyway, where was I?" he said. "Oh yes. Those three horses were there in the pasture by the house. And when my wife and our neighbors got down there, they looked up on the big hill behind the house and those horses went frantic. They were running and running in the pasture. And they got up on top of that hill and stood there. And I sold six acres to the Game Commission and they had three horses. And she said those horses just panicked. Running the fences, trying to get out. There was a little knoll at the end of the Game Commission pasture. And those three horses of the Game Commission got up on top of that knoll, it wasn't but four or five feet high. And here come a flood of water, hill to hill."

Orville was a little red in the face. "An hour or two after she got there, they drove through the cloudburst up on the mountain. But a flood only travels about two miles an hour so she got there quite a bit ahead of the flood. But those horses, just like the Indians, knew that flood was coming. Now that will make you think, won't it?"

"Do you think the Indians just know things like that?"

"Have to," Orville said.

"They just know," I said reverently.

"For the whole tribe to move up there and send a couple of women down to tell Hynds to come up, much water was coming. That was five or six hours before it rained."

"That's amazing."

"It's uncanny. We don't know it all, you know."

I looked out the window of the Jeep Cherokee and noticed the rancher in the Wagon Wheel was still watching us. Orville pulled slowly away from the curb and headed down the main street at a snail's pace. The waitress with the pink hair net ran outside and was trying to get Orville's attention, but he ignored her. I think it was probably his wife calling to find out if he had left the Wagon Wheel. The waitress went back inside, wiping her hands on the back of her skirt before she pushed open the big glass door.

Orville turned his head a little in order to watch her.

"Henry Heppner was a mule man. Did you know that?" Orville asked as he drove down the main street towards the fairgrounds at about two miles an hour.

"Didn't know that."

"Yep. He was runnin' mule freight teams between Umatilla Landing on the Colombia River and the gold fields. You know Canyon City had a gold rush and lots of gold was found. A lot of the fellows headin' for California never made it and stopped to try their luck in the gold mines around Canyon City and Seneca."

Orville would have been a gold miner, I thought to myself.

"Ol' Heppner was originally from Prussia and he and his family showed up in New York around 1850 something. He was down in California, always real successful at whatever he did. He was a mercantile man and knew what the people wanted and needed. So after he set up shop in the Dalles and Corvallis, he was camping on Willow Crick and set up a permanent camp in this valley. He was no longer a pack train or wagon man after that. He set up freighting and mercantile businesses all over the area around here with Jackson

Morrow. Heppner bought the goods that were needed and Morrow built the store because he already had one up in LaGrande. There were about twenty-five families around back then. See these sidewalks?" Orville nodded towards the street and its shops. "These were some of the finest boardwalks around in those days. The town was growing, and the wool and wheat was all brought in to town, so the Oregon Railroad and Navigation Company built up Willow Crick from the Colombia all the way down here to haul out freight. Oh, there were still lots of pack trains, then. The pack trains built this country."

He pulled over to the curb and stopped.

"Old Heppner and Morrow were out there pounding in the last spike when the railroad came in. There was a big depot out north of town. Oh, that was a big day in the town! There were big bonfires up and down the crick and there was a dance that night that lasted until dawn at the Opera House. So that was beginning of the end of the mule trains and freight wagons. All the fuss was pretty much over about the gold in California, but the towns that grew up around the gold, wheat, sheep and cows just kept on."

We pulled into the fairgrounds. Mavis and Sarah watched with interest as we pulled up in the Jeep Cherokee. When I opened the door, they saw me and brayed. Mavis' bray was starting to deepen a little since we left home, but it was still nothing compared to the sound that came from Sarah. Sarah's bray echoed off the back of the bleachers and the walls by the shuttered snack bar. Orville shook his head and laughed.

"Those mules could wake up the dead," he said as he adjusted his glasses and fiddled with his hearing aid. I could hear it ringing.

We walked together and perched ourselves along the red metal corral, both of us hanging our arms over the top pole. Mavis took her soft nose and nudged me with it. I scratched Sarah's soft ears for a minute and she dropped her head into my hands and enjoyed a good scratch. Mavis looked hopefully at Orville with those gorgeous dark eyes. He reached in his pocket and pulled out a peppermint and fed it to her. She decided peppermint candy wasn't her taste and with one toss of her head she spit it out and it disappeared in the hay.

"These are fine looking mules," Orville said to me as he patted Mavis with his old bent hand. She was gentle with him and didn't throw her head, even after the peppermint. He pulled up a plastic bucket and sat down, looking through the red metal gate. "They are a hell of a lot smaller than our big work mules, though. And that's good for you. Closer to the ground," he laughed. "Had any runaways?"

"Oh, one, up by Pendleton. They never run too far."

Orville took off his hat and scratched his forehead. He pulled out his handkerchief and wiped his balding head.

"So were there a lot of cowboys around here?"

"Oh yes, oh yes, there were cowboys all right," Orville laughed.

"Did you used to ride?"

"Oh yes, young lady, I've probably rode further than anybody in this country."

"Oh yeah?"

"We lived one hundred and seventy miles from Calgary when I was a kid. East of Calgary. And I had to ride to Calgary and back for the repairs for our thresher outfit when I was thirteen. We had a Hamiltonian trotting mare called Molly. She'd trot twelve miles an hour. We trotted her ten hours; that's one hundred and ten miles, ain't it?"

"That's what I need," I joked.

"Oh no you don't, no you don't. Dad would shorten the stirrups on that saddle and put one of us boys on that mare and head her for Calgary. And Bozana was about half way to Calgary, seventy or so miles from our ranch. And Dad would tell us to trot her a mile and walk her a quarter." I knew he could hear his dad's voice saying those words.

"Well, we'd trot her a mile and lead her a quarter. You can understand that, because that's what you're doin'. And that mare would stay right on your heels all the while you was leadin' her. Oh, she was a honey. They'd kill themselves goin' if you let 'em."

"They'd just go and go," I added.

"So we'd ride to Bozana and about six or seven miles beyond it there was a cattle ranch, and we'd stop and spend the night. We'd go to Calgary and back in four days. It was about three hundred and

191

fifty miles. And we never took a cent of money."

I smiled at him in disbelief.

"We'd stop at those ranches. And those folks would be tickled to death to keep us overnight, you know, and send us on our way, puttin' a sack of oats behind the saddle. Oh yes. I've rode thousands of miles."

"I don't travel that fast," I said. "I make about twenty miles a day with these mules."

"Have you ever heard of Ben Snipes?"

"Nope."

"Ben Snipes owned more cattle than any man in the world. He lived in the Dalles and his ranch went all the way to Yakima, ninety miles across the ranch. Around about 1870 or 1880, somewhere around there. And he'd gather eight hundred steers and trail 'em to the Kamloops up in the British Colombia gold fields. And that's where he'd sell 'em. And he shipped a Hamiltonian stud around the Horn and up the Colombia, you know. All the farmers did that in those days. The horses were all Hamiltonians."

"Is that like a Tennessee Walker?" I asked.

"A Tennessee Walker and a Morgan and the Quarter Horse are all descendants of the old Thoroughbreds. The Thoroughbreds come out of the Hamiltonians. Well, he got a Hamiltonian stud, and he headed up to Kamloops, seven hundred miles with a bunch of Indians. And he'd sell the cattle for gold and he'd bring the gold home to the Dalles, canteens full of gold on each side of his horse."

"Canteens full of gold? Wow!"

"Well, one time he trailed these cattle up there and he took two bands of Indians with him. They got caught in the storm with eight hundred head at Penticton. And so they had to leave 'em there for the winter. Well, the next spring they came up with eight hundred more so they had sixteen hundred head of steers. They took 'em into Kamloops, up on the North Thompson River, sold 'em and he got a couple of two-gallon canteens full of gold for 'em."

"Really?" I asked. Orville nodded.

"Ben Snipes was a great friend of the Indians, just like the Hynds brothers. If you treated the Indians right they was really friends. An

192

old squaw told him that a couple of half-breeds were gonna murder him and kill his horse and steal that gold when he started back for Oregon. So he crept out in the middle of the night, and he stole a mule. And he saddled up that mule and he had gold on each side. And he headed out for the Dalles. He swam the Colombia River twice. He had to, on that mule! And he rode from Kamloops to the Dalles in seven days on that mule, with eighty pounds of gold. A hundred miles a day on that darn mule. And he'd pat the mule as he went and say to him, now don't you tell my Hamiltonian stud, Baldy, but you've got the hell beat outta Baldy!"

"That makes twenty miles look like nothing, doesn't it?" I laughed.

"Mules know more than a horse ever knew. Why, it's a pleasure to be around mules workin'. They don't step on your foot and a big-footed old horse will step on your toe and won't get off! A mule won't. And you can walk around a mule and he won't reach around and take you by the shoulder and bite you clear to the meat like a wicked old horse will. If he knows what you want him to do, he'll do it. Just like a good dog. And a horse, maybe. And even as good as Prince was, my Tennessee Walkin' stud, he was one of the finest horses I ever rode. Even as good as he was, I'm like ol' Ben Snipes: don't tell Prince, but the mule's got him beat!"

My Idaho home from the top of the barn

na and Jody with Sarah

Photo by John Fuller

St. Maries, Idaho

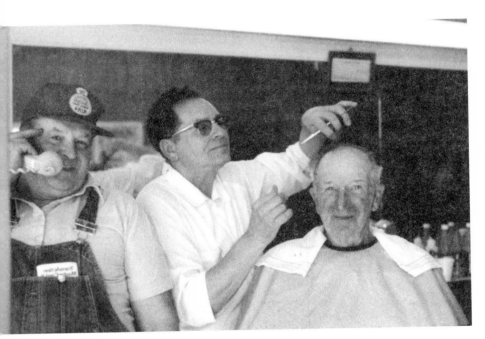

ayton, Washington

Idaho Road

Orville Cutsforth, Heppner, Oregon

reeze Looney, Pilot Rock

Walla Walla, Washington

Wayne Frey worked the mules

204

Chuck Young

Roscoe and Winnie Beamer, Weston, Oregon

Mrs. Dingle in Dingle's, Dayton, Washington

Crossing the Snake River, Lower Granite Dam

Pilot Rock, Oregon

Newport, Oregon

Sarah Metcalf, the veterinarian, Potlach, Idaho

Roscoe and Sarah Jane

Viola Waterman, Harlan, Oregon

Leaving Harlan

Chapter Fifteen

O.W. Remembers

I slept on a very comfortable couch in the living room of Joan Carlson. She and her son Paul drove down to the fairgrounds just to invite me over for a barbecue and a shower. Joan was a shy, well-dressed woman in her mid-forties. Her hair was dark brown and she wore red lipstick and was groomed impeccably. Her house was a comfortable one, but everything was so clean and white I watched where I walked, even after I took off my shoes.

The shower was heavenly, as was the barbecue that followed. A few of Paul's friends came over. I enjoyed the company of people around my own age. I stayed up with Joan and helped her clean up after everybody left.

I jumped up and walked down to the fairgrounds as the sun was just starting to arrive at the far end of Heppner. There was no one on Main Street and the only activity was over at the Wagon Wheel. I stopped in for a cup of coffee with cream and sugar, to go. I knew the mules would be waiting for their breakfast.

They looked so beautiful, their coats so shiny, staring through the bars of the corral with a look of anticipation. I threw them each a flake of hay and wished them good morning.

I sorted through the packs and tried to even them out. The sun filtered in and turned the round hills surrounding the town into big yellow mounds. The autumn light was warm and beautiful and every morning was bathed in clear yellow light. The air was so crisp and fresh that morning. A few of the neighborhood dogs trotted down to the fairgrounds to see if anything was going on.

I heard the engine of a car. Looking up from my pack, I saw Orville trying to get out of the Cherokee. It took him a few minutes. He walked slowly towards me, rays of light darting off of his glasses as they caught the early morning sun.

"Figured you'd be heading out early. I wish I had the ridin' legs to go with you," he said sadly.

"Me too," I answered. "You could tell me about everything from here to Clarno I bet."

"You're looking at a real horseman, little girl," he said in a broken, soft voice. He looked down at his legs and then looked away, out towards the round hills to the south. "Life's too short, but it's been a doozy."

The morning sun was shining on us now, and the mules pushed around their pile of hay, hoping to find something sweet. It was unlike me to get such an early start. I chuckled when I thought about the impossibility of rushing off, with the likes of Orville hanging around the old corral.

"My dad drove across the plains in 1880. Dad, mother and my oldest sister, she was about a year old. Mother wasn't well when they arrived in Spokane country. There wasn't any Spokane there then. The Spokane Indians lived there on the banks of the river where they had a permanent camp."

"They came out in a stagecoach?" I asked.

"No, no. In Dad's four horse wagon. They come out in a wagon train. They hitched the same old horses on the same wagon and went back to South Dakota in 1886. Mother wasn't well and they thought the South Dakota climate would help. In those days, they had to blame it on something. So they went back there and raised two more girls and a boy."

Orville looked up at me from behind his glasses to see if he had my full attention. He had come to tell me more stories, and I'd better be listening. I gave up then and there on an early departure.

"There were eight Cutsworth brothers that came out to a little town by Salem, out in the Willamette. Dad was the last one. This was in 1901 and I was hatched in 1902, so this is before my time. And these Cutsworth brothers were all prolific. Some of 'em had eight, nine kids. And one of 'em had fourteen. But one of them was a bachelor and they didn't have a check on him!" Orville laughed.

"What do you mean?" I teased. Orville looked at me straight in the eye.

"You can't kid me. You know what I mean. So as I was saying, the minute they got down there in that God forsaken valley, where it rains all the time, Dad got asthma and he couldn't live there. Doctors told him to come up to Eastern Oregon. He was down near Salem for nearly three years and he couldn't lie down. He had to sleep in a rockin' chair or he'd choke with the asthma. So they left that rainy spot and they come down to Ione, which is near the mouth of Rhea Crick. Ione was a real popular picnic site. Many pioneer gatherings took place through the years up there, and it's a real pretty spot. Anyway, he got himself and the family a room at the hotel and he slept in a real bed for the first time in three years. Oh, he felt so good!"

Orville had a big grin on his face. I had sat down on my pack to listen.

"So Dad got up and asked around town. Dad always had a little money. He was successful in whatever he done. He asked around town where he could buy a farm, see. In those days you had one mercantile in each town and they sold everything from silk stockings to wagons. They supplied the country. They told him to go over to the Trading Company; they had some farms to sell. People would buy their groceries by the year and pay for 'em once a year and if they didn't get a crop, they wouldn't pay for 'em for two or three years. And finally the grocery man would get the farm."

"Everything from pantyhose to ranches!" I piped in.

"They were silk stockings back then," Orville smiled sheepishly. "So this Trading Company had three farms to sell. Dad bought one. Paid the man at the Trading Company thirty-five hundred dollars cash, just like buying a horse. And in those days they didn't have title insurance and that sort of thing. And so Dad went out and settled on the farm and went to farming. Three years later, he got a notice that there was a mortgage due and payable on the farm! This young man who ran the Trading Company had sold three farms to three different people and Dad was one of 'em. Then that fellow went right across the street and mortgaged them to a widow woman and got paid again for the farms!"

"No kidding!" I piped in.

"After that, the son of a gun hitched up his trottin' team and trotted up to Heppner to record those mortgages before the fellows he sold them to had time to record their deeds, which made it legal!"

"How could he get away with that? What a rotten thing to do!"

"And so three years later Dad got this notice that the mortgage was due and payable. Well, three thousand dollars was a lot of money in those days. You didn't fool with my dad much; you didn't with those old men. Dad packed a pistol all the time. I was wondering just the other day what became of that pistol. It was the same kind of pistol that Wyatt Earp carried in that O.K. corral thing."

"Oh yeah?"

"Yep. It was best not to mess around with pioneer folks like my folks."

Orville walked over to the Cherokee and came back with a big bag of jerky. He tossed it my way. "Put this in your pack. It's venison."

I smiled and put it away in my red bag. I knew it would keep the knot out of my stomach all the way across the mountains.

"Going back to when my folks were headin' back to South Dakota. There were two horse thieves stealing horses. One of the horse thieves rode alongside their wagon all day and got acquainted with my mother who told about it lots of times. And he carried my sister on his saddle. Said he had a little sister her age back in Louisiana somewhere. What he was doing was seein' how much money these travelers had. Then they'd come in the night and run the horses off. They were part of Calamity Jane's gang."

"Really?" I asked in disbelief.

"Yep, really," Orville answered, adjusting his hat a little lower to keep the morning sun off his glasses. "Yep. They'd run the horses off and hide them somewhere until the wagon man wore his legs off hunting them. And then they'd agree to bring the horses for whatever amount of money they ascertained these people had. So this one fellow rode all day along the wagon and traded my sister apples for a ride on his saddle. That night the horses were making a fuss. Dad was a great man with horses. He'd call them and they'd all come to him. It was a moonlit night. Then it got real dark with the clouds. I heard Dad tell it a hundred times, and Mother too. Dad jumped outta bed and ran out there with his pistol and there were two men riding the horses off. My mother was a very, very accurate shot. I never knew her to miss a shot. And she had the rifle in the back of the wagon and it was on this narrow place, where the river made a loop. That next day one of those riders rode by her and she was gonna kill him. He topped his hat and said, 'ta ta, lady'. It was the cowboy who rode with them all the day before. And she couldn't shoot him. Mom and Dad told me that same story over and over again, growin' up, and I never forgot it."

"That must have been scary for them," I said seriously as I folded up my bandanna and put it away in my bag.

"You'd better believe it. But it gave them a good story to tell their whole lives. Anyway, back to the ranch. When Dad got notice that the mortgage was due and payable, well, to say the least, he was upset. The train ran once a week, clear down to Portland. Dad got on the train to go down and shoot this man. I can remember the row that my sister and my mother had in the kitchen. It was '09 and I was six years old. Mom and my sister got on the train the next day and went to Portland and got Dad. He hadn't found that man yet. And they brought Dad back before he killed him."

"So they went and got your dad and brought him back?"

"Yep. They brought him back before he shot that fellow from the Trading Company or history would have been a little different."

"No kidding," I said.

"So we lost the farm and went to Canada in 1910. We lived there for ten years. And we grew up about twenty-five miles from a little town called Carlson. We had three-month terms of school in the summertime and I spent twenty-one months altogether in the schoolhouse. That's all the education that I had."

"That was it?" I asked. He nodded.

"And in 1920, my older sister Maudy, she died in the hospital up here just about a month ago, had married a man named Charlie and stayed here and never went to Canada. When Charlie died, Maudy wanted my father to come down and run that ranch. And mother wanted to get the family out of Canada so we kids would get a little more education. So that's how we came back here, in 1920."

"Do you remember Canada real well?"

"Oh yeah. Last year my wife and I got a brand new motor home. It's a goody. We drove up there this summer and we went to the old ranch. All of the buildings are gone. Dad had the finest ranch in the country. We had the finest buildings and the best ranch up there. Three gas wells on Dad's old place!"

"Really?"

"Oh yes. Dad could see that would make him smart!"

We laughed.

"Well, anyway, the buildings are all gone. But he had planted four thousand trees and they're all growing wonderful! If Dad could just see those trees, it would tickle him half to death."

"Maybe he can," I said as I got up from the bale of hay I was sitting on and grabbed the little green plastic grooming brush I had carried all the way from Clark Fork. Sarah Jane had a look of delight on her face as I brushed her neck slowly while Orville hobbled back over to the Jeep Cherokee.

The sun was bright and had found its way into every nook and cranny of the fairgrounds. Orville walked slowly back towards me, and handed me a small yellow paperback book with a black plastic spiral binding. It was called "O.W. Remembers."

"It's all yours, little lady. And I signed it so you will always remember me. It's a book about my life and it's full of fun." His shaky hand passed me the book and I blushed with delight. I opened it and he had scrawled in blue pen, Jody Foss, Keep Ridin', O.W. Cutsforth. No. 596 was printed on the back of the front cover.

"Most of these are huntin' stories and some are pretty tall tales," Orville laughed as he patted Sarah Jane's neck. "It's my tribute," he said with a smile. "If there's anything anybody's done, I did it too. I've chased lions and tigers in Burma. I've been all over Africa two or three times. I've been to Thailand and the Philippines. I've been in the Holy Land and down in King Tut's tomb. And I've crossed the Equator," he said. "I've had a gold dredge in Alaska. Been everywhere in the world but Russia and Argentina, and I'm not goin'."

"Were you working?"

"No. I was playin'. Everything I did would come under the

heading of playin'."

"What made you want to travel?"

"I was always interested in archaeology. We lived next to the Red Deer River in Canada and it ran about a thousand feet below the level of the prairie, through the clay. What they call the cutbanks. There were petrified turtles! There were petrified bananas, snakes and fish! There was everything petrified up there on the Red Deer River. And I was always interested in that kind of thing. I helped a man by the name of Cutler dig out a ninety-foot dinosaur. Shipped it to New York. I read the other day that the longest one ever dug was eighty, but the one we dug was ninety!" Somehow, I was not surprised.

"So what was it like around here during the Depression?" I asked.

Orville looked upset just thinking about it and hit his knee hard with his old hat.

"Do you know anything about raising wheat?" he shouted, and I shook my head back and forth, no. Just for a second, I wished I hadn't asked.

"Industry is public enemy number one of the farmer. I heard my dad say that many a time, and it's really true. Industry wants to buy its raw products as cheap as they can. If you were runnin' the flour mill, you'd like to have dollar wheat instead of three-dollar wheat. And if you were runnin' the packing house, you'd like to have twenty-cent meat instead of fifty. And if you own a bunch of timber, that's the biggest wrangle in the world to get the price of that timber reduced."

He took a deep breath and he stopped talking. I could tell he was thinking back.

"I sold wheat for eighteen cents a bushel. Six carloads. I got less than six hundred dollars for six carloads. I got a penny a pound for cattle. I got a penny a pound for hogs. I hauled a truckload of hogs to Portland that weighed fifty-six hundred pounds and I got fifty-six dollars. Came back to Morrow County, that was in 1932, and I was the richest man in the county. The banks all went broke and closed their doors. And I had fifty-six dollars. Imagine that! The richest man with my fifty-six dollars."

"So what did you do with it? Did you try to save it?" I asked, only half kidding.

"A loaf of bread was fifty cents. Of course my wife was making her own bread. We had a cow so we had our own butter. We had chickens so we had our own eggs. Had a big garden with lots of taters. Meat was no price at all. We ate all right, but we had a problem buying gas. Bought a new tractor in '29, but gas was sixteen cents a gallon and I had a hell of a time getting money to pay for that gas to run that tractor. Now gas runs the world and folks don't think about it. They just take it pretty much for granted. I bet you don't even have to think about gasoline, being out here on muleback, do ya?" he laughed.

"Not for a second," I answered.

"I bought that ranch from the Hynds brothers in '44. Seven thousand acres. How'd you come over the hills, through Pilot Rock?"

"Yep."

"Well, you didn't pass it then. There are seventeen rooms in that old ranch house. It sits right in the middle of fifty-five thousand acres. You can throw a rock from that front lawn onto every field on that ranch. I don't know another ranch in the United States like it."

"This sure as heck isn't suburbia," I said to my paper coffee cup. Orville didn't hear me. He kept right on talking.

"When I was about forty-five, one of my neighbors came to me and said, 'Orville, this country's been awful good to me. It's been good to you. What will you do for it?' Well, the first thing that I'm gonna do, I told my neighbor, is put in an airport. Everybody wanted to fly, and there was no airport. So we bought sixty acres and we gave the town of Lexington an airport!"

"So how far is Lexington?"

"Just nine miles down the road. That's where the home ranch is. When I quit farming, what I had was nineteen miles long and two miles wide, excepting a little bit here and there."

He pulled a bag of Fritos out of his pocket and they were all smashed. But he opened the bag and offered me the first handful of broken corn chips, as if he bought them that way.

"It's time to go, Orville," I said. "I think it's about eleven miles over to Ruggs, and I want to make it before it gets too dark. I hate riding at night and Mavis and Sarah do, too. And they let me know it."

"That's when the dark unseen lurks behind every bush, just as the sun goes down," Orville laughed. "Horses and mules hate twilight, when they can't see clearly."

Mavis was stomping and pawing, looking at me with those big black eyes, her ears forward, signaling me to cut the conversation and get the show on the road.

"Thanks for the jerky," I said to him.

He grabbed my hand and gave it a strong squeeze. "Take care, little lady. And don't you take more chances than you have to. And remember us. Drop a card once in awhile, and let us know how you make out."

"Bye, Orville." I was sad to leave and dying to get going. I grabbed my leadrope and led Sarah out of the fairgrounds. The sun was real high and it was already almost eighty degrees.

Mavis walked out the gate and headed down the highway with Sarah right behind. I turned around and looked as Heppner disappeared behind the fold of a hill and the only sound was the mules' hooves on the road. The smell of the juniper and sagebrush filled my senses as I rode quietly. I half expected Orville to drive by to see how I was doing and when he didn't, I missed him.

Chapter Sixteen

Easy Riding

I loosened up on the reins and let Mavis have her head. She searched the road for broken glass, sharp rocks and unexpected pickup trucks that appeared out of nowhere. The trucks sometimes had to slam on the breaks as they crested a ridge in the road, least expecting a mule train.

The late autumn evenings had a bite to them. The night air nipped at my nose. I knew I had to keep the trip on the road, not get too comfortable in these friendly, welcoming towns with the good stories and the wood stoves burning juniper and pine, often with a warm bed with clean sheets just for me.

It was about eleven miles over to Ruggs, riding in the barrow ditch along the highway. Mavis and Sarah moved steadily all day. I think they had had enough of the corral at the Heppner Fairgrounds, but it wasn't easy getting away from the likes of Orville. Eagerly, they walked up and down the hills towards Ruggs, finally arriving in the tiny town around four o'clock.

"Where do you think I could pasture my mules for the night?" I asked the woman handling the cash register at the store.

"Across the road, the Wright Ranch," she said in a high voice.

I went across the silent road and approached the perfect porch that looked welcoming and cool. I was feeling weary and didn't feel like talking. When a neat, middle aged woman answered the door, I could tell she didn't feel like talking right then either. But once I told her my story, she took me in and put me in the junkhouse, as she called it. It was really the bunkhouse but it had long been full of boxes. Even so, it was clean and white and had an inviting cot with a fluffy mattress that looked comfortable. I longed to lie down.

There was the prettiest and most perfectly groomed vegetable garden I had ever seen next to the white board and batten bunkhouse. From my bed I could look right out into the deep coolness of tall corn waving in the evening breeze. I could have heard a pin drop on the street in Ruggs at sundown when I marched over to the store and bought a microwave pizza and a big bottle of sweet lemonade.

Sitting on the tiny white bed in the bunkhouse, I looked at my maps, trying to decipher which way to go. The moon came up over the ridge and lit up the whole town. It provided a white blanket of light, and luckily for me that evening because when Mavis sneaked into the vegetable garden for a little corn, I could see her clearly. I ran out to catch her before Mary woke up. Somehow that mule could untie just about any knot and did so whenever she had the chance. My quick release knot was just that for Mavis who was particularly agile with her lips.

The bunkhouse was warm and I had it all to myself, with Mavis and Sarah retethered safely along the edge of the garden, out of reach of the luscious corn that hung there waiting to be harvested. I don't think Mary noticed anything, although I was probably kidding myself. I'm sure that after I hit the road for points further west, she raked the mule's hoof prints from the precious garden.

I slept soundly on the neat cot, and pulled the blanket over my head to keep out the morning sun. It was comforting, but I knew I had to keep on, as the days were growing short.

Mary was alone as her husband was off in Portland recovering from surgery. She woke me up, or at least got me to admit that I was awake, and invited me into her home for breakfast. The coffee smelled so delicious and the aroma filled the whole kitchen. I knew then she would notice the mule tracks in the garden. I sat quietly, enjoying every minute in the dining room. So secure, so permanent.

The morning sun was shining on the carpeted, cool living room. Mary brought me a big white plate laden with bacon, eggs and with two pieces of white toast and homemade jam. I chewed slowly, enjoying that meticulous house sitting on a ten thousand-acre ranch.

They had buffalo, a hundred and nine of them, to be exact. They had sheep, cattle, moufflon and llamas. I had never heard of moufflon before. Mary told me they were deer that had bred with sheep, though I wasn't sure if she was just pulling my leg. Regardless, I believed her. They had two hundred and fifty cow and calf units and a thousand ewes.

"Oh yes, and seventy-five bison. I forgot about the bison," Mary laughed as she walked briskly towards the kitchen. "But the buffalo are fascinating. They are like a living locomotive. They walk where they want, never heard of a fence and they ignore the blizzards."

After I had eaten close to a half a jar of Mary's homemade berry jam, I pushed myself away from her perfect home and gathered my dirty packs; everything looked dirtier to me after being Mary's guest. I felt refreshed and wanted to take that cool, comfortable old fashioned bed with me.

"Hey, Jody, before you pack the mules, could I talk you into a little tour of the area?" Mary asked me. She handed me a tightly wrapped package of cookies and two oranges to put away for later.

"Why not?" I answered delightedly.

We jumped into the pickup and drove up to a little town called Hardman, which was about nine miles away. We took pictures, and Mary took my camera and clicked a few of me on a weathered, rickety old porch complete with Victorian woodworking.

Hardman was a ghost town far off the beaten path. I stood behind one of the weathered old Victorian houses, long faded and in need of repair, facing the open hills that went on forever.

Mary packed a lunch for me and filled up my Thermos with hot coffee for the road. There was little wind and I happily packed up and rode off toward Condon. It was a sunny fall morning and very few cars were on the road.

I walked Mavis and it felt so good. Sarah's packs were perfect. They were so light ever since I figured out how little I needed.

The countryside was beautiful, and across each hill, a new view took my breath away. It was a land dotted with tall junipers and sagebrush.

I pulled into the Martin's place, right at the bottom of the grade. It was starting to get late, evenings coming earlier and earlier. The Martins raised Paint horses and had a beautiful stallion.

They had some college kids from Pendleton up to hunt, and conversation found its way around to the Rajneesh, whose commune wasn't far away. Everyone had their own view, but all agreed it made for some lively dialogue.

Mavis and Sarah had a corral with some good looking hay and I slept under a street light, next to the barn. I could have chosen a better spot to put my bed since a snorting gelding kept me up. Also, the coffee I had right before bed didn't help. It had been a fun evening, with lots of tacos and a big salad and beer.

We had made eighteen miles in seven hours. Not a bad day and regardless of the noisy gelding, I managed to fall asleep.

In the morning, one of the young hunters came out and woke me up for breakfast. He reached down and grabbed my sleeping bag. I yelled and jumped up before I realized I was standing there in my long underwear with about every other button undone. Looking down, I grabbed the front of my union suit and he looked at me, but a little above my head. My face turned crimson and I reached down and grabbed my bag, pulling it up around my armpits.

"Breakfast is ready, Jody," the young man said in a low voice. He was so handsome and I felt embarrassed. "I fed your mules," he added.

"Thank you," I said as I hopped around in my sleeping bag, reaching for my coat without falling over in the process. I could smell pancakes and bacon and fresh coffee. The chill in the morning air sent wisps of cold air up the canyon across the road in long thin columns of white mist and clouds. I looked forward to the day and walked eagerly towards the house and the breakfast that awaited me.

The horses and mules were eating peacefully and the air was filled with anticipation. I entered to have a plate handed to me stacked high with pancakes and crisp bacon.

Chapter Seventeen

A Rancher's Wife

The road to Condon was spectacular, with rounded hills of
aromatic wheat and the healthy, warm sun shining down on us all
day. The hills rolled along rhythmically, one after the next. Mave and
Sarah were enjoying the day as much as I was. Their shiny, slick coats
glistened as they walked. It was a perfect day for riding.

I crossed Rock Creek, following it on the wrinkled map as it
meandered north to join the John Day River on its way to the
Colombia and the Pacific Ocean. It flowed past Cayuse Canyon,
Wolf Hollow and Spring Hollow. It went through Olex and Rock
Creek where the Condon Kinzua and Southern train came
thundering through. Then it passed Diamond Butte, Emigrant
Canyon and flowed out to the mighty Colombia. For centuries,
tribes had followed Rock Creek to the big river.

By the time the big buck deer joined me, I was not even a bit
surprised. The mules didn't pay much attention to him after a while,
as he lumbered along in front of us picking his way through the sage.
The sound of the sage brushing against his big powerful legs made
me stop the mules to listen. His light tan coat was glistening in the
sun. He heard the pickup truck long before I did and stopped.
Gracefully moving his huge rack and with perked, nervous
twitching ears, he stood still as a statue and listened to the rumble of

the engine far off in the distance.

I watched, as the deer stood there, frozen, staring at the road. Just then he bolted and moved his big legs so fast that they slipped out from under him and he started to go down on his knees. With the massive muscles in his legs, he managed to pull himself up and catch the ground securely as he took off straight up the juniper dotted hillside to the south.

The big buck ran for the top of the steep canyon. He heaved huge sighs as he pushed to reach the top. As he disappeared off into the thick juniper and sage, I said a breathless prayer on his behalf and got Mavis and Sarah moving again. He was a magnificent creature.

"God speed, buck," I said in a whisper.

The truck topped the hill and stopped. A man sitting in the passenger seat aimed his rifle directly at me. My blood ran cold and I felt like I was going to faint. I waved my arms frantically, and gave Mave a little nudge to get her moving. I felt a sense of panic as the truck started moving again. The hunter pulled his rifle back in the window. I couldn't breathe. What was he thinking? They drove slowly past us. "Seen any deer?" a big bearded fellow yelled out the window of the pickup.

"Nope," I answered. "What the heck are you doing pointing your rifle directly at me?" I was livid, and my voice was shrill and trembling. I was ready to cry.

"Oh, sorry, just trying to get a closer look through the scope. Guess I should've used my binoculars." He was apologetic, but I was fuming. I wouldn't have told them about that gorgeous buck if they had begged me.

Condon was a welcome sight on that beautiful sunny day in late September. I rode up Main Street and turned onto a side street with a "No Parking" sign to which I tied the mules. There was a little grass plot with rich looking feed at the base of the pole and so I felt comfortable leaving the mules there while I went into the little coffee shop for a cup of coffee and maybe something to eat.

It felt good to slide into the cool vinyl booth. I ordered from a large, tanned waitress who looked like she could wrestle steer. Hunters filled every table and the air was filled with the exaggerations of hunting stories. I sipped my coffee and overheard a conversation that was taking place directly behind me in a booth full of older hunters. I noticed three of them were wearing wool shirts with the same plaid.

"I saw it running, and it looked big. Must be that old buck from up Rock Creek, the one old Mansfield was after last year. Biggest buck I ever saw. Boy would I like to tie him to my roof rack." They all laughed and I blushed. They were talking about my buck.

I walked outside and was surprised when I noticed my picket rope was missing from the top of Sarah's pack. I was disheartened to think somebody would take it right off my saddle, so I figured I must've dropped it on my way into town.

"Hey, girlie, where ya goin' with those mules?" a low, raspy voice yelled from the window of an old station wagon. I looked over and saw a small round woman, her face covered by huge round glasses. She waved her heavy arm, motioning me to come closer.

"You the gal that rode from Idaho?" she yelled. She had a real loud voice for such a little person.

"Yep, sure am."

"Well guess what? You're stayin' with us. Who'd make a stink?" she said as I walked up to the window of the car. She slammed her hand on the outside of the old station wagon and the mules jumped. "We live right up here on the right. You can picket your mules in the back yard and let 'em eat that long grass, see?" Her voice ricocheted off the shop windows along Main Street. She pointed a round, short finger up the hill to a big lot.

"My name's Mary Squibb. This here's my husband, Leonard!" she hollered.

"I'm Jody. Glad to meet you. Thanks for the invitation."

I was starting to feel the sixteen miles we had come from Ruggs. I got back up on Mavis and followed them up the hill, their little white dog jumping from the back of the station wagon to Mary's lap like a little rocket.

Mary showed me where to tie up the mules. When I told her I had lost a rope, she walked over behind the old white house and instantly produced one, as if by magic.

"Here's your new rope," she said, smiling at me and tossing it my way.

"Thank you, Mary."

"Think nothin' of it. And you'll be stayin' in the house since we have a guestroom. None of this sleepin' out in the weeds. Not here. Come on in and have a cup of coffee and some cookies. I just made 'em."

I took off my hat and could tell my hair was looking pretty rough. I grabbed my brush out of the red bag and tried to get the tangles out as I followed Mary through the thick carpet of grass to the back door. I could smell the chocolate chip cookies the minute she opened the screen door.

Her little Cockapoo dog was upset that she had tied him in another corner of the yard to keep him out from under the mules' heavy hooves. He was shivering and whining and looking as miserable as he could. A cold, dark cloud had rolled in and covered the afternoon sun.

The wind came up just as the door slammed behind us and I stood there, awkwardly, in the tiny white kitchen. The counters were cluttered and magazines were piled high in several places throughout the house. But it was so warm and comfortable. The window in the living room looked out towards the west and the juniper dotted hills off in the distance.

I took one of the giant chocolate chip cookies and Mary poured me a cup of coffee.

"Ahh, thank you. I feel so happy to be inside even though it was a beautiful ride today from Ruggs."

"Oh God," Mary said, "I don't think I could ride a mule that far...all the way from where?"

"Clark Fork, up in Idaho," I said wistfully.

"Oh, my God, would my butt be sore." She poured herself a cup of coffee.

"When I saw you with that black mule and that pretty white one all packed up and headin' down the road, it really brought back some times," she said, wiping a place on the plastic table cloth with big red flowers on it. I looked up at the wall and thought the deer in the calendar picture looked identical to the one that had escorted me halfway into Condon.

Leonard came in and sat down at the table to roll a cigarette. He was much taller than Mary and was thin and hunched over a little after a lifetime of farm work. His white tee shirt was clean as could be and his red and black flannel shirt was ironed and neat looking. He methodically rolled a perfect cylinder out of tobacco and twisted the ends. I didn't feel shy about grabbing another one of the thick, warm cookies off the big green plate Mary had put in the middle of the red and white table.

I pulled out my new book, O.W. Remembers. "Have you seen this book?" I asked Mary.

"Nope."

"I got it from a man in Heppner. It's a crack up. You can read it if you want."

"Oh? What's it all about?"

"It's a collection of tall Oregon tales. So what did you do with mules, Mary?"

"Drove 'em on the stacker."

"Just you by yourself?" I asked her in disbelief.

"And one of these mowin' machines, the old type mowin' machine. Oh, let's see...I was married the first time in '44 and I used to drive a set of mules on a gol' damn mowin' machine!"

"With your husband?"

"Yeah, my ex-husband."

"In Nebraska?"

"In the Sand Hills," said Leonard.

"So you were a farmer's wife?" I asked.

"No, I was a rancher's wife."

"There's a difference," Leonard said quietly.

"We used to have to mow the hay and stack it. All with mules."

"Did you like it? Working with the mules?"

"Well yeah, until noon!"

"Then what?"

"They knew when it was noon!" Leonard said, laughing.

"HEE HA!" Mary yelled. Leonard reached up his long bony

hands to cover his ears. "HEE HA!" she yelled again. "They knew what time it was and they wanted to stop and eat!"

"Couldn't get nothin' more out of 'em," Leonard added, laughing.

"I might be clear across the gol' damn field, comin' around you know," Mary continued. "And boy, they'd start brayin' and brayin' and brayin', and I had a hell of a time getting 'em around the field to where we was gonna eat dinner."

"Same way at night," Leonard said.

"Same way at night," Mary repeated.

"Did you work with mules, Leonard?"

"No, I didn't. But my dad did."

"Your dad had some dandies, didn't he?" Mary said.

"Why, I remember him cussin' 'em!"

Mary picked up another one of my books that dropped onto the table out of my pack. "Heppner Indian War. Geez, I'd like to get me one of these books," Mary said, thumbing through it with her thick, worn fingers.

"Go ahead and enjoy it. I'll stay here until you finish it! And if you don't, I'll stay until you do!"

We all laughed, but I was only half kidding.

"Do you think mules are smart?" I asked.

"Damn right they're smart. I know darn good and well they're smart! Like I said, I drove them sea biscuits on a damn mowin' machine. And about noon, you might be clear across the field, they knew what time it was and they'd start brayin' and they'd start slowin' down. And you'd have to coax the heck out of 'em to get 'em around the field where you was gonna eat dinner, to where the wagon was at. And we worked 'em on these old time stackers. One thing about them mules, they never tripped over the single trees, they never fought the lines or anything else. But if they didn't want to go they wouldn't go. All my father-in-law and I had to do was holler at them sea biscuits, 'You'd better get to goin' out there!' And they'd go again and put the hay just where it was supposed to go."

Since the cookies were gone, I decided to walk downtown. Mavis and Sarah watched me with interest as I headed down the street on the edge of the wide-open fields surrounding town. They were happy in the yard, but looked at me as if to say, "Let's go." I decided to take them for a little walk.

I felt so at home in Condon with Leonard and Mary I stayed three days. It was the weekend. On Sunday I read the Oregonian from cover to cover and wrote my article for the Sandpoint Daily Bee. It was eighty-five degrees during those days and the nights were cool.

I walked the mules around the town, up and down Main Street. Then I sat in the window booth of the coffee shop and watched as the cars and trucks drove up and down.

I saw a dead deer tied to the hood of a pickup in front of the bar. But it didn't look like my friend.

Chapter 18

Jackrabbits for Supper

"Are you the gal with the mules?" a tall old man in blue overalls asked me as I sat down in the soft red booth behind him in the coffee shop. He had such dancing, cheerful eyes. He motioned to me with a big weathered hand to come and sit with him and his friend.

"Sure am," I answered.

"Will you join us at our table?" he said. He held out his hand and grabbed mine.

"I'm Jack Nelson. And this is old man Greener. Call him Bill."

I grabbed my coffee cup and slid in next to old Jack who had on a flannel shirt and overalls, just like his friend. "Thank you for inviting me to sit with you. It's nice to take a day off from riding."

"Well, we don't have very good manners," Jack said. They both looked at each other and laughed.

"See, I'm riding my mule along, talking to the old timers I meet along the way, asking them what they remember about the old days, what they loved about their life."

"Well, I don't think I was alive!" Jack said.

"Do you want to go first?" Bill said, looking at his old friend.

"Go ahead," Jack said. "God, where are you gonna start?"

"Well," Bill said, "I think I better start with my grandad, when he first came here. That was 1883."

"How'd he get out here?" I asked.

"Well, he come from Kansas, around the horn with a load of cattle. He first landed at Kelso, Washington. Then he broke his leg, a real bad break, it was. But he got down in the Willamette Valley. Down there he cut logs and made a farm, you know. But he figured that was too much work. So he come up here in this country and he picked this spot over by Mayville that he liked. He made a claim on it, you know, the government claim on it. And then he built a cabin. He dragged his logs sixteen miles from the mountains. It had a dirt floor and no windows. Just a door."

"They didn't have floors in the houses in those days, you know. And some of 'em lived in dugouts," Jack tossed in. He had a really fun sense of humor and I knew I had to watch him or he'd start stretching the stories.

"The door was about so high," old Bill said. He reached his arm up just a little above his head.

"And then he brought his family out. It was in November and they got into one bad blizzard. They had to come from the Dalles. He sold his wagon and horse down in Portland, purchased a boat ticket and they come on up the Colombia to the Dalles where he bought a new wagon."

"Sounds like fun, doesn't it?" Jack teased.

"He bought a new horse and a Guernsey cow and all his supplies up in the Dalles. He only had three hundred bucks and he spent most of that on his supplies!"

"That was a lot of money in them old days," Jack said.

Bill continued his story. He was used to Jack piping in. They had been friends since they were kids and they were in their eighties.

"It was Thanksgiving Day when they made it into the cabin. Of course they built a fire right away. And the only meat they had was a jackrabbit!"

"That's all they had to eat?" Jack asked.

"Yep, that's all. So jackrabbits on the table for the Thanksgiving feast!" They both laughed.

"So as soon as they got settled, it snowed about seventeen inches. But they was all snug in their cabin and they had plenty of wood.

246

He made himself some snowshoes and every day he'd go out and get him a jackrabbit. And oh, they went through some real poverty, then, you know. They used up all the money."

"I guess so, livin' on jackrabbits," Jack said.

"You see, this was all prairie land," Bill said quietly. He stopped and reached for his glass of water. The blond waitress had just filled it to the brim and he spilled some on the table as he lifted it to his lips.

"Not so much sagebrush as there is now." Jack mopped up the table with a big bunch of paper napkins.

"No, there wasn't so much sage in them days. Bunch grass, bunch grass that went clear up to the bellies of the horses. So he cut that to feed the horses and the cow. Of course the old milk cow gave milk for the kids."

"So where were you born?" I asked.

"Right there on the farm in Mayville," Bill told me.

"He was born at the farm at Mayville and I was born on the farm out at Prairie Canyon," Jack added.

"The day I was born, lightning struck and knocked my Uncle Fred off the ladder!" Bill laughed.

Jack looked at him with disbelief, like he'd never heard that story, like he didn't believe him. "How do you know?" he said.

"Because Uncle Fred told me!" Bill laughed. "Yep, it knocked him off the ladder, and started a fire, and I wanted to go back where I came from! I was scared to death! And I was scared of lightning for years!"

We all laughed. They were slapping the knees of their overalls and turning bright red. This is how they spent their days, outdoing each other with quips and yarns, as they had done for decades.

"The Indians used to trail through here, right by our house. We lived on the main road," Bill told me, his eyes lighting up. "They'd go through the mountains, see, and there were hundreds of them crossing through in a big long line that seemed to stretch out for miles."

"All single file," Jack interrupted. "Oh yes, I remember the Indians."

The door to the coffee shop slammed shut behind a big man in dirty work clothes.

"Hey, Bill," he said as he approached our table.

"Howdy."

"What're you doin' there, Bill? I didn't recognize you without your hat on!" the newcomer teased.

"We're havin' an interview," Bill laughed. I could see his face turning red. He was a little shy.

"Could I have some coffee?" I said loudly to the tall blond waitress behind the counter. "Thanks."

B. Shiler

"You better put that hat on, Bill. Nobody's gonna know who you are," the big man said as he stood with his hand on old Bill's shoulder.

"What about me?" Jack piped up.

"Oh, sittin' with Bill is one advantage. They might recognize you there, but not Bill without his hat. No sir! He's always trying to get close to the girls, you know, Jack."

"Oh?" Bill said.

This type of bantering back and forth is what moved the clock forward in Condon.

"Oh, here comes Blondie," Jack said, as the big blond waitress moved with ease towards our table with a pot of fresh coffee. She carried the full pot with the gracefulness of a buxom ballerina, sliding in between the big man who towered over our table.

"Thank you," I smiled.

"But, anyway," Bill continued, "the big braves used to be the first in the line. The young men would all be riding the young horses. Then, pretty soon, the older men down the line. They'd be riding in the back. And on the tail end, there'd be the squaws and the babies." The image of all those Indians walking single file haunted me.

"So what kind of advice would you give a younger person? What kind of advice from all the years you've lived, would you tell a younger person like me, to have a good life?" I asked as I tried to take a sip of coffee, missed my lips and felt it soak through the front of my tee shirt.

"Well, my God, there hasn't been a lot of excitement around, but, well, just be yourself," Jack started out.

Bill laughed. "Just be yourself," he repeated. "That's all I can think."

"Yeah, just try to get along," Jack said. "Stay out of all the serious trouble you can. And just take one day at a time," he added.

"Make the most out of one day at a time," Bill repeated.

"That's what I figure," Jack said.

"Yeah," Bill laughed.

"And just do the best you can," Jack added. "Whatever comes, you know."

"Whatever will be will be," Bill chimed in.

"Yep," they both said at once.

We sat there for a moment in silence. I think Bill and Jack were thinking about what they might have left out. I could hear Doris Day singing "*Que sera, sera, whatever will be will be, the future's not ours to see, Que sera, sera.*"

It was time for lunch. We ordered fries and hamburgers from the blond waitress. The food came in minutes and then we talked between bites.

"What do you think of that old guru over in Antelope?" I asked.

"Well, not very much. We would rather not mention his name," Jack said. I could see he meant it.

"You've been there, Jack. I haven't," Bill said, passing the buck.

"You have?" I asked in a high voice. "I'm not going through the ranch. I'm just riding through Antelope."

"Well, they say you better get the sheriff's permission. That's the safer thing to do." Bill sounded concerned.

"Me and another fellow went over there. And, by golly, we were treated real well. So I can't really say anything." Jack tapped the table. It was obvious they didn't like to talk about the Big Muddy.

"I'm sure I'll be fine. I'm not afraid of them, I'm just afraid of the tension." I took a big bite of the hamburger. "You know, being in the wrong place at the wrong time."

"The tension is kind of high over that way, but I must say, I was treated real well," Jack said. That was the end of that.

"So you have friends right here in town that you grew up with?" I asked.

"Oh yeah. But most of them are all dead," Jack said.

"Less and less every year," Bill said. "But we make new friends all the time. There's a few of 'em sticking around, but less and less every year."

"Lloyd Evans would be one. And old Doc over here, the old bald headed feller down there."

"So you both were raised on a wheat farm?"

"Oh yeah, wheat and cattle."

"Did you thresh the wheat by hand?"

"In the early days we threshed the wheat with a stationary machine. The engine ran the separator and threshed the wheat out that way." Bill said.

"But when my dad first started farming, he had what they called a horse power." Jack added. "And the horses went round and around this gear that had a tumbling shaft that went out to the separator."

"Both our dads were steam engine operators," Jack continued. "Then they graduated from that to ground powered combines and then from there to powered combines and then they went to pusher combines."

"But I spent a time in the service, though. In the South Pacific with the headhunters," Bill said casually.

"He almost got his head knocked off," Jack added.

"In the Hebrides. But they don't call it the Hebrides anymore."

"He almost got his head tore off!" Jack repeated.

"Well, I met a headhunter right down on the beach," Bill laughed.

"Now this is getting exciting," Jack quipped.

"The only trail back to camp, and here I was," Bill continued, "all alone in the jungle. There I was all alone and you couldn't get two feet in the jungle. But the old headhunter was comin' up to me on the beach. He had a great big club, and I didn't have anything! But I didn't show him that I was scared. I figured I was runnin' to save my neck and he was just after my head!"

Jack loved the headhunter story and laughed and slapped his knee. I was surprised he didn't wear out the knees of his overalls.

"Unbelievable," I said.

"And then I got right up next to him," Bill hesitated. "And so I got right up next to him and he said, 'Hi!' And I was glad." Bill laughed.

"So what did you say to him?" I asked Bill.

"Oh, I said 'Hi' and he said 'Hi' and I walked right by him."

"You kept your head!" I said.

"Yep! I kept my head. But I was ready to run anyway!"

"But you would have insulted him if you'd lost your head!" Jack laughed.

"But, I was tellin' Jack, they sold us cattle for seven cents a pound, these headhunters. So I guess they'd rather hunt cattle than heads! Seven cents a pound, dressed out!"

"What did they do with the heads, take the brains out and eat 'em?" Jack asked.

"I don't know. I never questioned because it was bad medicine. It was bad medicine to question headhunters and cannibals, too. But I went into the jungle that day, because it was my day off and I said, well, I'm gonna go into the jungle. And I got about three feet into the jungle because you had to chop through every inch of the way."

"Well one of them would be pretty good against the headhunters. One of them jungle knives." Jack was fun.

"Well, yeah, but I wasn't gonna get tangled up with him!" Bill laughed.

"Let's get up and stretch our legs and go have a look at your mules," Jack suggested.

The mules watched us from the street through the window. We took some old bread out to them, some dry toast and left over rolls that the blond waitress gave us. Sarah took them carefully and slowly while Mavis grabbed them as fast as she could, getting as much in her mouth as she could without dropping too much. Mavis butted Bill with her head and almost knocked the old man over.

"Do you think mules are smarter than horses?" I asked my friends.

"Sure," Jack said.

"Definitely," Bill said.

"Yeah. We used to raise mules," Jack continued. "You can't founder a mule, and a horse will founder easy. And a mule will get tangled up in a fence and won't cut himself all up like a horse. Mules are just smarter all around. And on hot days he'll out work a horse. He can take more heat."

"I go about fifteen or twenty miles a day," I told them.

"That's not too bad," Jack said.

"That's more than I'd like to do," Bill laughed.

"How did you manage to get a black one and a white one?" Jack asked.

"Luck, I guess," I told them. "I flipped a quarter in a Montana bar for Sarah eight years ago and I just bought the black one. She's out of Spokane." I held Mavis' head in my arms and she fell asleep. Sarah pushed her nose into Jack's hand.

"My grandad was here before the town was ever built, you know," Bill said.

"Yep! My grandad came in 1882, something like that," Jack threw in. "He come down and there was nothing but mud streets. Horses and wagons and mud. No sidewalks."

"Coyotes?" I asked.

"Coyotes, yep. But there wasn't too many deer back then," Jack added.

"But there was some bad Indians, you know, murderous Indians, you know, up in Piute Canyon. They'd waylay people, and bump off people," Bill said. "And we had an Indian War out here. Two tribes got in a fight. I guess we used to have a murder or two out here a year."

"Oh, it was shoot a man for breakfast!" Jack laughed.

Bill really loved everything Jack came up with and his laugh just kept on and on through our whole conversation. Nothing Jack could say was anything but funny to his friend.

"Oh, he's pulling the wool over your eyes, you know," Bill offered.

"Sounds like an old wives' tale to me," I said.

"Oh, I don't know. That's what they told me. That's all I know," Jack said, with an innocent look on his face. "Oh, heck, there were twelve or thirteen saloons in this town. A saloon on every corner."

"Guys would get in a fight at the top of Main Street and they'd roll all the way down the street fighting each other," Bill said.

"Do you remember your first car?"

"Oh yeah, it was a Model T, wasn't it?" Bill asked Jack.

"Yeah. No, by golly, our first car was a 1914 Buick."

"Mine was a Model T," Bill said. "The first one I really owned."

"We traded that thing off for a Model T which was a way better car."

"Then we got a big six passenger Studebaker," Bill added.

"Um hm. We had a Studebaker, too," Jack threw in. "That was a honey."

"And then I bought, or made up a Model T again, for myself." Bill said proudly.

"Yeah, I wore out a lot of Model Ts," Jack bragged.

"Then a Model A. Then I bought a little Crosley. Then I went back to a Studebaker again." Bill laughed. "Two Studebakers, then an Oldsmobile and a Pontiac."

"Well, now, she's wanting news, Bill," Jack teased.

"I just have to kind of think it over and think *waaay* back. What about the story about old Potter?"

"What story? I don't remember that," Jack admitted.

"Old Potter. Up at the cemetery his tombstone reads, 'Here lays, very deep, poor old Potter, herding sheep'," Bill continued. "He accused this feller up in Heppner of taking the hobbles off his horse and he went up there to kill him. But a horse on the prairie here, there was no end to how far a young horse could run with no hobbles. I don't think they ever caught that horse."

"When my folks came, there wasn't a fence in the country. Not a fence nowhere." Jack said the words quietly, like a prayer. "You'd just head out in any direction and never come across a fence. And there was bunch grass as high as a horse's belly."

For a moment we were quiet. The sun was heading out west and would soon disappear behind the Cascades. The changing light and shadows soared down Main Street and within minutes the street was in shadow.

"Well, Bill better get going home to his wife or he'll get spanked," Jack said.

"I'm sure glad I got to meet you guys," I said to the two old friends.

They walked back into the coffee shop to get teased a little by the blond waitress and their old friends who sat at the booth and waited for them to return.

The warmth of the coffee shop was so tempting, but, instead, I walked the mules back up to Mary and Leonard's and put them on their picket ropes so they could busy themselves with a late afternoon snack of Mary's back lawn.

Chapter 19

Mule Driver

Before I knew it, two more days had passed. The smell of the wood fires drifted through the wide streets of the little town and I thought about my beautiful home in Idaho. The apples would be picked. I knew Dorothy and Reid would make good use of every apple, and Dorothy would be baking pies.

It was hunting season and the deer would be reluctantly heading for higher ground. Walking quietly through the woods, they would look for feed and listen for the sound of a truck engine.

I loved to think about my cozy log home on the bluff. I knew the granary was cold. The wallpaper upstairs was probably peeling already, I thought to myself as I walked back up to Mary's place. I pictured opening the heavy wooden door and jumping up on my own big bed.

Mary smiled wide when she saw me, tossing me a beer in a can I didn't recognize. "Here you go girl. Take a load off. You've been running around all over the place. Sit here and have a piece of chicken."

The chicken arrived that next second. It was dreamily fried and smelled delicious.

"Thanks, Mary."

"Will ya stop thanking me all the time, gol dammit! You are an honorary member of our family while you're here, ain't she Bob?"

"Damn straight," Bob answered from the couch. He was in a plaid shirt and worn work pants and waved from his place in front of the TV.

"Take a look at the poem Bob wrote you," Mary said in a thunderous voice which filled the walls of the little green kitchen. She was tossing up a big green salad. Leonard sat at the table and rolled a smoke. I read Bob's poem. He called it "Poem for Mule Lady" and it was written on a brown paper bag. I pulled the white lacy curtain back in the kitchen and could see my Mavis and Sarah, in the middle of a pile of little apples the neighbor brought over.

POEM FOR MULE LADY

While I was sittin' here today, thinking over this young lady's plight
I thought I'd try to make it right, so here it goes:
Black in the body, gray in the mane,
White on the legs, but a mule all the same
Bearing her master, up hill and through dale,
Sometimes to follow the Oregon Trail.
From Sandpoint to Moscow, along Coeur d'Alene,
Always on bearing, come hail or come rain.
Across the Snake River, Pendleton go,
Take in the Round-Up, missing the show.
Then on to Heppner, Condon is next,
Spending the weekend, the mules are most wrecks.
Fed up and rested in Mary's back yard,
I'll have to remember to send her a card.
Then onward to Fossil, westward we go.
Taking in Antelope, watching the show.
Bagwans and streeters, all dressed up in red,
This is no place for finding a bed.
Then on to Prineville, Redmond or Bend,
Telling my story, make a new friend.
Onward to Sisters and Three Fingered Jack,
Looking for shelter, any old shack.

Sweet Home it beckons, parish the thought,
Seventy-four miles, I'm walking a lot.
North to Corvallis, then west, the last leg,
Looking towards Newport, driving my peg.
Feet in the water, setting my mule,
Caring not of being a fool.

Mule lady: I wrote this for you this morning at Mary's kitchen table.
Have a good ride the rest of the way from here and I hope you don't get snowed on.
Bob Messenger, Condon, Oregon

Leonard spoke up. "Yep, Jody, Mary was one heck of a mule driver in her day," he said, with his thin face winding up in a big smile. "Remember what you said you did that time, Mary?" Leonard broke into a laugh. "You said you backed the mules right up and buried him?"

"No, no, no, not with them mules," Mary barked.

"With somethin'."

"It was my ex-husband. He chewed me out because I wasn't puttin' the hay just where he wanted. I was runnin' the tractor by that time. He said, 'You ain't puttin' it where I want 'em.' When you stacked hay, like we did in Nebraska, you put one in the front, one in the back and one in the middle. And he was up there on the stack, my ex-husband. And he was giving me hell. And I thought, you son of a gun, I'll put it where you want it!"

Leonard was really laughing and so was Bob from the couch. He'd heard this story before, I could tell. So had Leonard, many times, but he loved it. Mary swung her arms around her head and continued.

"And so I backed that son of a you-know-what tractor up there, and I buried him!" she whooped. Leonard laughed some more. "And I said, okay fine. Did I do it right or didn't I do it right!? I done did it right because I told him before that if they don't go up there right I'm going to get in the car and I'm gonna go to the house. 'Cause I had three kids out there in the field with me! Young kids!"

"Do you want to go outdoors? Hmm?" Leonard asked the little white dog. He got up from the wooden table and picked up the bundle of fur. The screen door squeaked as he pushed on it. "Stay away from those hooves over there, little buddy," Leonard said sweetly to the dog.

"And then you had to do all the cooking too?" I already knew the answer.

"You bet. I did all the cooking and had a great big garden and fixed all the lunches and everything else!"

"So the woman gets the raw end of the deal in farming!" I said.

"No, this was ranching!" Mary yelled.

"Well, still," I said, a little embarrassed.

"Farming's fine. He works on a farm, but I don't. I stay home. If I had to go to work and do something, I would." It was quiet for a minute. "I tell you what, I'm almost ready to go to bed. What time has it gotten to be? Almost midnight! Geez! Here I am, standing here in my bra. I was almost there once already!"

"So is your family Italian? English?"

"No way!" Mary yelled. "It's all mixed up. It's a duke's mixture!"

"Same here," I said. "We are too."

"My mother was a full blooded Englishwoman and my dad was German. So there you go!" Leonard said. "I don't know what I am!" he laughed and shook his head.

"We're Scotch, Irish, French and Norwegian," I piped in.

"My mother was a full blooded Swede. The other half is a duke's mixture," Mary said, yawning. "And old Bob over there, is he asleep? I think he's got a lot of English in him too." Mary and Leonard looked hopefully in the direction of Bob who was definitely sound asleep, his arm over his eyes like a cat.

"And my kids are a real duke's mixture. They're a quarter Swede and the rest is something else," Mary said.

"So I always ask my grandma what advice she'd give me. Do you have grandkids?"

"Six," Mary said proudly.

"What advice do you give them?"

"I don't because they live back in Nebraska."

"If you had the chance, what would you say?"

Mary paused. "There is no way I would give any of my kids or my grandkids any advice."

Leonard was shaking his head. He didn't believe it for a minute. He looked at Mary.

"I would not!" she yelled at Leonard.

"You would if you thought they were gonna get into trouble, you would!"

"Yeah, if they was gonna get in trouble, I would," Mary admitted.

"Other than that, let 'em live their life, that's it!" Leonard said.

"When my kids was in high school I didn't give them any advice. I just told them what they should do and what they shouldn't do."

"Like with me," Leonard spoke up. "I've done a lot of things and I've often said, if I knew then what I know now, I'd probably do the same things all over again!"

"If I knew then what I know now, when I was nineteen years old and first got married, it would be a heck of a lot different," Mary said thoughtfully.

"You wouldn't do it?"

"Well," Mary said thoughtfully, "would you?"

"I don't know."

"I was nineteen when I first got married. I had three children and I was married for thirty years. My husband was basically, for the last ten years, an alcoholic. I worked and raised three kids all through high school. And when they was through high school, I said to them, okay, fine. I'm leavin'. And I left. I run into him," she said, nodding towards Leonard who was rolling another smoke, "and him and I come out to Oregon! I said, are you comin' with me or are you not! And we packed up and we took off."

"We didn't know where we were goin'!" Leonard said loudly.

"We didn't know where we was goin'! But we just jumped in the car and we took off!" Mary added.

Bob rolled over onto the floor and Mary got up to go help him.

"Night, Mary," I said as I stood up and stretched. "Time for bed."

"I'll wake you up early, girl, so you can get started before the sun gets too high."

I drifted off to sleep and pulled the nice worn blanket up around my chin. Mavis and Sarah stood still as statues against the black sky. I could have stayed the winter there in that tiny green room with the comfortable bed. I knew in the morning the frost would be on the pumpkin. It was time to get moving, to leave this little town perched on the edge of a world so wide open and golden with wheat fields that one could see the curve of the earth.

Chapter 20

Palisade Coyote

The morning came early with a loud squeak from the bedroom door. I looked up and there stood Mary, with a steaming cup of coffee. "I told you I'd get you up," she whispered. "Bacon's on. Get up." She disappeared back into the kitchen. I stretched, got out of the little bed and looked out at Mavis and Sarah who were searching the little back yard for anything tasty they might have missed. The wheat fields were dark gold and pink in the early light, a combination that was startling in its beauty. I looked down at my pack and grabbed everything in the little green room that was mine. "Goodbye, coziness," I said aloud as I reluctantly closed the door. I marched out to the kitchen table where my place was marked by the plastic placemat with a picture of the famous El Capitan in Yosemite. Mary carried a heaping plate of bacon and scrambled eggs and plopped it in front of me. I remembered not to say thank you because, as she said, enough already.

"Leonard's already gone to work. Bob said to tell you to have a good trip. It's gonna be good weather for a few more days at least. So we think you'd better make a bee line for the Cascades, and get them mules goin' so you don't hit snow, because, girlie, I tell you, the high country can sock in pretty damn fast, you know!"

"Time to go, I know it. I got the article finished for the

Sandpoint Daily Bee, so I'll send it off on my way out of town. I guess I'll get an early start for once." I looked out and could see there was not a cloud in that huge Oregon sky. The sun was up and massive golden rays shot their way down the wheat to Mary's house. The yard was bright yellow and the air was cold. That morning could've brought life to the dead.

Mary folded her arms and watched me pack Sarah. With so few things, the whole job only took me about ten minutes. Sarah stood still and I made sure her bags were even so I wouldn't have to stop and repack. I saddled Mavis as the red morning sky started to fade. The day was going to be hot and beautiful. I felt like crying. I smiled at that feisty woman and gave her a big hug. I jumped up into the saddle and waved goodbye to Mary.

"Don't forget to send us a card," was the last thing she yelled out as I headed down Spring Street and onto the dirt edge of the highway, the wheat fields a bright yellow road to follow. I reached into my saddlebag and pulled out *Poem for Mule Lady*. I read it over a couple of times, folded it up and stuck it inside my notebook.

It was at least eighty degrees. The miles flew by, Mavis walking briskly with Sarah close behind her. I chuckled when I thought about Leonard and Mary and Bob. I had forced myself to leave and I missed them. Once in awhile in life people like that come along, people who feel like family.

We came over a hill and there was a little scrap of a town, quiet and abandoned. We had reached Mayville and it didn't look like anyone was around. The houses stood up as straight as they could, faded in the hot sun. Boards were askew. Paint peeled. Doors boarded up. I tied Mavis and Sarah under a big willow tree just off the road, and let them graze. The wind rustling the ancient willow was the only sound. The town was singing its own song. I listened and my imagination ran away with me. The old wagons came to life again and there were horses and people in the streets. The houses were for a moment shiny and new and the picket fences were straight and painted white.

I walked around in wonder and thought about the stories Bill and Jack had told me. I pictured the long lines of Indians who were walking to the reservation. There was the livery stable, the old store...and that old place must have been the hotel. I could picture the hustle and bustle when Mayville was a stage stop and the wagons rolled through, stopping for supplies at the little store.

I stretched my legs, walked around and met a woman named Lois who lived there. She was one of the only people who did. She didn't mind a bit and liked having a town all to herself.

"Is it lonely?" I asked.

"Not really. If I get lonely, I can jump in the truck and head over to Fossil."

I took a nap on Mavis, the three of us resting under the willow, waiting out the hottest part of the day. The sound of the tree rustling above us was soothing and cool.

Once again on the road, the mules were moving fast. Before I knew it, I arrived in Fossil, a quick twenty-one miles. The town was such a welcome sight. It had a few streets and most of the houses were painted white. It was such a nice welcome feeling to ride into Fossil, nestled between the hills. The town came as a surprise to me. Juniper trees dotted the hillsides around the town and the neighborhood dogs came out to meet us.

I found a good pasture with Dub and Wilda Freeman and their kids on the edge of town. They had a nice modern home with a big barn next to it. They took me in and cleaned me up. Dub gave the mules some hay and grain, showed me to the shower and did my laundry for me. Wilda asked me to sleep in the house, but I stayed out by the mules behind the barn.

I had a burger down at the cafe and when I returned fell asleep out behind the barn. I was dead tired and didn't hear the rooster crow in the morning. Wilda made me a cup of coffee and a delicious breakfast and sent me on my way with a bag full to the brim of freshly baked cookies and another filled with beef jerky. Dub and Wilda's kids showed me a road on my map called Stone Cabin Road that would save me a good twelve miles.

I headed into the juniper and sage along that quiet dirt road, the country stunningly beautiful. It was like a wonderland, one of sharp rocks and outcroppings that looked like Indian faces and animals. I

sang every song I could think of and the hours passed, while Mavis and Sarah walked briskly.

The moon was almost full and by five it was showing itself in an already darkening sky. I arrived at the Clarno Fossil Beds around six and it was almost dark. I picketed the mules out to the fence and found a place to put my sleeping bag. I had the whole place to myself.

Dub had told me about the Clarno area and the Palisades, but still I wasn't prepared for what I saw. The red rock outcroppings and the sheer stone cliffs shone in the moonlight as I made my camp in the dark. I walked the trail and thought about the Indian tribes who called this home. The Teninos traveled this country, as did the Umatillas. This was their borderland. They fished and hunted, setting up a village in the winter months. The river basin provided their every need.

It was not until the late 1800's that homesteaders settled in the area. Joseph Clarno homesteaded on Pine Creek in 1866. Dub told me that Joseph Huntley had a homestead at the Palisades and he operated a stage station there.

The Clarno unit of the John Day Fossil Beds has some of the most incredible fossils in the world, the shells and nuts and seeds and animals found in the rocks telling a story, set in stone, of another time.

As I closed my eyes to settle into sleep, the place was so silent. I listened and could almost hear the sound of the thundering hooves of the tiny horses that lived there in a lush forest shared with enormous rhinos and ferocious giant pigs which are forever entombed in the ash laden mud flows.

A coyote started to howl, coming closer. I sat up and watched as he approached me. I was trying not to stare at his shadow. To take away my growing fear, I clapped my hands at the night and yelled.

My voice echoed off the red cliffs that glowed in the moonlight. I listened to the coyote's song for an hour or so, with my head under my down parka, trying to find a way to convince myself that it was safe to sleep. Finally, I jumped out of my ragged sleeping bag and headed for the trail.

The moon bathed the sandy earth in gentle, comforting light as I walked briskly up the path along the Palisades. The spires rose up like jagged church steeples making me feel safe. The Palisades were full of fossils, the remains of seeds and nuts uneaten at the time of the ash flow. I walked as far as I could without losing sight of the mules and returned to my camp as they watched me with anticipation since they had long ago tasted every blade of grass within their reach.

Later, the coyote tipped his rabbit ears towards the three of us. His soft, cream colored fur shimmered in the moonlight as he danced silently in front of my sleeping bag. I lay there terrified and thrilled by his presence. "I think he's hoping for a treat," I whispered. I don't think he was used to nighttime company. Finally, he disappeared from view and I settled into the security of my warm sleeping bag as the moon set behind the spires.

It was the sun in my eyes that woke me in the morning. There were coyote tracks right next to my bag. I reached out, lightly tracing them with my finger.

Chapter 21

Big Muddy

I was only twenty miles from Antelope and was excited to finally see the controversial commune for myself. I sang the song I had made up somewhere between Condon and Mayville: *Oh Bagwan of Rajneeshpuram, Gandhi's rolling in his grave, sayin' you're a slave to that pretty car.* I had ten verses by the time I finally got there. But I forgot them as I sang them and it was probably just as well.

I was hungry and tired when I first rolled into the tiny town. A big sign along the highway read, "Welcome to Rajneesh." An old, beat up highway sign that read "Antelope: Pop. 39" was tossed off to the side of the road and covered with dried mud. I looked back at Sarah and her orange tarp, and reached up and touched my bright pink bandanna.

I felt a little embarrassed as I rode through two large groups of men who were waiting for the bus out to the Big Muddy, or Rajneeshpuram, as they called it. Mavis pranced by unfettered and I looked back at Sarah who was staying close behind.

"Hey, where you comin' from, mama?" one of the men yelled. They had just arrived on buses from places like Chicago and Miami to take a shot at a community with no violence, drugs or crime. That's what they had been told when they boarded a bus bound for Antelope, way out in the west.

"Sandpoint, Idaho!" I yelled back. Mavis saw the store and I could tell she and Sarah were ready for a stop. Break-dancers boogied on the road while strains of soul music filled the air. "Where you all from?"

"Everywhere!" one of them yelled.

Mavis pulled to a quick stop in front of Zorba the Buddha restaurant. I tied the mules to one wooden post on the side of the building in the shade and walked into the small cafe. I ordered a cup of coffee from a young girl who had skin like peach yogurt and bright, believing eyes. By the second cup, I was chewing on a black licorice rope. So much for healthy eating. I sat there for a good half an hour while young and old red and purple clad people came and went, people from all over the world. The screen door of the little purple store slammed in a friendly way. But no one approached me as I sat there, drinking coffee with cream and wondering where in Antelope I would find a quiet spot to sleep.

I found the rich, greasy carrot cake too much to resist and ordered a big piece of it, perfect with licorice and coffee. The Bagwan's books and tapes lined the walls and everyone was noticeably quiet in tone. I already missed the absolute silence of Clarno and the sound of the John Day River bubbling by the Palisades with only a coyote for company. It was a busy place, or busier than anyplace I had been for awhile, with street people and folks in pink and purple, many with a picture of the Bagwan sealed in plastic hanging around their necks.

My pink bandanna wasn't quite enough. My worn green pants stood out like crazy and I could see that the outfit required pants, coats, shoes, everything to be in colors of the sun and fire, "to symbolize the vibrancy of one's life, committed to truth."

After two more cups of coffee (it was the fresh ground kind), I asked the man behind the counter if he had found a place for me to camp with the mules that night. I had been in there almost an hour and the sun was sinking behind the hills. He said to be patient, he needed to make another phone call. He was trying to locate someone to give permission for me to pasture the mules in the town of Antelope. But of course, they didn't call it Antelope, ever. It was Rajneesh.

It got dark as I sat waiting, outside, on a stump next to Mavis and Sarah. Where would I sleep? Finally, he came out just to tell me there was no exception to the rule; I could not pasture and camp there. He suggested I talk to one of the twelve "holdouts," as he called them. The holdouts were locals, people who had refused to leave. They simply turned their stubborn heads away and believed that it would all pass, that soon the Big Muddy would be the Big Muddy again and the town would again be restored to how it was before the Rajneesh came to Antelope. These outsiders had come quietly at first. Then their numbers gained momentum and size like a snowball in spring.

I found an Oregon State Patrolman, which really wasn't hard. For each of the State Patrol, there was a Rajneesh Officer, or Peace Force, the only police in pink shirts I had ever seen. The State Patrolman was big and strong and seemed to have things in control. I knew he'd find me someplace to sleep. He made a phone call from a little maintenance building that sat next to the highway.

"Hey Betty and Jack. I've got a mule skinner down here at the store whose name is Jody and she needs a place to put her mules. Can do?" he yelled into the receiver. The mules were nervous now that night had arrived and they were still in their walking clothes. The nice Patrolman followed me all the way up the hill to the very edge of the biggest little town in Oregon, his lights shining on the mules' rears and mine too, for that matter.

We got to the gate and there was Betty. She was a tall and friendly lady, in a plaid cowgirl shirt tucked into her Lee's. She smiled and said, "Well, she isn't the Jody I thought she was, our cowgirl friend who rides all over the place. I figured it was *that* Jody! But you're welcome, anyway. Get those mules unloaded and come in for a cup of coffee and something to eat."

I quickly unsaddled Mavis, took the pack off of Sarah and covered up my gear, piling it high under my tarp. I picketed out the mules in the lower part of Betty's yard. The moon was still pretty full. I stopped, turned around and stared at it to quiet my soul before I entered the house. I looked through the window in the door leading into the kitchen and could see Betty getting started on dinner. The home looked inviting and I could see the coffee was on. Antelope was quiet and only a few lights were shining, down by the store.

"Have you eaten yet?" Betty asked.

"I'm fine thanks. But I'd love a cup of coffee."

"You bet. We haven't eaten yet. Jack's still out doing his farming."

"Thanks. This is great. Betty is your name, right? I asked.

"Yep."

"Well, it was real interesting riding into town."

"I bet," she answered.

"But they were real nice, even though they wouldn't let me camp."

"Oh, they are real nice. The only one I've really talked to is a little gal cop."

"I talked to her today."

"Yeah. Real nice. But she has her downfalls, too," Betty said, as she cut up a big thick steak into chunks and threw it into a stew pot. The meat sizzled in the already hot pan and she stirred it, while cutting up carrots from her garden. She cried as she cut up the onion and I watched, drinking my coffee.

"I've heard everything about this place. It's funny to finally be here. I got tired of hearing about it."

"When did you leave?" she asked, wiping her hands on her apron.

"August twentieth."

"Oh is that right?"

"Yep. I rode out August twentieth. I've gone twenty miles or so a day, 'cause that's a lot, you know. I watched the mules very carefully the first month. In fact Sarah went lame in Potlatch, near Moscow. And I said to myself, there goes my trip. Out the window! But we put her foot in a bucket of Epsom salts for three days at the vet and she's fine!"

"Oh, thank God!"

"Are you a horsewoman? Because I thought it was a miracle that she healed so fast."

"But they're pretty sturdy, aren't they?"

"They are. But, still, she's been lame for a month before. Right now my horse Cowboy is injured with a bowed tendon and he'll be lame until next summer. When I look back on it, it was a hard

270

summer before this trip. My dog died and my older friend Nina, who was going to come with me, got injured only three miles from Clark Fork."

"Oh, dear," Betty said sadly.

"And she was an old girl, a seventy-two year old woman."

"Oh, you're kidding," Betty said.

"But it was almost like the good Lord said 'Nice idea kids.' Something could've happened even worse. But it was bad enough as it was."

"What did she do?" Betty asked curiously.

"She got dragged by this pack pony named Easter Boy that I bought at the last minute. Something scared him and he took off and so she wrapped the rope around her hand and she was dragged by that little pony."

Betty looked horrified.

"It was only about twelve feet, too far for her old bones. So she's been back in Seattle this whole time. She was just heartbroken."

"Oh, yeah, missing out on all that fun."

"But the town had sponsored me, so I didn't really have a choice but to go. And it was pretty scary leaving alone."

"Oh, yeah. But you haven't run into anything too frightening?" she asked.

"Broke my Thermos. That was the most trouble I've had."

She loved that. She had a nice laugh.

"I'm not kidding. It's been great, you know. But you hear so many rumors about this place. Everyone said don't go there, don't bother stopping by because it's so tense. Do you think it's getting more tense?"

"Well, we're not in it. We're not exposed to it. I know that when I go down there I can feel the tension. I can just feel it, like I shouldn't be here, like I don't belong here. I've only been out to the ranch twice. The first time was curiosity and the second time I took my mom down. I could hardly wait to get out of there. I swore I'd never go back. And I won't."

"So they're doing all this building. Are they planning to take over the whole town?"

"They already have."

"How?"

"Well. . ."

"When I rode up the street it was just so eerie, to see all the empty homes. It's strange."

"They bought the Muddy Ranch, which was a working ranch. Some people in Texas had owned it. And they bought it for several million dollars, I don't know, but it's quite a few acres. And nobody objected. They just said fine. They're gonna farm out there and do their own thing. And they are just going to live out there. But that wasn't enough. Then they wanted to build a few buildings in town, and it got voted down. They got the school board. Then they got the City Council. So the whole town was theirs. People just sold or just moved out of their houses. They're all taking a loss, those that just left their houses. But most of them were retired folks and it was a neat community. I guess they used to have potlucks down at the school. But now only the Rajneesh kids go to the school. Anyone else would have to pay tuition."

"Really?" I asked. She nodded.

"They used to have a lot of fun. They used to have card parties and everybody was really friendly. There used to be a little restaurant where the post office is now. Everyone had a post office box because there wasn't any delivery and so you'd go get your mail, stop by and get a cup of coffee and a piece of pie or something and you'd chat. I mean just a friendly, real low key community. It was changed when we got here, but that is what I was told it was like. But the Rajneesh want a thriving metropolis, so they're gonna get rid of this entire back woodsy thing and get this historical stuff out of the way because they don't believe in old things. They want to tear it all down but they can't because most of the buildings are still privately owned. They changed the street names to all their names, changed the fire hall to Jesus Fire Hall, and I can't remember what they call the dump."

"Jesus Fire Hall?"

"Yep. Jesus Fire Hall. Guess they figured it would annoy people."

"I bet it does the trick," I said. "Have you talked to the street people they brought in here?"

"Well, no."

"They aren't anything to be afraid of, are they?"

"Well, no," Betty said. "Jim picked up this street person and dropped him off down by Willowdale. You'll go past there tomorrow."

"I heard it was twelve miles but the sign says fifteen. But it's flat. Not like the fifteen I did today."

"Oh, no. It's curvy, but it's not too bad. Anyway, this street kid was talking to the police and Jim and I stopped to pay for his meal. He was telling the cops some of the stuff that was going on down there. He said they had him register to vote, but they didn't tell him how to vote. That's too much of an investment, pulling all those street people in here. I don't know what they're up too. I really don't. But now they are pulling them out of here faster than they're bringing them in."

"I figured I'd have some company on the road to Madras."

"No, no, they won't let them leave that way. Oh a few have escaped, but they haul them in buses. They don't want them straggling out that way. They put them in buses."

"What does Madras think of all this?" I asked.

"They are concerned. I can tell you where to go to talk, and that's the bus depot. It's right across from Jerry's Restaurant. It's a little hole in the wall right across the way there. And it's at the bus depot where they're dropping them off. Of course Madras is worried sick. The churches are really trying to pick up the slack."

"So what do you think will happen?"

"I don't know," Betty said thoughtfully. "I just know something will happen."

The view of the hills to the east was really beautiful from their living room. Jack came in and looked surprised.

"That's not Jody," he said, smiling at me.

"Sure is," Betty said. "Just not the Jody we thought it was."

"Well, when I heard Jody was riding a mule and needed a place to stay, I wasn't a bit surprised. That girl will take off and ride almost anywhere," Jack said.

"You mean there's two of us?" I asked.

"Guess so. Anyway, welcome to Antelope," he said as he washed his hands at the sink. "So what do you think of the circus downtown? Like anything you've ever seen? It's like New York, Chicago, Los Angeles and Atlanta all on one corner. I'm starting to think there's more of the street folks than the Rajneesh."

I lay in my sleeping bag on the hill overlooking the little town with its spice cake and spiritual books and tapes and new street signs with five syllable names. I thought about the fact that only three years before the houses with the "no trespassing" or "for sale" signs were full of families and farmers and ranchers and a few folk who probably came for all the fresh air. Simple homes or not, they were somebody's home. Most of the locals were gone. After so many miles of riding, after so many conversations with Oregonians, I would have to wait no longer. In the morning I would board the Buddhafield Shuttle and go see the infamous Muddy Ranch for myself. The moon poised itself over the dark hill across from the town and I looked to it for comfort.

A beautiful Mexican woman with long, straight dark hair drove the bus to the ranch, twenty-four miles from the city of Antelope. I practiced my rusty Spanish on her, until I knew she wanted me to take a break. In the back of the van was a girl from New York, another from Sweden and a German, all dressed in beautiful shawls, cloaks and skirts in shades of purple, red, and orange. I started in with my questions, and I knew right away that I should have gone back to attempting Spanish with the driver. New York, in the back, made it very clear.

"I'm suggesting you wait until your tour. They'll answer all of your questions."

The sign along the narrow dirt road read: "Curvy, muddy, hilly and dangerous next 20 miles. Good luck." I bounced along in silence and thought about Mavis and Sarah, safe in Betty's yard eating away heartily, not giving a second thought to the Bagwan and his ways. To be a mule and search, but only for a good place to camp. They wouldn't have liked that road anyway. I was missing them before I arrived at the entrance to the ranch.

We arrived at the Gateway building. A sharp-eyed woman asked

me for photo ID at the desk. I had failed to bring it, never thinking about my driver's license when I'm out with the mules. Papers were shuffled and I was allowed to board the bus without it, much to my delight. New York looked disappointedly in my direction as I pulled myself into the back of the shiny white van. The sharp woman followed me out and asked kindly, in a soft voice, "Oh Jody, you don't have any weapons of any kind, do you?"

"No," I answered. "Just my camera."

Our tour began. We were informed that the Rancho Rajneeshpuram, formerly known as the Big Muddy Ranch, was purchased in June of 1981, 64,000 acres for six million dollars. The Bhagwan and forty followers had come from Puna, India, and were looking for land that had been abused by man to restore and reclaim. The land had been overgrazed for years and the lush bunch grass that once grew had been claimed by the sagebrush and the juniper, the "cowman's curse." Their vision was to find an area to practice their beliefs in an isolated, quiet way, in a drug, crime and violence free environment. They would guard their city with a great deal of pride and hoped to make a model of how people can live creatively in harmony.

"So what happened?" I blurted out from the back seat. Perhaps they had accomplished their goals out on the ranch. But they certainly didn't seem to be geared towards harmony when it came to the State of Oregon. New York turned and glared at me before she realized it and turned away.

"The sleepy town of Antelope was inhabited by people dedicated to fundamentalist, non-growth ideals," the tour guide continued. "Of course they were threatened when we voted to incorporate their city and change the name to Rajneesh. We are a group of people dedicated to activity, inner and outer growth, and assertiveness. It was very disruptive to them, as it would have been if thirty circus performers had moved in. We applied for city permits to build and they were not granted. We took the city to court and the court proved us right. This started the controversy that continues to this day."

New York turned around and smiled. I guess she was trying to apologize for being rude. I didn't really care. All I wanted was to safely complete my tour and get the heck out of there before I was asked to join up. I shuddered. I wanted to get back on the trail as soon as I could.

"The Rajneesh have been criticized for everything they have done. The latest problem is the homeless program. Three or four busloads of homeless people arrive every day from all over the country. Now if the Lutherans were doing it, it would be accepted. We're the first city in the history of the world that has opened its doors to the homeless."

Just then I looked out and saw another bus pull in. Bewildered men filed out into the hot autumn sun. Four older men, obviously old friends from a mission or park bench somewhere, sat together on a bench and watched. The older homeless were the ones who tugged at my heartstrings. Maybe the mission wasn't much. But I wondered how many longed for that other, more familiar bench in the city they had left behind.

The tour continued. "We have the third largest transportation system in the state of Oregon. And during the summer festival when 15,000 join us, it's the second largest. We reuse 100 percent of our liquid waste and 70 percent of our solid waste. Krishnamurti Dam holds 330,000,000 gallons of water and an irrigation design to make best use of that water is in the making."

We passed the Rajneesh International Airport as we continued up the narrow canyon. "We have three DC3's, a little Islander, a helicopter and a Conveyor. There is constant air traffic from Portland to the ranch."

He explained about the five-fingered building on our right, Rajneesh International Meditation University. "Books are discouraged, except those written by the Bagwan, of course," he added.

I thought to myself how I would like to interview the father of the masses, but he wasn't talking.

After touring the very impressive truck farm at the end of the compound, and the dairy farm, we returned to the downtown area, built around the only original buildings in the city, the original Big Muddy Ranch. I wandered alone around the mall. In the boutique, there was an extensive selection of clothing, lingerie, accessories and shoes, all in purple and scarlet shades.

I sat down on a bench next to Antonio, a young Puerto Rican from Atlanta. He'd been at the ranch two weeks.

"It's a dream come true for some," Antonio told me. "All the basic necessities are covered. We work—worship, they call it—twelve to fourteen hours a day without pay and it's kind of hard to get used to. But there's lots of love people all over. There are no gangs, no violence, and just a lot of good harmony. Especially at two o'clock every day when the Bhagwan drives by. You really get a good feeling from him because his spirit fills you, when you get your beads. You've got to see it."

We walked out as the crowd lined up to see the Bhagwan. It was a colorful line-up. The song for the Bhagwan was being sung in as many variations as there were people. A Chicano man played the bongo. A saxophone whined, a trumpet tooted, a guitar was strummed, a snare drum rattled. Then I spotted the Rolls Royce rolling slowly down the line of rejoicing followers that was at least a mile long. The peace force officers with M16's marched around the car. Bodyguards carefully watched the car and the crowd. There he was, the famed Guru, seeming to pantomime a bumper car ride, teasing the crowd from behind the bulletproof window. He looked like a playful, mute, Moses.

I shuddered, as he passed, to consider the power he had over these people.

I carefully watched the guards with the guns as they carefully watched everyone in the crowd. I could feel my blood go cold when I thought about all the weapons there. And anyone could see how fully armed Oregon was, especially during hunting season. Both sides had made threats. As the numbers of pilgrims increased, the tension mounted.

The homeless were brought to Madras and Portland to find their own way home from there. The Salvation Army put $20,000 up to purchase bus tickets, and Oregon followed. But as many left, that many more arrived every day to live in the crime-free city of Rajneeshpuram.

The forty that first came to the Big Muddy Ranch, less than four years before, now numbered five thousand.

I caught the last shuttle out and packed up the mules. Their innocent brays were a comforting sound. I was more than ready to hit the road towards Madras, the gateway to the Cascades. As I rode out of Antelope, the sound of the crane and the bulldozers building a new housing complex on the edge of town eventually drifted out of earshot and the clip clop of the mules' shoes never sounded so much like home to me. That was my first night ride, but I knew I didn't want to stay another night. The moon rose.

"How appropriate," I said aloud. "An orange moon over Antelope."

Chapter 22

When Heaven is a Cinnamon Roll

Sleeping on the side of the highway behind a big plywood sign didn't leave me rested. Visions of the Bagwan behind the glass in the Rolls and the music, that one song, kept spinning through my mind as I lay in my bag watching Mavis and Sarah graze down the bunch grass around weathered juniper fence posts that held up ancient barbed wire.

Even though I had slept little that night, I felt happy when I awoke to a crisp, cool morning, the smell of sagebrush in the air. I stood up, shaking away my bag, and took a deep breath. I made a little fire at the base of a water tank and fixed a quick cup of coffee before I packed the mules at the side of the road. It was not the best camp. Even so it took me awhile to leave it, as I watched the parade of snowbirds pass heading south on the highway as we walked on.

It was later than I thought and, before I knew it, the sun set and it got dark. Once the sun went down on those fall evenings everything turned cold and I was restless to get inside by a fire. Riding at night never seemed like a good idea to me. But Willowdale continued to elude me. I had almost given up hope of making it that night when I saw a big neon hamburger glowing in bright pink and purple hues. My stomach growled but I ignored a pang of hunger and gave Mavis a little pat.

"See that, girl? When we get to that big hamburger, there will be lots of good pasture and I'll give you some oats. So just keep walking." I never really had to encourage Mave or Sarah to keep going at the end of the day as they were always as anxious as I to get there, especially once the sun had gone down. Mavis was afraid of her shadow.

She walked double time towards the pleasant looking sign of civilization. I pictured a hamburger sizzling away next to a nice green salad and a steaming cup of coffee. And the perfect jukebox, chock full of my favorite songs. There would be a place to sleep near the mules and plenty of good, green pasture at the base of a big willow tree. "Why not?" I asked myself.

The Dalles-California highway was busy with snowbirds flying south in rigs big and small. Many of the motor yachts had bumper stickers from every tourist trap in the west and beyond. Every other vehicle was a big rig hauling to California. I stayed off to the side of the road in the sagebrush and weeds and worked my way towards the giant neon hamburger. Suddenly, it flickered once and went out.

"No, don't tell me! We missed it!" I wanted to cry. The mules flapped their ears and laid them flat at the sound of my unhappy voice.

A few minutes later a friendly woman in a big station wagon drove by me slowly and waved. She did a U-turn on the highway.

She pulled slowly up to me and rolled down the window.

"Are you Jody Foss? We've got your mail at the restaurant. Follow me over there and I'll get it for you."

"Oh, my gosh. I've been riding towards that big pink and purple hamburger for miles," I smiled and gave Mavis a little nudge. The mules' ears, beacons of all emotion, pointed forward again towards the big neon hamburger. The woman raced off in the car and pulled up in front of the dark coffee shop. A moment later the lights came back on and the giant hamburger once again glowed deliciously against the last dark purples of the sunset. I was covered with goose bumps and wanted to cry I felt so happy. The mules trotted towards the big hamburger in long strides.

I loved my life and I never wanted this trip to end. I was heading for the Cascades as the last warm day hit the high country. At any moment, an unexpected snow could arrive and blanket the whole region. We were living in a world where the cafe owner turned on the sign just for me. A place that would unlock its door and big hot cinnamon rolls were free. That's what happened.

I was handed a big pile of mail that the postman had delivered to give to me. She opened the oven and pulled out a giant cinnamon roll. She opened the refrigerator and splattered a big spoon of butter on the top and handed it to me.

Heaven was that coffee shop in Willowdale. After that, she turned off the lights again and I slept under a big willow tree next to the restaurant. There was plenty of good pasture and the mules relished the greenest grass they'd seen for a while. The only thing missing was a jukebox.

I woke up to see my friend Dan, from Sandpoint, standing above me trying to wake me by shaking the top of my tired old sleeping bag. I sat up, startled, and tried to straighten my hair but, instead, just reached for my hat and crawled out of my sleeping bag. I was fully dressed and ready to go on into the cafe for breakfast.

Dan and his family were on their way to California to work since Sandpoint could be a little barren in the winter. They had their own land and the trip to California helped pay for the dream. I was glad to see some friends from home. We said goodbye there in front of the store and they sped off in an old pickup truck loaded with everything but the kitchen sink. Their kids and a dog shared the passenger seat.

I packed up and left that perfect camp under the willow tree. As I tied the ropes to Sarah's pack, a very old man with white hair and a cane tugged on my shirtsleeve.

"Want some tomatoes?" he asked, smiling.

"Sure do," I answered.

"I've had a hard time getting rid of them all. People are funny. If you say, here, have some free tomatoes, they wonder why they're free. Free makes them suspicious," he said, laughing.

"I'd love some."

"Well, then, I'll see you up the road." He drew a simple map for me in the gravel.

I rode up to his place and sighed. Roots ran deep. It was a two-story farmhouse that looked as if it had stories to tell.

Eddie Bolter had lived in Willowdale his whole life, as had his father. He walked with me slowly out to the hay barn, past some big Arabian horses. He had a rosy, healthy face and was a pleasure to look at, a vision of health. He was neat as a pin and looked like he was dressed for church. But it wasn't Sunday. The barn was so quiet and cool. We sat down on a bale of sweet smelling grass hay.

"Sure wish I had some hay like that," I said to Eddie. He nodded.

"When I get home I won't have any hay in for my animals."

"How many do you have besides these?"

"Just Cowboy, my horse. But I didn't bring him because he sprained a flexor tendon. And that's bad news. Have you ever had that happen?"

"I don't think so."

"Look at this Arabian horse," I said to the old man. "He's beautiful!"

"You should see the gal ride this horse! She rides him in the parade with no bridle. I've never seen anything like it. She just nudges him with her legs."

"No bridle or halter? That's amazing."

"Yep. She trained him to leg signals."

"What's that mountain there?"

"Mt. Jefferson."

"It's so nice in here." The hay smelled sweet.

A little black and white cattle dog came up and licked my hand.

"So what year were you born?" I asked Eddie.

"1900."

"Eighty four years old."

"Yep."

"So what were your earliest memories?"

"Well, the earliest thing that happened that I don't remember was, they sent a man on a horse over to Antelope. They had to get the doctor, and it took him two hours to go and an hour to get the doctor ready, in his buggy, and two hours to get back, and by then I was already born!"

"You were in kindergarten when they got back." I joked.

Eddie had a sweet laugh. His whole face lit up.

"So they just turned around and went back to Antelope?"

"Well, I suppose they looked things over a little."

"So tell me a little bit about your dad and how he got here."

"Well he was only three years old when they brought him here. His folks came from Dallas and they were in the furniture business. I think they made furniture because he built our house, windows, doors and all."

"He lived on the same spot in Willowdale eighty three years and lived in three counties and had nine different post office boxes and he never moved."

"Boy that's something," I laughed.

"Isn't that?" he replied. "Shows how the country changed. Used to be no houses and no fences. Just open country and Mt. Jefferson as a backdrop." He nodded towards Jefferson which was framed in the door of the huge, timber frame barn.

"Tell me a little bit about Willowdale and what it was like growing up in the old days."

"It was called Cross Keys then. And it should have been kept that. Oh, we just played like other kids. We rode horses and then we got bicycles and motorcycles and finally we got old enough to have a car."

"Whats the longest you've ever ridden in one day?" I asked Eddie.

"Sixty-five miles."

"Oh, that's a long way to go in one day."

"Sure is. But it was different then. The horses were always hard. And now you get on one and ride five miles and, well, they're soft you know, and they can't do anything, even if it is a good horse."

The little dog reached up and timidly kissed the old man's wrinkled, worn skin. Eddie was surprised. "What do you want?" The little dog just wagged his tail and crept off. He was a real shy pup.

"Shaniko was the big town. You haven't been there?"

"Nope."

"There isn't a whole lot there now. But when we were kids, it was quite a busy spot."

"How often would you go into town?"

"Oh maybe once a month. But I doubt it. Dad would buy a thousand pounds of sugar and a ton of flour in the fall. And lots of cased goods."

"So your mom was in charge of the kitchen and taking care of everything?"

"Feeding these freighters. She worked hard. I used to wait on tables when I was pretty young. Our place was a stage stop and the freighters with their teams would stop by to rest the horses and have a meal."

"You waited on tables in the cafe?"

"Well, it was just a ranch house. One long table."

"So how many guys did you have living with you then?"

"Well, at night there would be different numbers. Average four horses to the man, maybe six. There were a few eight horse teams."

"How many acres did you farm?"

"Oh, not that many. Only about one hundred and sixty. But we accumulated three hundred and thirty-nine irrigated acres. We finally got 16,000 acres all tolled."

"That's a lot of land."

"Sure is."

"What's the scariest experience you've ever had on a horse?"

"I've had lots of falls, but I never got hurt," he said proudly. "I fell off a load of baled hay and broke this heel bone about ten years ago and it bothers worse all the time."

"Do you have any Indian stories?"

"Well I was afraid of them when I was a little kid. They'd travel in hacks. Do you know what a hack is? It's a heavy buggy. And you could hear them coming up the road, trotting and, gosh, I always went in the house. I was scared to death. By the time I was growin' up around here, the settlers had pretty much broken every promise they ever made to the local Indians and they didn't have much faith left that anything would change. Many of them just plumb gave up fighting and trying to hold out and moved on to the reservation."

"What reservation?"

"Warm Springs. The reservation is only fifteen miles from here."

"So there were a lot of Indians at Cross Keys."

"They'd camp there."

"I overheard you talking down at the cafe about the big horse race. What was that all about?"

"Oh, heaven's yes. That was in '22. I was twenty-two, and my sister fed that man. I think his name was Houston. The race started in Bend about five o'clock in the morning. And they galloped to Prineville and then over Grizzly Mountain Road and down by our place, and through Shearer's Bridge to the Dalles. It took 'em eleven hours. That was an awful thing to do to horses. I think that feller Houston had a horse change at our place, but I don't think the rest of them did. I can't remember that. That feller had lost an arm in a mower, as a kid, so he only had one arm."

"So you'd cowboy with your dad? What was that like?"

"Well, we'd turn 'em out in the spring, and they could just go for miles, you know."

"No fences."

"No fences. And along in October we started to bring 'em back and we'd have some pasture to put 'em in. It was a big job. There were at least three of us and sometimes four."

"Did you enjoy that?" I asked Eddie.

"Oh yes. We camped out, slept on the ground."

"What kind of food would you take with you?"

"Oh, some potatoes and bacon. We cooked. A little bit of coffee, and this and that. Lots of coffee. That's the only time I ever drank coffee until I was twenty-four. But I drink it for breakfast now."

"Eddie, how did you meet your wife?"

"Oh, she was raised up in Metolius here. The next little town up the way. Do you know where that is?"

"I'm going through there tomorrow on my way to Cove Palisades."

"Her dad had a store. In those days there was a dance about once a week in maybe Madras or Metolius or Gateway or Antelope or Shaniko. I met her at one of those dances. She went to Prineville High School, like I did, but she was behind me two years so we didn't go to school together. And then after school she went to the University of Oregon. But I got left out of that."

"How did you propose to her?"

Eddie laughed. "Are you sure she didn't propose to me? Do you mean what did I say? I said, 'Let's get married!' And away we went."

287

"That same day?"

"No!" His laugh came easy and often.

"So where was your wedding held?"

"We just went over to Goldendale and got married. Not one of these big weddings like my grandchildren has. It costs a fortune. Are you gonna have one?" he asked.

"Oh, I don't know. I'll probably get married when I'm about sixty!"

"How old are you now?"

"Thirty!"

"Thirty! Why I didn't think you were that old!"

I reached over and gave Eddie a big hug. He blushed and so did I.

"Have you lived in the same house your whole life? Your whole life so far!" I added.

"You're kinda careful what you say! Well, I was born in the house my dad homesteaded in. And then we lived in the house my grandfather built. But I say I did because the houses were right next to each other. Right close."

"So you had to go all the way to Prineville for school?"

"Well, there was a school here but it was new and we didn't think it was as good. We still go to the school reunions at Prineville; they have it for classes 1917 to 1940. Over sixty people still come, and only one was in a wheelchair."

"Pretty healthy group. Must be all that fresh air."

"Must be."

"So did you hunt in the mountains a lot?"

"Not at all, I never killed a deer," Eddie said proudly.

"Is that right?"

"No, I never wanted to kill a deer. Have plenty of them around here though. And I have a high and tight fence around the garden. But I never wanted to kill one. They are just too beautiful. I fished a lot though."

"Tell me a little bit about your mules."

"Oh they were very tall mules and they could walk four miles an hour easy. We liked them a lot. They didn't kick worse than any horse."

"It sounds like someone's here. Let's go see," I said, standing up and wiping the hay off the back of my jeans.

"Sounded like the door slammed!" he said as he slowly got up from the hay bale and moved in measured steps towards the house. A tiny cowgirl, who was walking around with spurs on her boots, had arrived with her kids. Eddie gave her a bag of tomatoes. She grinned, grabbed the bag and hugged the old man with her free arm.

"She's not afraid to take your free tomatoes," I said.

"No. She eats a lot of them. And she likes my squash. Do you like squash?"

"Sure do." It wouldn't hurt me to eat something besides popcorn.

"Well, before you leave, let me give you one. I'm just one old man and I've got squash and tomatoes coming out of my ears!"

"Thanks, Eddie."

I walked down the street with my paper bag full of free tomatoes and a bright yellow squash.

Chapter 23

Phyllis and Babe

Once again the mules' shoes had worn thin. It was impossible to keep the metal from grinding off and it wasn't easy to find a new place to nail the new shoes on. The shoes wore out faster than the mules' hooves grew out. It had been a long road since Dayton and the last set of shiny new shoes.

A man down at the coffee shop in Madras gave me the name of Al Short, a horseshoer. I called him on a pay phone and he and his wife, Luann, invited me to stay in their barn and have dinner with them. They were great company. It was warm and comfortable and Luann's candlelight dinner was deluxe. The mules were in a corral right outside so I could talk to them. During the course of the evening, I brought them treats from Luann's kitchen. The Shorts had a mule named Molly and so Mavis and Sarah had somebody to tell their adventures to that night. They stood nose to nose with the little brown mule, on opposite sides of the fence, while I sat at the dining room table with the family. Al told me about their dream to sail off into the sunset.

"I don't think the mules like to sail," Al said jokingly. We laughed and talked into the night, pouring over maps, tracing my long trip from Idaho. Once in awhile I would run into someone who wanted to hear about the journey from beginning to present. Telling the stories cemented the adventure in my memory and the story got longer and longer as we rode towards Newport. I looked back and remembered camps and places where I had slept with a fond sense of familiarity.

Al and Luann argued over which way to send me over the Cascades. Al shook his head slowly back and forth when he looked up from the newspaper and announced a big storm was coming within the next week. He was pretty sure I would get snowed on up on the Santiam. I wasn't a bit looking forward to that because I knew how hard it was for the mules to walk in the snow, especially with shoes on. The ice balls would get bigger and bigger, packed hard into the mules' hooves and held tight by the shoes until we'd be skating. We'd probably make good time sliding down the other side of the pass, but I didn't want to ride in the snow and had never really fathomed a snowstorm on muleback.

They sent me off with a big bag of fresh homemade cookies and smoked salmon, suggesting I eat the fish before I got to the high country and had to share it with a bear. Bears can smell smoked salmon from miles away, and they love it. I planned to eat it all and dispose of the bag by the time I reached the high country.

I took the side road up to Babe and Phyllis Moore's. The folks at the coffee shop said I couldn't leave Madras without meeting them.

Phyllis and her husband Babe lived on the edge of town in a cement block house they had built themselves. That was their business, cement blocks, and their buildings were all over town.

Their house was a wonderland all its own. There were more rooms than I can remember and, like in a child's dream, each one was designed around a separate theme.

Phyllis walked me down to the yard where they used to make the cement blocks and pointed out the trees I should picket the mules to. She was a pretty woman with cat eyeglasses held on with a pearl chain. She had a fun sense of humor, dry and witty, and welcomed me in like I was a long lost cousin from far away. Phyllis was a poet and storyteller as well as a wife and mother, grandmother and gardener.

She took me through each of the rooms of the house and

explained in detail every item, from the old worn pool table to the plastic flowers in the gravel yard. And, finally, we looped back around, past the cement gnome in the back yard to a door leading into a dark room.

"Well these are the dolls," Phyllis said proudly as she led me into the cool cement block room with the high shelves. The dolls looked out at us from their perches and I shivered. She pulled a string cord and the light came on.

"Well, let's see, what one shall I show you? I can show you this one. They are all different, but I stuck to the fairy tales, so they are all strictly fairy tale dolls. This is Goldilocks." Phyllis held up the beautiful doll with the gold hair.

"Oh, she's so pretty," I said.

"Sometimes I can remember the poems, but I better go get the book." She turned Goldilocks upside down. Under her skirt were the three bears, Papa, Mama and Baby Bear. She looked around for the book and I held onto Goldilocks.

"Do you sell these dolls?" I asked.

"Oh, I've sold a few. But actually I haven't made them to sell. I made them to show. I belong to the Eastern Star and the Rebekkah Lodge and they ask me to do skits. I've been doing this for fifteen years. I take them to the nursing home and they enjoy them, too."

"What fun," I said.

"So here's Goldilocks," Phyllis said as she held up the doll with the yellow hair and started to read:

> In a clearing in the darkest woods once there lived three bears.
> They had three of everything, big and little and small sized chairs.
> They even had three different bowls to put their porridge in
> Which is just what they had done,
> When to their chagrin,
> They found the porridge much too hot.
> So they decided to take a hike.
> And who should timely happen by, but Goldilocks,
> And, maiden-like,
> She went in and looked about

293

And resolved to examine the cottage there,
Not knowing that one of every thing belonged
To a fuzzy, growling bear
She ate and sat and rested in nearly every chair
She didn't know the owner
And she didn't really care
She finally found the beds
Where she fell fast asleep.
The bears came back and found her,
And she woke and began to weep.
They tried to tell her not to cry,
They only wished to be her friends
But she ran home as fast as she could,
And that's where the story ends.

"The dolls are so beautiful. You must stay busy year round with all this," I said.

"Well, this summer I was working in the yard, so I didn't get any dolls done," she said a little sheepishly.

"So has Babe done a lot of horse packing?"

"Yeah, he has."

"He said I threw a pretty good diamond hitch."

"Not everybody does that well."

She held up a doll and took a pose. I knew another poem was about to begin. I listened intently.

"Well, this is Red Riding Hood. Most everyone likes this one. You know the story of Red Riding Hood!" Phyllis flipped over the red cape and underneath it there was the wolf. I laughed like a little kid.

"Nobody gets hurt in my stories!" Phyllis said proudly.

"How long does it take you to make these dolls?"

"It takes about a week because it takes me a full day to write the story, to figure out what I want to do. It takes me a few days to figure out the fabrics, to get it to come out right. The big share of the fabric is scrap. A doll only takes about a third of a yard!"

Phyllis showed me doll after doll.

Sing a song of sixpence, a pocket full of rye, four and twenty blackbirds were baked into the pie, and when the pie was opened and all the birds arose, to sing before the king, one pecked off his nose. Wasn't that a dainty dish to set before the king? He paid through his royal nose to hear the birdies sing.

I was fascinated, hypnotized by the show.

"See, a lot of the nursery rhymes were written in political satire," Phyllis said. "So I have changed the poems, but have kept the political satire. Like so many politicians, they think we don't know what is going on. They spend two days saying that's what they said but that's not what they meant. I am not voting for Reagan. He has so much charisma with so many people, but he hasn't convinced me. But I'm hard to convince," Phyllis laughed.

"This doll is little Miss Muffet. Look at the spider."

I laughed. "He sure has a smug look on his face," I said, as I turned Miss Muffet right side up so the spider was once again hidden under her skirt.

"That's Pinkie Snuggle Bunny and the mouse is Deacon Solomon. He's a little church mouse."

"So, Babe's not here?"

"No, he went hunting."

"Overnight?"

"No, just for the day. He'll be back." Phyllis carefully turned the page. "I have twenty of these dolls made now," she said proudly.

"Does Babe like the dolls?"

"Oh, he doesn't say much. Guess he figures it keeps me out of trouble."

"The dolls are beautiful," I said quietly.

"I have to write the story first because I don't know what the doll is gonna be. And that takes some time."

"Where do you buy all these faces?"

"Anywhere I can find them. Some I send away for, some I buy at dime stores." Phyllis rustled through the dolls and the little book that held the verses.

"I wanted to show you one that is pretty cute," she said. "Ha,

295

here it is."

> Snow White was a beautiful lass
> With a stepmother haughty and proud
> Who was jealous and hateful and mean,
> And she had a mirror she would talk to out loud.
> When she said to the mirror out loud,
> Mirror, mirror on the wall, mirror, who's the fairest of us all?
> And the mirror answered back, "You all."
> She was happy and stood tall
> But one day the mirror answered back
> And said that Snow White had the where with all.
> The angry woman threw Snow White out
> And said, Now who's the fairest of us all?
> Snow White went out in the darkening woods
> And suddenly she spied a cottage small,
> This was the home of seven wee men
> And Snow White captured the hearts of them all
> And she dearly loved the seven wee men,
> Bashful and Grumpy,
> Both made their mark
> And there was Sneezy and Sleepy and Dopey and Doc,
> And the one always happy as a lark
> Snow White lived on happily in the woods.
> The stepmother less happy,
> And the mirror, less happy I fear.
> But what do you expect from a mirror that talks,
> And says all the things you don't want to hear?

"Is it really six o clock already?" I looked up at the old clock in the room.

"I think its seven." Phyllis answered.

"I can't believe that it could be this dark at six." I said.

"Once in awhile, somebody asks me to write something special," Phyllis continued. "This little girl down in California used to live here. She comes back to visit once in awhile. I suppose Oregon is

Utopia to her."

"I can see why. It's so beautiful here."

"So this is Shirley's Oregon Summer," Phyllis said quietly.

Summer's disappearing,
And just around the bend,
Autumn's chasing shadows,
Have chased summer's end.
The sultry season's storms build
As clouds roll in
And the rumbling of billowing skies
Is a distant threatening din.
Intermittent lightning unzips the blackening skies
And rains come cascading on the wind's erotic sighs.
Then, as fast as it began,
The clouds all roll away
The sun descends a gold horizon
And bids farewell
To a summer's day.
The spicy scent of juniper
Brought a freshness to the air
The fragrance of gin flower needles
Is pungently everywhere
The aromatic sagebrush
Presents a coat of silver gray
With its terminal cluster of yellow
In a dazzling display.
Summer's grand finale has not been in vain
There will be nostalgic memories
Of sagebrush after rain.

"Do you have anything more about Babe?"

"Sure. I have another whole book that's just about Babe." She slowly closed one book and opened another. It was tattered and the cover was torn.

Babe and I have been married so long you'd think we'd have great conversations. We don't. When I speak he says 'huh' four times in a row, and I repeat what I've said with four variations. It really is monotony. Or he says "I know," and I know he doesn't. As you can see they are not very extended conversations. Anyway, what would we talk about after all these years that both of us haven't already heard? Several times. Of course, we don't really work at it, both of us already know what the other is thinking, no matter what we say. I have an idea we've even had some arguments and we've never said a word. To show you a typical conversation, it goes something like this. He says, "I see a couple of birds have found the new bird feeder." And I say, "Oh?" What else? I thought about making up some bright, animated comments to fit these occasions, but a real thought provoking thought eludes me, so I have devised at least nine ways of saying "oh" to verify that I am there and that I heard. There are of course a variety of eye manipulations and eyebrow maneuvers to accompany and accent the "ohs." Some of it's noticed and appreciated and some of it's lost. Seems like a good idea, but a lot of times my carefully executed "oh" turns out to be a well-modulated dud. I guess in this particular case you could say it was for the birds. However, these "ohs" are not always a dud, sometimes they are quite effectual. Babe came in one day, a beautiful day for mowing the lawn, and said, "Guess I'll go fishin'." Nothing startling in that, or unusual. But I looked again, and it still looked like a beautiful day for lawn mowing. So I said, "Oh," with one of those special inflections and a lift of well trained eyebrow, and a look at a tall lawn. He studied a bit and went out to get his fishing gear and came back and he resolutely announced, "I'm leaving to go fishing. Just as soon as I mow the lawn." See? Lengthy discussions aren't necessary. There's the good old stand-by-conversational bit, "What's for dinner?" But I already know what I'm cooking, and he already knows he's eating anything I fix. By this time I know not to fix anything he fiercely dislikes, and he knows better than to adversely comment on anything I fix, and so experiments, at least as far as he knows, have escaped my kitchen long ago, so what's to discuss? We have sort of agreed not to discuss finances; there's no point to it.

298

There's just so much money and so many bills, that kind of sort of balance each other so there's no money left to discuss, and hopefully no bills left over to discuss. Anyway, the whole thing is kind of depressing so we avoid that one. After so many years we have found the weather is there whether we like it or not, so talking about it is not going to change it. Any chitchat there is of short duration. Maybe we've just said all that we have to say. Maybe we ought to just sit back and relax and enjoy television. Somebody ought to be able to watch TV with a clear conscience. I think maybe it's us.

We sat quietly for a moment. I was lost in her world of verse, for the moment forgetting that summer was part of the past and winter was just around the next corner.

"Do you guys go hunting together?"

"We have," she paused before continuing. "But I don't really enjoy watching things killed. He goes out and does a lot of hiking and I'm not that great at that."

"Does he still have horses?"

"He has one. He had a couple of horses and a burro for a long time. They were for elk hunting."

"Where's his horse?"

"I don't know. Out on a ranch out here someplace. Some girl wanted to use it, and so she takes care of it to use it. Sometimes he doesn't use it for two or three years at a time."

She closed up the book and I felt a little sad.

"Thank you so much, Phyllis. I really enjoyed them."

"There's a book in there that is just about our life. And when we were going together, and what happened, and some of the hunting trips we went on."

"Did he propose to you?"

"Well that's a moot question, too. He says he didn't and I didn't ask him, so I don't know who did. I don't know how this thing happened. It's kind of like when you see a couple holding hands because they are afraid to let go? We'd known each other, but we didn't get along. Every time we opened our mouths we were fighting. I guess we got married to settle the fight, I don't know. We didn't fight after that. It wasn't as much fun. A fellow named Mike asked me if I wanted to go to the November eleventh Armistice Day Ball, and he meant with him and Babe. So the three of us went. We hadn't been there very long and Mike got to drinking and got drunk and Babe had to drive him home. Which left Babe and me alone. And so we finished the dance and Babe took me home. All the way home we told each other why we weren't gonna get married, ever, either one of us. I found out a couple of years later that he had gone home before we had ever gone out and told his folks he was getting married. He always has made fast decisions. So he had already decided. The second date we sent my ring back to the other fellow I was engaged to. Not in a letter. It was a telegram. We sent the other kid a telegram to tell him I was marrying someone else. The third date we had our rings. And that was in December." Phyllis sighed. "We got married in March. It was a good thing we got married in March because in April fishing season opened. That would have been a disaster. He was gone fishing. Oh, I went fishing with him a lot in the beginning."

"How many kids did you have?"

"One. She was born two days before our first anniversary. She's forty-three and has two kids. Our oldest grandson was Valedictorian at Redmond this year, out of about 235 graduates."

"So, do you like being a grandma?"

"Oh yes. Being a mom was pretty great too. Aurolyn and I have a great relationship. We get along great. She calls and Babe thinks it's so silly. She calls long distance and we just stand there and laugh and laugh over the phone. Yes, Aurolyn and I get along great together."

"Arlin?"

"Aurolyn. It's English and it means the light of day. Fits her too. There's a picture of her in the other room. I tell you who she looks like. She looks like Wonderwoman!"

"She does?"

"Exactly. She looks so much like her over a dozen people have told me they have seen her on TV."

"What advice would you give a younger person?" I asked.

"Actually, I don't give advice much. I listen a lot. Several young people call to tell me their troubles. They don't really want advice. I don't know what I'd give as advice." She paused, thinking for a moment. "I think you have to be able to live with yourself. You have to be able to get up in the morning and be able to look in the mirror and not cringe. I think if you like people, they'll like you back. You have to live your life in such a way that you are happy with it, so that you think you are doing the right thing. This is the one I was looking for." She pulled out another poem and began to read.

I met a friend today,
She's been there all the while,
But today I heard her voice and saw her bubbly smile
I knew I'd found a friend, although we'd never met
We talked politely and displayed our very best Sunday etiquette.
She was a stranger yesterday,
But now a friend to greet.
She was that certain friend
That I had yet to meet.

"You know, how they say, a stranger is just a friend you haven't yet met," she said, softly.

"That's how Oregon has been, the whole way across," I told her.

"I think most people are what you reflect. Whatever you are, you redefine in people. You see two girls move into the same neighborhood, and one says everybody is so friendly. Well, that's because *she* is. The other person says it's an unfriendly place. That's because she's not looking for friends."

Phyllis and I stayed in that dark, cool cement room until eight that night. She made me hot cocoa and walked me down to my camp, admiring the mules as they carefully took the dried apricots from her hand with finesse. Babe finally got home from hunting. I hoped he would be around in the morning so I could get to know him a little bit before I headed on my way up into the mountains.

When I woke up, the ice was heavy on my sleeping bag. I knew Al was right. It was only a matter of days before the first storm.

I had coffee with Babe in the kitchen. He was a bear of a man, soft spoken and confident. I smiled, thinking about Phyllis' funny story about their conversations, like I had been let in on a humorous secret.

I followed Babe into his study. It looked like a museum, every inch of the place covered with a picture, a skin or a fur, some beadwork or some leatherwork. He was an honorary member of the Warm Springs Tribe and he had many gifts from the Indians.

He played me a song on an ancient phonograph, the kind with the big horn sticking up. The song sounded scratchy and very old.

"My great-grandfather and my grandfather and my father were all freighters. They carried freight in big wagons from the John Day Valley to Prineville in the early days. Shaniko, Portland and the Dalles were places they freighted to. You came through Shaniko, didn't you?" he asked.

"No."

"There isn't much left of Shaniko. And they crossed the bridge down here to Mecca. But that's all gone. You'd never know a road even went through there. But I did have a chance to cross it before they tore the bridge out. I've been over a lot of the old roads," Babe told me. I've been over the Indian trails. The Indians, when they used to have to travel through the country, they'd come through. It's like you, going on your trip. You've gotta have water. That's all there is to it. When they crossed over to the John Day country they went through Rooper Ranch. When they got to the top of the hill, that was the divide. Then they ran out of water. They went up Ward's Crick. And before they hit the top, they'd run out of water. Then they'd break over the other side. And the draw started forming, and it went down into the John Day River. Once they hit the river, it was clear sailing. They went in for the summer into the mountains between Mt. Vernon and Dayville, on my grandfather's ranch. They'd go up Field's Crick for the summer and they'd hunt and pick berries and everything. Field's Crick and Field's Peak was named after my great-grandfather, on my mother's side. In those days, the Indians didn't have too many rights, but they could stay at my grandparents' ranch. And they did. They'd come through and they'd camp."

"So you've known Indians your whole life."

"Yep. In fact my people are said to be part Indian. My dad hauled

Typical Freighting
Outfit

B. Shields

freight from Portland and the Dalles. But I do know they went through Shearer's, on the Deschutes River. The Molala Indians had their winter village there. I go through there, quite often," Babe continued thoughtfully. "I try to figure where the old road was. And here, the other day, I saw parts of the old road. It's hard to see. And it was a toll bridge in them days. And Shearer's had a barn and they'd charge so much to cross the river."

"Oh yeah? How much did they charge to cross?" I asked.

"I'm not sure how much they charged. My dad told about stayin' in Shearer's barn. And it wasn't much. He said there'd be half a dozen freighters in there. It had a dirt floor, and they'd have fires goin'. But it was shelter, and that was about all. About the only shelter they had out on the mountain was under the wagon. But when you got to Shearer's, he said, it would be so smoky in there, you'd have to lay down on the floor to see what you was cookin'!"

Chapter 24

Jack Frost

The ride up to Cove Palisades State Park was so beautiful, the storm already settling in over the mountains when I pulled into the State Park Camping area. I chose a camp on the edge of everything in case anyone did show up, but there wasn't a soul there.

It started to rain just as I unpacked Mavis and Sarah. I quickly slipped my gear under a picnic table and covered it with a small tarp. I put my poncho on as the rain slashed sideways and the thunder cracked and lightning split the lake in half. Boom! I could feel my heart. Then, again, another bolt blazed its way into the dark sky. The thunderous pounding sent a chill through me. It didn't take long to figure out how miserable I would be if I got all my clothes wet and so once the mules were picketed out and watered, I moved into a fish cleaning room. It was a little place with big windows that ran all the way to the floor. It had a stainless steel sink and a table which was my bed. The best thing about it was that it was inside and there was safety glass between the storm and me which slammed furiously into the little building. Whoever built that fish cleaning room did a good job; there wasn't a leak. It was cozy and dry and I read a book by candlelight and made a cup of tea and Top Ramen as I watched the storm rage outside, lightning cracking and rain pouring down in torrid sheets. I was at once terrified and awed by the storm, and filled with relief when morning came.

Al and Luann came and found me way up on Green Ridge that next night; we built a big campfire and Luann brought a good dinner. They felt like old friends. We laughed and talked until about eight when they decided to head home. What had taken me two days would take them an hour. I listened to the sound of their engine while they drove slowly down the dirt road back to Madras and then, after that, it was too quiet.

The country had changed and I felt tiny as I rode under some of the oldest, tallest trees in the world. Relieved to have finally reached the Metolius River, I headed south along it as I was told it was the best way to go; Al and Luann had argued long and hard over that one. I felt confident in their direction and the mules loved the dirt road and the sound of the rushing Metolius. It flows endlessly from the earth near Black Butte and transforms into a river that's level varies little throughout the year. Worn by the boots of fishermen, the banks of that stunning river glistened with shining pine needles.

Homesteaders made her banks their home, their trail well worn by settlers who crossed the mountains with pack trains of mules. They were bound for the Willamette and the land they had always imagined, a land so fertile they would flourish and thrive. Long before that it had been an Indian path. I could imagine the pack trains and horses and the people who had walked that trail before us. I worked my way towards Camp Sherman.

Since the early 1900's farmers from Sherman County had come there to beat the heat in the valley and to fish. I rode along quietly and listened to the sound of the rushing river, lost in the thousands of trees that engulfed me, many dripping with moss. Everywhere I looked was deep, endless forest. The country had changed so fast; I was amazed at the wonderland I found myself in. All new smells and sounds; sometimes the smell of pure pine would fill the air and then the aroma of the cedar would drift in. Down the same road I traveled, along the river, thousands of men and women had passed as they etched their way across the passes of the High Cascades. Now the trail was quiet and there was no sound aside from that of the river. The mules' feet fell silently on the pine needle carpeted forest floor.

Someone had put a shoe box top on a post that said Camp Sherman along the trail and the name stuck. The Camp Sherman store was a welcome sight under the tall ponderosas, smoke curling up through them like silk. I tied up Mavis and Sarah and walked up onto the wide porch and into the old store which had been serving the needs of flatlanders and fishermen and hunters for generations. Everyone was talking about the storm which was due in that evening. A cup of hot chocolate helped warm me up as I stood there in the welcoming store feeling my body starting to thaw out a little, my feet frozen.

"Do you know anyone who might have a place where I could leave my two mules for a few days?" I asked the woman behind the counter at the Camp Sherman store who was unpacking frozen meat, dialing the phone and working the register all at the same time.

"Head down the road and you'll see the red cabins and an old house, the one with the corrals. Try there."

"Thanks. I have to get to a wedding in Anacortes, Washington. My friend Amy's getting married the day after tomorrow and I've just got to get there. I rode down from Idaho and it's already taken me almost two months. Figured I'd be to the end of the trip, out on the coast by now. But, of course, things like this take time." I was blathering away. I hadn't talked in a couple of days, except to Mavis and Sarah. I was excited about the wedding and I also knew it was foolish to take time to go since Old Man Winter wasn't invited and he was going to come anyway.

A round, friendly man answered the door of the little red house. He had lived there for many years and had done quite a bit of packing himself. Before I knew it, the mules were unpacked and rolling in the sawdust in the little pen. They would stay in the nice corrals under the ponderosas. He promised to feed them twice a day, grain and large flakes of sweet grass hay.

Winter would come to Camp Sherman while I was off in the real world, leaving Mavis and Sarah buried in snow.

I crowded into the back of a station wagon with five hunters, each one expanded by their heavy black and red jackets. They were heading over the mountains and agreed to carry me to a truck stop where I

307

could get another ride. They had been hunting in the mountains for a week or more and smelled of wood smoke and pine. Conversation was lively all the way to the Interstate as we swapped stories of the trail. I already missed Mavis and Sarah but looked forward to the wedding and seeing Nina, who was waiting for me in Seattle.

The night was pitch black by the time we arrived on Interstate 5. The hunters waved goodbye as they headed off to their homes to recover. I stood there, bewildered in the rain, feeling lost without Mavis and Sarah. The rain was coming down in sheets. I hunched my shoulders and walked towards the cafe, opened the door and shivered as a warm gust of hot air that smelled like french fries hit me in the face. There were a variety of truckers sitting at the counter, each one doing his best to make the stop count. The waitress looked at me with disdain. I sat down feeling like an underdressed mule skinner drenched and cold and lonely without my mules. Funny how much confidence they gave me and how ridiculous I felt without a place to sleep, sitting in that truck stop late at night. I needed my four legged good luck charms.

"You better wait until morning to get a ride out of here," a tall, skinny cowboy said to me as he put his coffee cup down and paid his bill. "I've got lots of room in the cab of my truck. It's parked right over there. You're more than welcome to stay in there and catch a ride with me in the morning. That way you'll stay out of trouble."

I trusted him. His eyes told the story. It was his co-pilot I had to worry about. When the tall skinny cowboy led me back over to the beautiful blue Peterbuilt, I could see his fellow driver sitting in the seat reading.

"Oh, Eugene, what did you bring me?" he said smiling at me with his gold teeth, his thick bushy eyebrows dancing up and down.

"That's enough. You're sleeping in the back tonight."

He kicked his partner out of the tall cab and I listened from the passenger seat, already warmed up by the strange looking man who Eugene had instantly banished to the trailer in back. The skinny cowboy was going to watch out for me and would get me safely to Seattle with no funny business.

"He's got plenty of blankets. We just finished moving the innards of a mansion to San Francisco. We're empty to Seattle. Now you sleep here and don't worry about him; he's harmless. And he's locked in the back," he said casually.

"You locked him in?"

"Yep. Don't trust him that way. You know."

I stretched across the comfortable vinyl seats and tried to sleep. I was exhausted and did my best to block out the country music that was playing on the radio. Eugene was snoring; I thought he was asleep so I reached up and turned down the radio. Once it was turned down, Eugene stirred and reached out from the sleeper and turned it back up.

"Can't sleep without it," he woke up to tell me.

I lay there through three sets of country road music and gave up on the idea of getting any sleep. Somehow morning came; the rain had stopped. I felt embarrassed as I jumped down from the tall cab. Another trucker looked at me and smiled and I felt my face redden as I rushed for the bathroom out behind the gas station. I slipped on the slick tiles and stumbled towards a look in the mirror which was a piece of polished stainless steel. It was like looking into a frozen pond. I thought about Phyllis Moore and her Snow White poem that went something like this:

Mirror, mirror, on the wall, who's the fairest of them all?
Y'all, the mirror answered.

"I promise not to tell Mom about this night in the truckstop," I said to the mirror.

I sat in the sleeper all the way and was up in Seattle before I knew it. They dropped me off close to Nina's. I walked over to her house and knocked on the door, a little weary but glad to be there.

"Oh my God, Jody! Come in! You made it! Where are the mules?" she asked in a childlike way. Her eyes sparkled and she was still limping. Out came a big box of homemade meringue and we sat and ate half of it, the sweet fluffy crumbs falling all over the sofa. Nina lived in a cozy house in the company of her dog and three cats. She listened intently to all my stories about the long trail from Idaho.

"It feels like three years ago and it has only been two months," Nina said sadly. "Jody, you will never know how heartbroken I was on that bus trip back to Seattle. Also, the happiness I felt on the back of sweet Sarah Jane as we rode up that trail, what was it called? Dry Creek? Or Crick as you say?" She laughed. Nina had told me that life was a succession of losses. Even though she had lost so many people she loved in her life, she held her memories fast, continuing on and living a life in which she found joy beyond all her suffering; making her own yogurt, scaling Mt. Rainier, riding off across the west on a little white mule. I idolized her. We talked about all the roads I had traveled and I told her in detail what she had missed. It was almost too hard for her to listen but she wanted to know all the places we had slept, when I was most scared, what she would have loved the most, all about dear Sarah and Mavis, and what I planned to do about the snow that was expected that weekend in the mountains. Everyone asked me that question.

I came back to see Nina after the wedding which was a wonderful, fun time with dancing in a log cabin on a huge dance floor. I felt as if I had dropped in from another planet. I knew it was snowing in the high country and I could tell if I stayed away another day I would not finish the trip to the coast. The thought kept tapping me on the shoulder the entire time I was away. I wanted to stay but instead went back to Nina's and she drove me to the place where I'd catch the bus back to Camp Sherman. There was no way I was going to hitchhike out of there.

Nina drove like a bandit, in her long fur coat, her small gray head barely reaching over the dash. She often drove through yellow lights and although she respected the law, she never let it slow her down. As she explained, who would throw a little old lady with an accent in jail? Her driving scared me. She dropped me off at the bus. Just before it pulled away, there was Nina in her long fur coat.

"Remember, Jody! Wheels over the pass! Wheels over the pass!" she yelled. Everyone on the bus turned and looked at her and then at me.

"O.K., Nina! Don't worry! I'll give Sarah a hug for you!"

The bus pulled away as I watched the tiny woman hobble to her old Buick. She looked so old to me. "Going to let my hair go gray the minute I feel like an old woman. And that time has come!" she had told me jokingly. But sure enough, her gray hair made her look older and her knee injury did not help matters. I was anxious to get back to the trail, before I wanted to move into her spare bedroom and eat meringue all winter, adjusting the thermostat for heat and watching TV or reading.

The bus pulled into Camp Sherman and I didn't recognize the place. Snow has a way of changing everything. The old store looked different.

I slipped in my tennis shoes across the big parking lot and laughed out loud. I ran down to the corral to see Mavis and Sarah. They both had snow on their manes and eyelashes—a wonderful, magical light snow, the first of the winter. The hunters had packed up and hit the highway for the lowlands. Little neatly kept trailers were heading down the road as if in a parade.

"Now you better be careful riding out of here," my corral host warned me. "The highway is slick as a whistle and people aren't yet tuned into the snow. Oil on the roads and maybe a little ice makes dangerous conditions for you on the side of the highway."

"So I might as well just pass by the Pacific Crest," I said sadly.

"Forget about it. When it's buried in snow, which it is, better to stick to the highway side. You could travel that way all the way down to the valley. It's just that people aren't used to it. The road is so slick; they slam on the brakes and bam! they're heading right towards you. I wish you'd let me carry you down to the other side, I don't know...just out of the snow."

"We'll see. I'll give it a go and see how I do!"

Mavis and Sarah were glad I was back and, even though they had been fed heartily and given grain, they still were anxious to get going. Once we got on the snowy road Sarah did her best to balance and not slip. Mavis was skating behind us. For a change I was riding Sarah. Mavis had taken to the pack like magic and was proud to carry the load which, I must say, was much lighter than I was. We skated and I held my breath, always planning a way to get out of the saddle as quickly as possible if she slipped and fell. Sarah's height made it easy

to make such plans and I never worried about getting to the ground. It was nerve-wracking riding and I looked hopefully up the road to see if the old man would come down with a horse trailer. We rode the quiet Metolius Road and made it to Highway 20.

After a mile or so of riding on the side of the road, with big trucks rumbling past with little distance to spare, I caught my breath, pulled down my hat and patted Sarah on the neck for encouragement. She understood the danger and kept off the road as much as she could, ears poised and ready to move to catch any sound, listening for the next truck or car. Just then I looked back and saw a big black Cadillac swerving towards me, obviously getting ready to spin. I choked out "Sarah, go girl!" as I gave her a good kick and pushed her down the mountain into the deep snow. Mavis followed and we turned to see the Cadillac pulled off to the side of the highway a few feet from where we had been only seconds before. It took a minute to catch my breath. The mules were breathing hard, too. We were not having fun. And then in my mind there would be an image of little Nina, in her long fur coat, when she jumped on the bus yelling, "Wheels over the pass! Wheels over the pass!" We moved off and stood under some tall ponderosa pines, big chunks of snow falling from their giant branches. A couple of huge clumps landed right in front of Mavis and she practically shed her skin. Sarah remained calm through all of this but I knew if she could talk she would be echoing Nina's stern command.

I heard an engine and looked up ahead on the pullout to see the pickup and the little horse trailer.

"I think you'd better let me carry you off the pass and down to the edge of the snow. It's only about fifteen miles or so," the round man said with authority.

"Great," I sighed with relief and the mules could hardly wait for me to get the door of the little yellow trailer open. They dug into the sweet grass hay that filled the feeders and warm steam rose off their cold, snowy coats. "There," they must have thought. "That's more like it."

We rolled past the Pacific Crest Trail. The little sign was covered with snow. The season was over and now only the very hardy would ride up there. I smiled sadly as we passed Suttle Lake and some really perfect campsites along the Santiam River. I swore I'd be back another year...earlier.

He dropped me off down the road where the snow ended and the rain began. The cedar trees were huge and dripping, the pines filling in all the spaces in between. The old trail to the Willamette ran right along here. I walked on the old wagon road, through some of the most beautiful fall colors and huge dripping gray pines. Cascadia State Park was a good place to camp where I hurried to make camp before all my gear got wet. Without a tent, I had to rig up my tarp next to a picnic table to stay out of the cold rain. I made tea and had some cookies and some jerky and fell asleep in my watery little room under the picnic table. The pine needles fell all night in the forest, and the sound of the creeks flowing into the South Santiam made beautiful music.

I rode the old wagon road all the way to the bar outside of Sweet Home. I put the mules out in a pasture under some tall pines next to the river. Everything was so wet and lush, green and rainy. My poncho kept me dry but not warm.

I sat at the corner of the long, long bar and sipped a cup of coffee in the first restaurant that looked open, a big place called The Point. I listened to the rain pouring down outside, my frozen hands just starting to thaw out. It was heavy, consistent rain and acted as if it had come to stay. A couple of drunken guys were sitting way down the bar. I could barely see them the bar was so long and the room so dark. One of the cowboys disappeared for awhile and came back with Sarah who was walking with great concern across the green and white linoleum floor. The cowboy danced in front of her at the end of her rein and his laughing friend practically fell off his barstool. I just sat there in disbelief and watched the whole scenario unfold. The cowboy tried to get up in the saddle which had my poncho draped over it. He got about halfway on when the saddle slipped off to one side and the butt breeching got caught up underneath her tail. I got up and walked across the dance floor to rescue Sarah as the cowboy slid off and on to the hard floor, his legs sticking underneath the little white mule. Sarah stood as still as a statue, her eyes wide as saucers, looking down at the cowboy on the floor.

"Wanted to buy the poor water-logged critter a hot toddy," he said as he got himself up off the floor and hobbled back to the bar.

I tiptoed back outside with Sarah following me in careful steps. Mavis brayed and the sound echoed off the walls of the front porch of The Point.

Chapter 25

Paved or Growed Over

Bernice didn't have to convince me to stay at her house. "Who would care? It's raining and it won't let up," she said matter of factly, her hands on her hips. She was a tall woman in her fifties and walked with confidence across the floor like she owned the place. Turned out she did. "I've got nice neighbors all around me. Nobody would say a word."

An old man sat at the bar next to me. He leaned over a beer and started talking to me in a whisper. His voice was gone, probably from smokes.

"Sweet Home Valley was a real quiet valley until the 30's when the freight train came through here. Of course Indians fished and hunted and lived here long before all that. Then the first settlers came in here in 1851 or so to build a little saw mill. And that was the beginning of the town. The road back in the old days was nothing much and it used to take two full days to get up to Lebanon with a team of horses and its only fifteen miles." He smiled at me and his eyes twinkled.

"I'll be there tomorrow night, I think. The road is much better now, isn't it?"

"Oh sure, the highway is. But the old wagon road still can be ridden along there in places. Old roads like that, if they don't get paved over or growed over, well, they're etched in the woods forever. I worked the woods, first for myself and then for the big guys. Worked the sawmill, too. But I preferred the woods. It felt good to use a big saw, and boom!" He made an excited movement with his left arm and it came down on his beer like a wrecking ball. The glass broke and the beer went flying. Bernice walked over with a bar towel and cleaned it up without a word, the old sawyer giving her an apologetic glance. Then he continued. "When those giants fell, the earth groaned under their weight. No big trees left like that, you know. Only a few groves here and there. But most of the big ones are gone. Went to build boardwalks and buildings and wagons and every bit of this place that ain't rock or mud."

I looked at the old man, deep into old eyes that were so light blue I found myself staring. His arms and hands were rugged and crooked from years in the woods and I couldn't help but notice the missing finger. I smiled and laughed a little.

"What's so funny?" he asked, glancing at his four-fingered hand, then raising it up in front of his face.

"Nothing. Sorry."

"I lost it to a chain saw. And a little one at that. Don't take much of a saw to do a finger in," he said gravely. "You know that wagon road is really something. See, a lot of the pioneers who first came over here, well they tired of the rainy weather and many were sent away for their health. Some, they thought back to the good graze they passed by on their way over here. Sure, it was good for growing crops in the Willamette Valley, but the cattle were getting squeezed out and so they headed back to Central Oregon through here. Santiam was always a trail, though."

"Have you lived here all your life?" I asked, sipping my hot coffee. I kept my eye on the two drunken cowboys at the end of the bar who were still laughing over Sarah's unexpected waltz across the dance floor.

"Since forever," he said and suddenly reached his old hand out, grabbed mine and squeezed it pretty hard. "Wanted to try Tucson and dry out, you know, but never did. Went to Old Mexico once; liked it down there. I came back and built my cabin here in Sweet

Home and stayed here all along."

"It's beautiful here," I said quietly.

"So then," he continued, taking a sip of his new beer, "with the gold discovered over in Canyon City and Granite, they had even more of a reason to head east. Of course they always give the credit to a guy named Wiley but the pass was an Indian trail and a deer trail before that. You probably saw Wiley Creek on your way down."

"All the creeks were so loud," I said. "Not like on the East Side."

"You know," he continued, "they charged a toll for the use of the road. There were roadhouses all along the way, one at Cascadia where they have that old natural soda spring, and another at Mountain House. Mule trains hauled freight over the pass and down the other side. It was a lively time, all horse and mule power. Every bit of everything depended on livestock before the train came in. Then the car. And you know the rest."

"I heard a story today about how the name road hog came about," I piped in. "An old Oldsmobile called 'Old Scout' came along the road around 1905. The gatekeeper had never seen such a contraption and didn't know what to charge him for passage. But the gatekeeper could see that the horses and cattle on the road were not comfortable with this noisy form of transportation and steered clear of it, just the way they do with hogs! So they called it a road hog and charged three cents, the same price as for a load of hogs to cross at the tollgate. This guy crossed the whole continent in that old car, in something like forty days."

"I know all about that trip. Wouldn't that have been something, crossing the whole country in one of them old cars? Imagine!" the old man said.

Bernice made a map on a cocktail napkin with her phone number at the bottom in case I got lost on my way from The Point. As I was leaving to ride over to her house, a man on a motorcycle pulled up and walked over to me, sloshing in his big black boots through buckets of rain in the parking lot. He was carrying a black Arctic suit in his arms, pressing it close to him to keep it from dragging on the ground.

"Here. Take this. Came all the way down from Alaska and I'm

heading to Florida," he said. "Don't need this anymore." He walked away without another word, jumped back on his bike and rode off, disappearing down the corridor of tall fir before I could say thank you. I stood there holding the big Arctic suit in the rain. It would protect me in any weather, a shield from the torrential downpours I knew were in my immediate future. I whispered "thank you" to the empty highway that gobbled him up in a flash of water and speed.

The woods were so thick I was feeling dwarfed, buried beneath dripping fir trees and cedars and gray sky. That time of year the rain came... and it stayed. I gladly took Bernice up on her offer to spend the night. She told me that she lived on a suburban cul-de-sac and that she had a big backyard with a tall fence.

I listened to the sound of the mules' shoes on the pavement. They made so much more noise in this neighborhood as we clip-clopped on the slick, black pavement towards Bernice's house. The mules had to walk gingerly to keep from slipping. I felt relieved when I saw her address on the curb.

A tall blond woman with a big smile, Bernice stood in the door and waved me through the side gate and into the most perfect back yard which I was sure had never seen the likes of a mule. Bernice was pleased to have such unusual company and I could tell she was an animal lover. The mules were very enthusiastic about trimming the lawn which was long and luxurious. I was concerned that by morning she would regret having such voracious dinner guests but Bernice wasn't the least bit concerned and went to making us fried chicken she had pulled out of the freezer. We sat on the couch and watched TV as the rain poured down outside. Later on she made us a big bowl of buttered popcorn.

"I practically live on popcorn on the trail," I told her.

"You're kidding," she said.

"I'm not. It's easy to pack and expands when cooked. It's the perfect trail food."

Mavis and Sarah ended up with their noses to the big sliding window in the shelter of her little cement patio.

"So did you ride the wagon road, coming down from Cascadia?" she asked.

"Part of the way. It was so quiet, so buried deep in pine needles, I couldn't even hear the mules walking and the only sound was that river. What beautiful, majestic forests you've got out here."

"Sweet Home wouldn't be here if it weren't for the trees," Bernice said, laughing. "Did you know this place is built in an ancient forest? You should see some of the arrowheads and agates and petrified wood people have found around here."

"Oh yeah?"

"The South Santiam is good fishing too, you know. And the Calapooia! You should see the trout that come out of that river. Miles and miles of trout fishing, so much around here you could spend the rest of your life with a pole in your hand!"

"That's one thing I want to bring next time. A fishing pole," I said through a mouthful of popcorn.

"Once the railroad came in, the wagon road wasn't such a big deal anymore. In the early twenties the road was closed and began to be buried in pine needles. Then the highway was built over the crest and that was that. Now it's just a bunch of crazy drivers slip sliding down the other side. It's a nightmare to drive up there after a storm before they sand the road."

We sat and watched TV until eleven. I slept right there on the couch in my sleeping bag which Bernice had dried out for me in her clothes dryer. She was good company and we laughed about my trip and some of the things that had happened between Clark Fork and Sweet Home.

The house was so warm I couldn't sleep. After being so cold and wet, the contrast was too much. I listened to the sound of the heater as it smoothly filled the room with comforting, warm air. What a luxury it was to be inside with electric heat. I cherished each moment I was out of the storm that was pounding the town.

The rain really had come to stay and wouldn't let up until spring. I could see why some settlers headed back over the pass.

I got up to use the bathroom and had to laugh at Mavis and Sarah asleep standing side by side on the tiny patio in the perfect back yard. It was a pretty tiny pasture for two hungry, cold and wet mules. I wished I had blankets to wrap them in. But, as they always did, they were making the best of what they had and that night it was a patio over their heads and all the lawn they could eat. We enjoyed the night spent at Bernice's place on the cul-de-sac.

Bernice and I had breakfast together. I pulled the mules out of the backyard and packed up for Lebanon.

I had grown so used to the quiet roads of the East Side; but on the West Side, the big trucks and the cars whipped up the rain adding a whole new dimension to a long, wet ride. Sarah did her best not to slip on the wet shoulder since there was obviously no room for mistakes. The mules' shoes slipped on the black pavement and, whenever I could, I followed the old wagon road that appeared now and then paralleling the busy highway. It was a pleasure to ride that quiet old road.

The tidy sagebrush campfires and the starry nights were behind me. I had a funny feeling I would be living in my poncho all the way to Newport. The rain brought out the friendliest people helping me along the trail. It was as if they each had a piece of the same, long, red carpet.

The mules and I were accustomed to the trail and the open dirt roads of the high desert had left us hardy and happy. Mavis was a pro and carried the pack happily as Sarah carefully measured her position on the soft, grassy shoulder of the Lebanon Highway.

I knocked on the door of a cheery looking trailer home. I found Lew, Bernice's ex, in a little trailer park a couple miles from Lebanon. The neighbor's trailer had a window box of red plastic geraniums which I stood admiring as I waited for Lew to answer the door.

"How're ya doin? Come on in. We'll get the mules settled over here along the woods. They'll be fine. My neighbor brought over some carrots so we'll make sure the mules get to chew on those. You get changed in the back room and I'll get these clothes dry for you." He was a tall, handsome man with a booming voice to match and a shock of white hair. He took to me as if he was entertaining an old friend. He laughed often and when he did, the sound echoed through the tall trees dwarfing the trailers. I led the mules down the small paved road that circled around to a variety of single and double wides. There were open woods behind Lew's small but tidy trailer, and I hoped Mave and Sarah wouldn't tear the place up too badly.

We came out of the trailer to discover that Mavis had wrapped her lead rope around a sprinkler and a pipe. She stood there looking a little guilty, waiting to be released from her shortened rope. The pipe was broken but Lew didn't seem worried. Before I noticed, she had dug up the lawn with her foot, her way of working out her frustration. Meanwhile Lew and I were over at the neighbors for pie and hadn't noticed what had happened. None of this bothered anybody except me because I had not wanted to see the place ripped to pieces.

"Mavis, what did you do?" I wailed. She responded by taking off with a fence post that I had tied her to. She put her head up and dragged the fence post by the rope as I followed her through the trailer park.

She knew better than to go too far without Sarah who paced at the end of her lead. Mavis pranced around the trailer park, her legs stretched out and her head held high, her ears flashing back and forth and her eyes wide much to the delight of the mostly elderly women who looked out of their trailers. I smiled embarrassedly and coaxed her in with a treat, a piece of candy in a noisy wrapper I found in my coat pocket.

It was never any use to chase a mule; there was no sense in it. You had to outsmart them, talk them into what you wanted. Mave knew that too. I grabbed her rope and heaved a sigh of relief, looking out at the fast moving traffic on the highway.

"This is where the rodeo ends, Mave," I said to her as we walked back to Lew's. The floral and lace curtains started to close and the trailer ladies went back to their couches and kitchens.

Lew sent me off towards Corvallis, warning me to be careful on the road.

"I will." He stood there and waved as I rode off down the busy highway.

On my way out of town it started to pour again and I felt the rivulets gather in the neckline of my cold green poncho. I hunkered down and the mules laid their ears flat to keep out the rain.

A friendly man stopped in a pickup and asked if I needed a place to stay. It was almost dark again since I had stayed at Lew's until after noon.

"Need a place to stay tonight?" he asked, keeping his shoulders hunched since it was pouring. "My wife and I have a place up the highway about three miles. You are more than welcome."

I said, "Yes." What else? My socks and pants were soaking wet. My tennis shoes were sopped and my poncho was soaked. I would just say "yes" and "thank you" without seeming anxious or at all desperate. There was a knack to it.

It was a long three miles and Mavis and Sarah walked as fast as they could towards Wes Lester's. Finally I reached a perfect red wooden home to the liking of any Palomino and his cowboy. I pulled in and Wes took Sarah and Mavis to a stall deep in straw just outside of the tack room, in the spirit of Mr. Ed. I looked around the simply furnished room and smiled. The smell of the wet leather filled the air. Saddles lined the wall and looked so perfect in comparison to my road worn gear which sat in a dripping pile on the floor.

"We fashioned this place around a horseshoe door knocker," Wes told me. He was proud of his place, and with good reason. It was neat as a pin, and would've made Roy Rogers and Dale Evans green with envy.

I slept on my saddle blankets. In the middle of the night I got up and tiptoed in to see the mules. They were both lying down in the soft straw. Slowly, I crept into the stall and lay against Sarah's warm, soft coat listening to the sound of her slow, even breathing. I stayed there for a long time and listened to the rain on the shake roof.

Chapter 26

A Man of Letters

I finally reached the big city of Corvallis and my only desire was to get off the road. I had had some close calls with a couple of big trucks that afternoon and once saw my reflection in the stainless steel drum of a gas truck. I was tired and strained from road riding. I looked down at the beautiful Willamette as I crossed it, entering town, and couldn't resist that grassy riverbank. Darkness protected me as I disappeared into the huge trees along the river, down a long bank under tall pines.

I quickly unpacked and tied Mavis and Sarah to trees close to each other. Digging around in my pack, I found the grain that Wes and his wife had given us and gave it to the mules in heaping piles. I found my town shirt and changed into it, taking off my hat to try and straighten my hair. At least with the good cowgirl shirt I would look halfway decent.

I entered the big, dark steakhouse called Michael's Landing and headed straight for the ladies' room to get a good look in a mirror and clean up in the sink. When I exited the ladies' room I felt like a new girl. Washed hair back under my hat, skin scrubbed and shirt ironed by throwing a little water on it. I sat down at the bar and ordered a beer and a dinner salad with Roquefort dressing. The waiter brought tons of crackers, which I had sweetly suggested, and I sat there for two hours, watched TV and warmed up. The restaurant had a gorgeous view of the Willamette.

There was a fellow at the end of the bar drinking martinis, one after the next. He kept looking out the window through the deep fog towards the river, shaking his head. Then he'd scratch his head.

"If I wasn't so wasted I'd say there's a white unicorn by the river," he said to the bartender.

"Sure, Pete. You're cut off."

"No, really. Come here."

The bartender reluctantly walked down to Pete's spot by the window. "See it?" he said excitedly.

"Wait. Oh my God. I do. Pete I thought you were out of your mind."

I stayed real quiet, paid my bill and left the two men wondering. Was it a unicorn or just my pure white Sarah disappearing in the fog as it blanketed the river then reappearing again, just for an instant?

At four in the morning, there was a flashlight in my eyes and three uniformed men standing close by.

"You can't camp here, you know," the one cop said.

"Oh, I'm sorry." I sat up in my sleeping bag and glanced down at the buttons on my shirt. I wanted to get up but I didn't have my pants on so I just smiled.

"Can we see some I.D.?" an officer asked.

"Don't have my license with me, but I have this newspaper article with my name in it."

I dug around in my red bag for my journal and pulled out a little newspaper clipping with a picture of the mules and me in front of the Heppner City Hall. I looked at the picture and pointed to my name. They focused their flashlights on the picture and then back to me.

"You rode from Idaho?" one young cop asked.

"Yep. I'm going to the coast."

"How long have you been riding?" another cop asked. "And on mules?"

The pressure was off and I could tell they weren't going to make me move. Everyone realized it wasn't realistic to send me off towards the fairgrounds in the middle of the night. Anyway, it was foggy and

B. Shields

frosty and the cops were rubbing their hands together.

They bent the rules for the mule train and decided it was easier to leave me alone. There weren't all that many mule trains coming through Corvallis anymore.

It was so magical on that big river with the mules grazing in the fog and a light sugar frost all over everything. I was sleeping under some very old trees, once shelter to families of Indians who lived upon the banks of the Willamette.

After the officers left, I sat up in my bag and listened to the river. The spirit of that place was so strong, I could hear a low murmur. Maybe it was just the river, but I believed it to be more than that. That spot was once one of the premier places to camp on the river the Indians loved and respected, the river that the settlers longed for. Next to the busy highway, even with all the noise of the cars passing by, I knew I was sleeping on very sacred ground. And I was thankful to the officers for bending the rules.

I rode out the bike path all the way to the university to collect on a bet I had made with young Ron Heller, a University of Oregon football player who I had worked with in the summer season up at the Lighthouse, in Hope, Idaho. He had bet me five dollars I would never make it as far as Corvallis on my mules and I had to go and collect.

I wasn't sure how to find him so I just went straight to the football field. I hoped to find him on his way out of the locker room. I rode Mavis and led Sarah all the way up to the door and let them eat the lawn along the building while I waited for Ronnie. Then there he was, a big lumbering man in a football uniform amongst his teammates on his way to practice.

"Hey, Ronnie," they yelled, "so your girlfriend's a mule skinner!"

He was bright red. Luckily he had money on him. He handed me a five-dollar bill and smiled.

"Congratulations, you made it," he said. He was as handsome as ever. I dropped the five-dollar bill and jumped off Mavis to pick it up as it swirled around in the wake of the football team as they ran in their noisy shoes towards the field. I crumpled up the bill in my pocket and rode off towards the fairgrounds.

I had been over to the Corvallis Gazette-Times for an interview as the cop had suggested, and there I learned of the town historian, Ken Munford, who wrote a weekly history column for the paper. I called him and he met me downtown. The breakfast looked so good and I was starved after my night out at the fairgrounds. I ordered two eggs over easy.

"So this is where you are now," Ken said, pointing at my map. He

330

had on a Pendleton red and gray plaid that was perfectly pressed and was a distinguished man, balding, with bright eyes. He had a scholarly look to him and his hands were not so worn. I could tell I was in for a treat spending the morning with him because he loved the area and had been working at Oregon State University since the late '30's, first as an English professor and then as an editor in the Office of Publications. He taught school, wrote, and learned everything about the history, both local and statewide.

He pointed to a spot on the map along the mountains, just outside of town.

"So this is where the Blodgett's lived."

I stared at the map.

"They came to this beautiful little valley in 1867 and staked a claim. Then they heard about the gold in California, so they went down there."

"Did they come back?"

"Yes. They didn't do so much as far as gold mining was concerned. They had the Blodgett Family Freight service and they brought goods and equipment up from the Sacramento River to a mining camp called Grass Valley."

"That's where my aunt and uncle live. Can I have a little real milk for my coffee?" I asked the tiny waitress as she whisked by on her way to cut pie. They had been cooling for about ten minutes and were ready to serve.

"Sure," she said.

"I'll have two eggs over easy with hashbrowns. And can I have my toast done on the grill? Thanks. Do they have waffles here? How are they?" I asked, hungrier than usual.

"I don't know because I don't eat them," the waitress said, looking at her figure in the mirror above our booth.

"I'm always tempted to get a waffle but I'll just stick with my eggs over easy."

"Would you like a waffle?" Ken asked.

The waitress stood there looking at Ken, her pen poised.

"Nothing for me. I've already eaten," he added.

It was already nine-thirty and Ken was an early riser, I just knew it.

"So tell me a little bit about the Blodgetts. William sounded like a real character," I said.

"It's all right here in my column. William Blodgett, in his later years, became a drunkard. William had many problems. His worst was a craving for strong drink. He mortgaged his half of the claim and bought liquor. Whenever the neighbors would see a driverless team trotting up the road they would laugh saying, 'There's Bill Blodgett, going home again,' knowing he was asleep in the wagon.

"It's a good thing those horses knew the way home," I said.

"That's for certain," Ken laughed. "The temperance minded editor of the Corvallis Gazette noted in his personal column that 'William Blodgett was in town last week in his usual condition,' or 'Mr. Blodgett and Mr. Logsdon were seen in town this week and were both sober.' That was news, you see."

"Two men tried to pick a fight with Big Bill when he was in his sixties. He picked up one in each hand and threw them through the solid door. One man who was badly hurt sued and Blodgett was ordered to pay him ten dollars. When Blodgett's mortgage was foreclosed he went to the doctor to have his throat examined. The doctor could find nothing wrong with his throat. 'But Doc, there has to be,' William said, 'I just poured three hundred and forty feeders, forty cattle and a team of wagons down it.'" Ken laughed. The waitress arrived with my breakfast.

The Blodgett family story was only one of many that Ken knew by heart. He cherished history like a cowboy loves a good horse.

"For thirty years the Blodgetts lived in their cabin and raised their family. In 1877 the children were grown and gone, except Rufus who stayed in the valley. Asideth, Bill's wife, had left the old man's bed and board and struck out on her own, which I tell about in the next column." He patted the newspaper with love.

"His wife left him?" I asked.

"Yep."

"William homesteaded ninety acres above the old home and proved up on it but he became unmanageable and was banished to a small house two hundred yards from Rufus and his family. Grandsons Rufus, six, and James, eight, had the duty to watch the old man while the hired man was away. He asked the boys to bring him a drink. When they brought him water he swung his cane at them hitting a teakettle and knocking boiling water all over. He didn't want any water to drink! The boys refused further hazardous duty."

"Nasty old guy," I said.

"The next column here is about Asineth who for thirty-six years of her life was his faithful wife and a mother. But at the age of sixty she was fed up with Blodgett's Valley and struck out on her own!" Ken said proudly. He spoke as if he knew her.

"She packed her possessions, hitched up the wagon and left. Her mother, for whom she had made arrangements to stay in Philomath, was with her. Halfway to town they remembered the pigs were still in their pens and William would probably forget to feed them. They went back, let the pigs out to forage for themselves and then left."

I could picture the two of them racing towards town in the wagon never to return to Blodgett's Valley.

"She went into Idaho and took a homestead there and proved up on it."

"Just by herself?" I asked, "Or with her mom?"

"No. Her mother stayed here. She signed up for it for herself and her mother. But by the time she had proved up on it her mother had died. Then in her older years she went to Grass Valley to be near her son James. Eighty years later her granddaughter, Myrtle Rose, remembered Asineth sitting at her table renewing her subscription to Ladies' Home Journal. On the table was a stack of dimes that she had saved for the payment. Asineth got up, tripped over a small Mexican dog, struck her head on the door and never regained consciousness. I was thinking, if you were going through that valley there, you could stop by the old homestead," Ken said, with a lively expression.

"I might be going through there. I still might be. The lady at the Forest Service office has me routed in a way that takes me out to Ona so I could ride up the ocean instead of ending up in Toledo. My friend Lew over in Lebanon said the Red Dog in Toledo is so much fun I might get detained there and never make it to Newport!"

"Anything else? Would you like more coffee?" the waitress asked.

333

"Well, there's a road, a not too busy road that goes right along the side of the Yaquina River and you go right on down into Newport," Ken told me.

"Anything else?" the waitress repeated.

"Can I have a little real milk instead of creamer?" I asked her. She was annoyed with me.

"Do you want some toast?" I asked Ken.

"No, I ate a big breakfast."

"Did you get up early?"

"I walk the neighbor's dog every morning at 7:30. He's what they call a Chocolate Retriever," Ken said.

"That is sort of what my dog was, a brindle Labrador. She just died this year. I had her ten years, and I took her everywhere."

"That's a great loss," Ken said.

"She would be sitting right out there in front of here and she'd never go in the street. I took her everywhere with me. She knew how to close the door and turn off the lights. But she never could have made this trip though."

"The dog I walk is attending obedience school. They talk about dogs going to obedience class but it's the owners, they're the ones who need to learn. So my neighbor learns and teaches me so we have the same set of symbols. Dogs are great. They aren't like seals where you have to be feeding them fish all the time! Just a kind word now and then."

"The mules are really fun to be with."

"I bet," Ken said.

"That black one is only three and a half."

"Do you give them sugar lumps?"

"Oh, yeah, I gave them some brown sugar yesterday. I give them all different kinds of grain along the way."

"You must have been on the road a long time!" Ken said.

"Two months. So I have mixed feelings about it being over."

"If it wasn't for the approaching winter you could just keep on going."

"You're right about that. I could just keep going. But I'm afraid in this rain I'd have to camp next to a laundromat every other night."

"I know what you mean. The indoors beckons on a Western Oregon fall evening."

"You said it." I finished up the last of my eggs and hash browns. It was such a good breakfast and the cafe was so warm. There was an endless supply of coffee and I could see the next storm outside, creeping towards Corvallis like a freight train. I could tell I was getting more than a little desperate. When a downtown cafe starts to look like home, its time to move on.

"So, how would you like to take a drive out to Philomath and see the museum?" he asked.

I wouldn't have turned him down. I had learned not to rush. One would think this wouldn't be a problem on mule back, but it is. And what was being in a hurry going to get me?

We headed out of Corvallis in Ken's big, comfortable car stopping at the fairgrounds to give Mavis and Sarah a flake of hay. It was strange to be traveling so fast. His car was so warm with an incredibly powerful heater that made me wish we were driving further.

Walking into the stately brick building, I caught my breath as I looked at the beautiful wood floors and the high ceilings. Ken smiled when he saw my look of wonderment. I tiptoed around and looked at the pictures of the old days on the walls.

"A bunch of the original woodwork is still in here," Ken said proudly, "except for the windowsills. And this is specially sawed vertical grain Douglas fir, just like the original. They've really done an excellent job of refurbishing it," he said as he reached over and touched the windowsill. He looked out the window for a moment, as if to see if the storm was still coming, to gauge the weather I would find on the trail later that day. He looked hopefully at the sun as it broke through the deep gray storm clouds which hovered expectantly over the hills.

"This is the library," Ken said as we walked into another huge room full of a million histories.

"It's beautiful, isn't it?" I could practically see my reflection in the floor. The words echoed off the high ceiling. "Is this where you do a lot of your work? Your studies?"

"Oh, yes. My next article is about the first newspaper here in

335

Philomath. They had four copies of it; that was all they had."

"Look at the floors in here. This is really something!"

"We had quite a time getting this in the door."

"I bet. So this is an old print machine?"

"It's an old Linotype. Have you ever seen one of those operate? All the type, the matrix, is all up in here. You press a key and it lets a letter come down here and then you can go, with a simple adjustment, from capitals to small caps to italic. Then, when the whole line is cast, hot lead squirts through here and makes a line of type. That's the way papers were set between the time they were all hand set until the time they got to phototype; that's the way it was done, on that printing press there."

"That's really something." We walked upstairs into a gorgeous theater room. On the way up the stairs, I stopped to look at a map of the area on the wall where I traced my route from Philomath up towards Mary's Peak.

"Here's Woods Creek," Ken said. "That's probably the way I would go. It's a real good dirt road and hardly any traffic."

"Here's the one they told me to take," I said as I traced my finger along Shotpouch Creek.

"You've got it all written down?" he asked with concern.

"Yep. But I don't know if I have it all right or not. There's a lot of little roads up there."

We walked over to a big display on the wall.

"Hops, used for making beer, was a big crop around here in the valley. Until they got the downy mildew and prohibition came along. But this is the early 1900's."

"So they'd say 'wire down, box full, weigh 'em up!'" I said loudly.

"Yeah. Yeah. And they'd bring in big sacks like this and dump 'em on the floor. And there were fires underneath here, of cordwood, to dry them out, and sulfur pots burning in there to kill the insects in it. Lots of hand labor, of course, in those days."

"Two hundred to four hundred pounds of hops daily," I read off the display. "Do they still have hops around here?"

"Not much. There's some in the valley. But most of it is up by Yakima. Irrigated hops."

"And everybody built their own kilns to dry the hops. Eighteen hours or so of slow drying on an elevated floor, the hops were dried." I read off the display.

"Each yard built their own dryer," Ken added. "Well, let's go upstairs. This is where the old chapel was in the college. The college operated from 1866 to 1929 in this location. But times were getting tough and it was hard to get enough students. This makes a nice art gallery. We have speakers and programs of various kinds. See, they really did a first class job with donations from people to put these seats in."

"So this was the old university," I said.

"Philomath College. See, this is a picture of the original building which has solid brick walls and was built in 1866. And when they added on to it, they added these wings which are frame buildings with a veneer of brick on them."

"So that's four walls thick!"

"That's right."

I looked out the big windows at the sun. I was so glad to see it was out. "Looks like it's turning out to be a pretty nice day!" I said with surprise.

"We better get you headed back towards the fairgrounds. We can see a few things on our way."

We drove off and headed towards Corvallis. Ken pointed out that in the days when the Indians inhabited that beautiful valley fires were allowed to burn. Fire was viewed as a healthy thing. They used it to help round up game. It cleared out the old grass so the new grass would grow better which made better grazing. He was quiet for a moment and I could picture the valley without a building in it.

"So they made settling here pretty easy with the Donation Land Law of 1850. It made it possible for a man to get three hundred and twenty acres if he was a citizen, eighteen years of age; but if he were married, he'd get twice that much. Now the men had to have certain qualifications. He had to be a citizen, he had to be at least part white, and he had to live on it, regardless, for a certain length of time; but the wife didn't have any qualifications for age, or color, or previous condition of servitude so that made teen age marriages very popular. It wasn't unusual for girls thirteen years of age to get married so she would get her three hundred and twenty acres. This

337

was the first federal law that made it possible for women to own property in their own name." Ken was quiet for a minute. The heater was blowing wonderfully hot air on my legs and feet.

"What we're following here is the old pack trail, what they call the Applegate Trail; the wet weather trail went up the stream. You haven't seen the Mary's River yet, have you?"

"Nope," I answered. "This is the way I should come into Philomath, wouldn't you think?"

"Sure. You've got to get off that highway."

"I'm so glad the weather's cleared up."

"We're gonna get a good clear view all over the valley," Ken said proudly.

"Do you think it's gonna stay cleared up for awhile? I guess you never know around here."

"It'll be pretty good. It won't be very cold, in any event. It doesn't get as cold as it does in Northern Idaho," he said confidently. "There's an operating mill," Ken said, pointing to the west. "This is kind of the milling center of the county really, around Philomath. Corvallis used to have sawmills and planing mills and flour mills but they all moved out here around Philomath. That's old Baldy off to the left. They call it that because of its bald face."

"I rode out by the university on the bike trail. It was really nice."

"You were along the river there?"

"Yep."

"So, you camped at Michael's Landing there by the river?" Ken asked, giggling a little.

"Yep," I laughed. "And I almost made the Sheriff's report."

We pulled into the fairgrounds and I saw the mules' ears when we were still far away. They were anxiously awaiting my return and somehow knew I was in Ken's car.

"The mules are still there," I said. "Thank you, Ken."

"You take care of yourself," he said, grabbing my hand.

Mavis was banging her hoof on the bottom pole of the corral, letting me know the hay was long gone and it was time to move to greener pastures.

Chapter 27

The Deluge

Woods Creek Road came up on my left and I decided to go up it instead of staying on the highway to Shotpouch Road. It was a so quiet with the old growth Douglas fir, spruce and hemlock towering above.

I headed around the corner and up the long hill. Mavis and Sarah were so happy to be off the main road. I could feel Mave's relief with every step. The smell of the trees in the rain filled my senses and I felt excited to be off the highway once and for all. It seemed by the map the rest of my journey would be on dirt roads. I really looked forward at that moment to the silence I would once again find in the high mountains, on the dirt roads that would eventually lead me to the coast. I had grown so comfortable out there in those quiet places, under the big trees. What a wonderland it must have been before the automobile first came to that place.

Highway 20 disappeared as I came around the first bend in the gravel road. The sound of the highway faded and the silence was comforting. What could I do? I wondered how I could find a way to keep going. But with Cowboy waiting for me down at the Diamond T, I knew I had to quit riding and go home once I got to Newport. Vine maple lined the creek in a gorgeous weaving of bright yellow and lime green. The fog swirled around us as we worked our way up Woods Creek and crossed into the Suislaw National Forest.

The creek sang a happy song as it came cascading down beside the road on its way to the Willamette. I was really content.

I rode along watching the mules' ears flicker back and forth, Mavis' one black ear whipping around at the sound of a deer as it leapt past us and disappeared into the forest, its long dark tail waving like a flag. Her light gray ear remained still since there was a truck coming and she had to listen for that, too.

I led Sarah up the road and tied Mavis to her saddle horn in a quick release. It felt good to walk. My tennis shoes had been wet for days and any dry socks were long since gone. My shoes went squish squish as I walked. I don't think we went further than eight miles or so, though it seemed longer.

"How's this for a camp, girls?" I said, Sarah following me into the perfect camp next to the creek. They instantly dropped their heads to get a mouthful of the thick, luscious grass at their feet. I unpacked them and put my gear and the saddles under the tarp to keep it all as dry as possible because I knew it would rain soon.

I built a fire and made myself some coffee. I had a little carton of whole milk and I dumped it in my cup mixing the rest of the brown sugar in. The brown sugar was hard as a rock and I had been chipping away at it since Walla Walla. The sky broke blue and huge billowing white clouds moved across the sky, what I could see of it above the tall Douglas fir and cedar.

I slept like a baby that night next to my little fire, halfway protected by the tarp, warm in my bag, under the canopy of some huge, ancient trees. We were heading up to Mary's Peak which was about four thousand feet elevation. I had been told of the meadow on top and the big Noble fir that rimmed the crest. It was the highest point around, a special place, not like any place else. The mountain was named after the same woman the river was named after. She must've been quite a person. I wondered who she was as I rode up the hill and around the bend. In modern times, a woman would be lucky to have a dead end street named after her.

The next morning charcoal gray clouds darkened the sky and they were thick with rain. It started about ten or eleven in the morning and didn't quit all day, a steady, thundering rain consistently drenching everything for miles. We walked on, following the signs to Mulkey Creek. After a mile or two that rutty muddy trail ended at another road where I had three forks to choose from. I sat there on Mavis while she grazed and tried to decide which road to take. I took the highest one. There was a myriad of logging roads intersecting and we were soon lost. The paper from the Forest Service had shriveled into white pulp, burying itself at the bottom of my red pack and I quit searching for it. I was as lost as I had ever been, only this time it was pouring rain and I was at that moment wetter and more miserable than I could remember. Once it got dark, I sang a few cheery tunes to keep me afloat.

"At least it's not too cold, just like Ken said," I told the mules. I finally pulled off the road, much to the relief of the mules who were steaming and soaked to the bone, their beautiful coats in a thousand ridges. Water splashed off their knees as they moved rapidly up the mountain.

I unpacked as quickly as I could, unloading the saddles and gear into a pile next to a big log. It wasn't much of a camp; a big loader had cleaned off an area so logs could be piled there. The ground was muddy and a pile of big logs off to the side looked like the best place to call home. Any camp would do. By the time we stopped we'd been a good fifteen miles and we were tired. The cozy camp on Woods Creek seemed like a long time ago. Every mile seemed like two the closer I came to Newport and the Pacific Ocean. Why was that? I knew it was only because of the rain and the approaching end of the ride. The whole thing was growing surreal and I longed for the magic days of September.

My little shelter seemed good enough. Mavis and Sarah had finished eating their dinner of oatmeal and some uncooked spaghetti, and any bit of graze they could find in the forest, as far as their picket ropes allowed. I could only see their shadowy figures as I lay down in my damp sleeping bag, on one tarp and under another, curled up next to the pack bags and the saddles. The saddle blankets felt damp beneath me and I could feel a deep chill cooling my bones as I tried to get warm. I missed my dog Robin terribly and when I thought about her and how much less lonely I would feel if she were there, I cried like a baby. No one could hear me; the wind and the thundering rain drowned out my voice. I hadn't had a good cry in a long time.

Thunder clapped its hands in my ears and I rolled over and tried to sit up. I had gone to bed with a pan of popcorn half-heartedly popped on a fire that never lit. The pan was filling up with rainwater and the burnt duds were spreading out onto my bag right by my head. I thought it was raining hard before but then the storm reached a new crescendo and it sounded as if it couldn't rain any harder. The entire forest was groaning and there were streams surrounding our soggy, pathetic camp. I hid under that log like a scared rabbit.

I heard the water coming from up the hill. It sounded closer. I sat up again, the water dripping in my face, to see what was going on. Then it reached my log. Hovering on the down side, with my face buried in my corn kernel covered bag, I felt it hit me. Within moments the stream of water arrived on my side of the log cutting away the soil beneath it and filling my bag with little sticks, dirt and enough of a wave to send me down the hill three feet, surfing in my sleeping bag. I grabbed at the side hill, at the duff and needles, and stopped myself. I stood up and, in my own potato sack, raced for the huge log. I jumped madly up and down in the wet sack, back towards the log uphill of the stream that now ran freely where my bed had been a few seconds before.

Knowing I couldn't get any wetter, I started to laugh. My voice could not be heard above the thunder and the rain and the crack of the lightning. It was pure bedlam.

I woke up and saw the blue sky and big white, friendly looking clouds. I couldn't believe I had ever fallen asleep, but I guess I ran out of steam around four or five in the morning. I had never been so happy in my life to see morning come.

Wringing out the saddle blankets and the bag, I started to pack. Each saddle blanket weighed at least ten pounds and was full of water. The leather in my saddle was soaked and cold to the touch. Even the sawbuck saddle had soaked up a bunch of the storm and was a few pounds heavier.

I heard the far away hum of a pickup truck. The sound grew closer. I walked up towards the road and, sure enough, a truck pulled up and stopped.

"Hey, what are you doing out here on the mountain? Boy, you must've gotten wet last night. That was the biggest storm so far this year and you were out in it!" The man in the plaid quilted shirt shook his head in disbelief. He held a steaming cup of coffee in his gloved hands, wrapping them around it to stay warm. He smiled as I looked longingly at his cup. "Do you have a Thermos? I'll share this with you," he offered.

"Used to, but I dropped it and it shattered, just south of Antelope."

"Antelope? You came all the ways from Antelope?"

"No, Clark Fork. Up in Idaho."

"Well, how about a cup? I bet you could use a jump start."

"Sure!" I said and ran off to get my beat up yellow plastic coffee mug. The coffee warmed up the plastic and I could feel the blood returning to my fingers and they stung.

My knight in the white Chevy drove off leaving me to pack up and head for Mary's Peak. The bright sun broke through and it was dry all the way down the other side to Harlan, down the Harlan Road.

The vine maples followed the river and outlined the quiet dirt road with a gold lining, spreading up the hillsides amidst the fir trees like sunlight. Mavis was steaming and kept my legs warm as I rode along. The mules were as glad to get down off that mountain as I was.

Later that day that nice man came back with his wife and insisted I sit in their heated station wagon with a cup of hot chocolate in my hands, to warm up. He had told her I was gloveless and she had brought me a pair. The rain was starting up again and I sat in the car with them for about twenty minutes. They were really lovely people and had driven an hour and a half up Mary's Peak to come find me and bring me fresh baked banana bread as well as a new little Thermos full of hot coffee.

Any suffering was long forgotten as I got back on Mavis and headed down the tiny road which we had entirely to ourselves. We took the center lane and walked right down the middle, singing, "When I get off of this mountain, you know where I'm gonna go, straight down the Mississippi River to the Gulf of Mexico," over and over again until Sarah stomped and looked cross, convincing me to stop.

343

Chapter 28

Downtown Harlan

Elk Creek tumbled along as I rode in the hard rain and hail towards Harlan, dropping down the hill towards the spot on the map I hoped to reach by nightfall. I had eighteen or nineteen miles to go.

I kept my head down, hidden in my poncho. My big black Arctic Suit was protecting me from the storm. It was a beautiful ride, enjoyable in the hard rain because of that wonderful black suit that made me look like Big Foot. Mavis walked about four miles an hour and Sarah kept right up.

I stopped and let the girls graze after eight or nine miles and sat listening to the rushing Elk creek as it cascaded towards its destination, the Pacific Ocean. I wiped the raindrops off of Mavis' long white eyelashes and hugged her big neck. She radiated warmth even when she was sopping wet.

Douglas fir and the vine maple shared hillsides of startling colors.

"A show just for me," I laughed as I trotted along at a good click down the perfect rain soaked dirt road ahead that looked silver in the light. When I came close to Harlan, blackberries rambled alongside the narrow dirt road. Old apple trees stood proud but forgotten, and apples covered the ground beneath them in mushy piles thick with bees. There was an old forgotten cabin buried in berry bushes. The old cabin had been claimed by them long ago and they grew heartily over the ancient, weathered boards that split and fell under the massive bramble, returning to the earth. There was a mailbox, a perfect garden with corn twelve feet tall and rows full of plump cabbages and carrots. Bright red mums and huge yellow marigolds and white daisies grew in thick rows of late color. A large sunflower lay on its back, picked clean of seeds. Other sunflowers stood with their heads nodded forward.

Beyond the garden a huge deep green Douglas fir tree stood watch. The mules saw it, too, and planned on stopping once we turned the corner and came upon the old clapboard two-story store with the tall porch and cement floor. There was a pay phone out in front.

Viola Waterman came out of the large green door; the screen slammed behind her. She was a short woman in her late seventies with large pink glasses that covered a third of her face. Her shirt was neat and well ironed and I noticed she wore penny loafers with real pennies in them.

"Jim stopped by to say there was a mule train crossing the peak," she said, in a soft, shy voice. She smiled at me, and I stopped immediately in front of her, but not too close, under the protection of the tall porch. Mavis and Sarah were happy to get their ears out of the rain and hail and were noticeably delighted that we had stopped at a civilized spot like Viola's. Both mules had sweet, smug smiles on their faces as I unpacked them in the backyard next to the garden. Sarah knew better than to head straight for the tall corn and ate the long, lush grass that had been flattened by the recent hail, one eye on the tall luscious corn that reached towards the heavens. I wondered how Dorothy and Reid had done in their garden and how they had enjoyed their summer in my little cabin on the flat, way up north.

I thought about Dorothy and the garden. By then it would be harvested, only a few forgotten squashes along the edges. She had probably tilled under everything but the asparagus. Perhaps it even had a light layer of snow because winter could come early in the North Country. I hadn't thought about my home by the bluff for a long time.

Mavis was gentle with Viola, sensing her age and frailty, and was

347

careful not to bump her with her nose. Viola confidently held onto Mave's gold halter keeping her still while I took off her saddle and the green and white Mexican blanket. Then Viola walked slowly into the garden and grabbed two ears of white corn, one for each of the mules. They didn't spill a kernel of it and ate the corn silk, husks and all.

"The store has been closed for eleven years," she told me, "since my husband died upstairs. Since then I've been lucky to have such nice neighbors to keep an eye out, you know," she said seriously. "I only go to town about twice a month, anymore. Get supplies, you know, over in Eddyville." We went into the kitchen and sat at the big, worn linoleum table. She put on her favorite Dolly Parton album, and the sweet voice filled the tall tongue and groove ceilings that had long ago been painted a light green.

"So, what advice would you give to a younger person, Viola, since you've lived a lot of years?" I asked.

"I really don't give much unless somebody comes up and asks me something." She was real quiet for a few minutes while the song changed and a Don William's song came on. "Young people need to learn to have consideration for other people," she said with conviction, her voice soft and sweet. "If they learn to do for others, it always comes back. That's why I had these pens made," she stuttered. There was a big box of white pens on the table. On each one was printed, "*Count your blessings. Do unto others as you would have them do unto you.*"

"I had a big bunch of these pens made over a year ago and I've gave quite a few to the kids around here. I also gave quite a few to folks at church. I learned years ago that if you help other people, why, when the opportunity comes up, it always comes back. I've been helped a lot of times by just helping someone else. Just like with me here, if the opportunity comes up that I can help somebody, and I'm situated where I can help different ones quite often. I've got a tire breaker and a compressor and I've helped a number of them that's got stuck out here with flat tires. That's really the only way you can get any real pleasure is helping somebody else."

"That's good advice. What memories do you have from when you were growing up?"

"I was raised in Nevada and Idaho. I went to Idaho on my fifteenth birthday, after I lost my mother. I lost my mother when I was fourteen. And I was the oldest of five of us. My youngest sister was just a year and a half old. My uncle and grandfather came down and got me and took me back up to Idaho. And my dad sold the place that next summer and came on up to Idaho. That was in 1930."

Viola took me into the living room and sat me down next to the big stereo she kept immaculately polished. Several of her favorite albums stood face out on the shelf above the stereo, her favorite stars smiling at us reassuringly. Viola lived out in the middle of a million acres of wild forest, yet she was not alone. But when a neighbor was not around, the place would have been too quiet if not for the singers on the stereo that kept her company.

She walked slowly over to a big scrapbook, pulled it open to a page and smiled. "Ever think you'll marry?" she asked me, her smile wide and her eyebrows arched above the big round pink glasses. "If so, here's a little advice for you:"

Then she read aloud, "*How to Cook a Husband.*"

Many husbands are spoiled by mismanagement. But they are really delightful when properly treated. Do not blow him up or roast him. Do not keep him in hot water. Do not freeze him with indifference. Do not keep him in a stew, by irritating words or ways. Do not keep him in a pickle. No husband will be tender or good thus treated.

First, when selecting a husband, do not be guided by a silvery appearance as in buying mackerel or the golden tint when selecting salmon. Select for yourself, as taste differs. Do not go to the market for him. The best is always brought to your door. It is far better to have done if you are not willing patiently to learn to cook for him, as to cook in a preserving kettle is always best. See that the linen in which you wrap him is nice and mended, with all strings and buttons securely tied on. If this is neglected, he is likely to fly out of the kettle and become crusty on the edges. Since, like crabs and lobsters, he is cooked alive; it is well to tie him in the kettle by the cord called comfort. The one called duty is likely to be weak.

We laughed. She took a big sip of the ice tea she had brought over on a tray that looked like it had come with the store. It was old and tarnished, with a girl in a bathing suit on it, drinking a Coca-Cola.

I sat there on a light green booth below the huge, paned window in the living room. There was merchandise left on old tarnished metal racks. There were old sewing patterns and boxes of canning jars, all with the lids. Every place I looked there was some interesting relic from the days when she and her late husband ran the store, busy from dawn to dark.

"So, have you been collecting poems for a long time?" I asked.

"Oh yes. I have a box and a big scrapbook that I've had for years. There's a box in there that's full of poems. I find them in papers and stuff and I get the Grit Paper all the time and there are always poems in that."

"The Grit Paper?" I asked.

"Yep. The Grit. I've been getting the Grit Paper for a long time." She carefully turned each page. "Some particular one I like, why, I cut it out and put it in this here book."

She pulled out a poem on a worn piece of paper, and read aloud, "*Happiness Cake.*"

> *One cup of good thoughts, one cup of kind deeds, and a cup of consideration, two cups of sacrifice. Three cups of forgiveness, two cups of well beat faults. Mix thoroughly. Add tears of joy, sorrow and sympathy. Flavor with love and kindly service. Fold in two cups of prayer and faith. After pouring all this into your daily life, bake well with the heat of human kindness. Serve any time, and it will feed the hunger of a starved soul.*

We sat there quietly and listened to the sound of the hail on the tin roof. She pointed out a couple of leaks on the back porch and told me how she really missed having her girls around since she couldn't really get to things above her head anymore.

"It was the tall jobs, that's what they really helped with around here. I'd do the low scrubbing and the girls would go up on the ladder for the high part. I sure do miss them. The house is a little too quiet. If it weren't for the music, oh my, I'd go crazy. And the neighbors. Always someone is comin' by to check in on me."

"What's your favorite song of all time?" I asked her. The rain was coming down so hard it was ricocheting off Harlan Road.

"Don Williams and Marty Robbins have always been my favorites. Merle Haggard, too. I like most all your western singers. I've got all kinds of tapes and records. I've got a metal container in there that's chock full of eight track tapes. Besides all the cassettes up on the back of the couch. And my record collection. I've got all kinds of records."

"So, do you have any Willie Nelson records?" I asked hopefully.

"I think they're a few in there," she said. "Some older ones."

"My favorite," I told her.

"So, do you play your records more than your cassettes?"

"I've got where I play my cassettes quite a bit. When they get through playin', they'll shut themselves off. The eight tracks don't. The tape plays over and over and over if you don't catch it and turn it off."

"Last year I had two young fellows come over here from the valley. And they had a camper on their truck and they backed right in, right here," she nodded to the cement porch where the gas pumps once were. "They backed in here, right up within three feet or so of the front door right here. And they backed in right before dark. And they opened up the back of it, and went up on the hill right there, and they must have set there, right at my front door for better than two hours."

"What did you do?"

"I happened to be upstairs in front of that front window up there. And the window was open and I could hear them. They had seen some deer tracks. We have a doe around here and last year she had twin fawns. She lives right around here. That's why I have a no hunting sign out there on that corner. At the tree, because people get to shootin' on that bank and they shouldn't. It's too close. They're not supposed to hunt around here close, but some of 'em do. And one of 'em said, 'Here's where we'll set, because here's tracks and we'll find us a deer so we just as well set right here.'"

"So I come down and I called my neighbor. And I didn't tell her why or anything. I just called her and asked her to come up. She come up and said, 'what's this doing at your front door?'"

"I told her they'd been sittin' there better than two hours, so she went out there and yelled, 'Is this your rig?' And they said 'yes,' and boy one of them slammed the door shut real hard and that one got snotty as all get out. And that's the only time I've ever had anyone come up and have that kind of attitude."

"I bet lost people are a lot friendlier," I added.

"You see, upstairs I have a big chair and a nice lamp where after dark I sit and read, right next to the window overlooking the road." She got up and walked into the kitchen and came back with a package of cookies.

"I've been here going on nineteen years. My husband came up here and made a deal on the place on Thanksgiving of '65."

"Do you know how old this building is?"

"No. There used to be a date on the cabinet in here. I don't even know if it's still there."

I looked up at the tall front door of the old store. "Don't you ever wonder about an old building like this, who all came through that door?" I asked.

"There used to be some pretty rough times around here. This was the old stage route and they used to have big dances over here at the hall. I understand one fellow got shot out here, right out here on this corner. He got in a fight at the old dance hall."

"See! Here it is!" Viola said excitedly, rubbing a tiny, tarnished plaque on the old cabinet. "This date was for the old post office. It says 1865. I think that was when they first had a post office in here. They didn't have this road coming from Burnt Woods. They used to all come down that watershed road, like you come in. They used to all come down that road. Into the valley this way, like you did. The mail, everything, used to come in the way you did. There used to be a cabin up there, years ago. But somebody got smart and went in and burned it down." Viola shook her head slowly, in disgust.

I pulled out my skin lotion and offered her some. "Keeps my

wrinkles away. I sure appreciate you hanging all my stuff up in here," I said, looking around at all my wet clothes. She had hung them up all over the front room of the old store on lines she had strung from wall to wall. Each piece of clothing was hung up with old wooden pins and everything looked like it was ready for the trash. Covered with charcoal and mud, worn from hard wear. Back in Corvallis I lucked into a brand new pair of tennis shoes at the thrift store for three dollars.

"In the morning you'll have to set me on the vacuum cleaner, to make sure I get all these pine needles off the rug. So you won't think of me when you see dirt," I laughed.

"They won't stay here long. I've got an Electrolux."

"Well I think everything is gonna dry, don't you?"

"Yep. See, I got busy turning things around a while ago. I did that to get them to dry more. I switched it all around," she said proudly.

"Can you imagine how those mules felt this morning when I took those sopping wet saddle blankets and plopped them up on their backs? It was the only time I felt really sorry for them the whole trip. They were shivering from the cold. They didn't like it one bit!"

"And you! Up there on that peak!" she said. "You were up there, where you were catching full blast of the wind. Well, you'll sleep warm tonight."

Her oversized penny loafers with the real pennies in them kept the beat on the old, worn, linoleum floor. Her dog, Pepper, was the smallest Chihuahua I had ever seen and he trembled at the sound of anything or nothing it all. She held him most of the time, or he danced in fragile steps around her feet, avoiding the tapping toes of the penny loafers.

"Do you love to dance, Viola?" I asked.

"Oh yes. I'd rather dance than eat."

She put on her favorite Johnny Cash album and we danced around the big living room. The rain never let up for a minute. After that, it was Don Williams again. He was her favorite.

She gave me my own room, a bedroom. The high tongue and groove ceiling was peeling paint. As I curled up in my bed, under four thick blankets and a comforter, I tried to remember exactly how miserable the night before had been, and I couldn't. Funny how sweet and cozy the rain sounded, beating down on the tin roof.

Chapter 29

Rio Dulce

It was the hardest spot to leave. Viola had a breakfast fixed for me by the time I opened my eyes in the cozy bedroom off the living room. I smelled coffee and awoke to a day I would never forget as long as I live. The rain had stopped somewhere around four a.m. and I stayed awake, wrapped up in the crazy quilts, and waited until the sun was over the hill warming up the big old store before I crawled out of bed.

I walked outside and looked down the Big Elk Creek Road towards Harlan. I imagined the stage rumbling by heading towards Elk City. The wet road glistened in the morning sun as the next storm loomed dark somewhere over Newport and headed our way in a huge, solid bank of dark gray clouds. The mules had their fill of the pasture behind the garden, the one Viola's neighbor called the hay field. They were filled to the brim with rich Oregon grass and heaps of corn that Viola had dropped in front of them in a big pile. They ate every bit of it.

Saddling up Mavis and Sarah, I walked them to the front porch to finish packing as Viola watched from the front door. All of the saddle blankets were warm and dry thanks to her expertise with the indoor clothesline. She kept an eye on my gear all afternoon and evening turning my jacket and my sleeping bag so they would dry on both sides. The saddle blankets were once again light as a feather and even fluffier since their big soaking up on the peak.

Neighbor kids came by for a ride and after they had their fill, I rode away. Viola Waterman stood on the porch and waved until I disappeared around the corner, heading down Big Elk Creek Road, with only forty miles to go and a jar of her fresh blackberry jam in my bag.

The Big Elk Creek Road followed right along the creek all the way down to the flat known as Elk City.

Once Elk City glowed as a hopeful contender to Portland and other big, important towns. Dressed in the best a rugged wilderness could offer, Elk City was considered an important harbor being the end of the stage coach route and the gateway to the world on the water as steamers carried travelers out to Newport and beyond. Many people traveled that road, stopping in Elk City for a night and then heading out on a boat down Yaquina Bay to the busy town of Toledo. There, at Sawyer's Landing, the train track ended, and the world on the water began. There was a time when steamers brought travelers from San Francisco and beyond. There was a cooperage there that made wooden boxes and butter containers. It was the county seat, and was once the biggest town for miles and miles.

I rode into the tiny town more than ready to get out of the saddle and stretch my legs. The mules were hungry and had walked almost twenty miles from Harlan.

Elk City Store was a big, old, weathered wooden building with a pair of old elk horns nailed to the front. With its rugged appearance, it looked as if it had been sitting there in a time capsule and never had changed. Built in 1866, it had been a store ever since. There was a big wood stove in the middle with a couple of comfortable looking chairs close by. Old signs, tins, wooden boxes and cross-cut saws covered the walls; huge elk and deer heads peered down with a variety of expressions from all corners of the big room. The wood floor was worn and was full of grooves, little pathways where travelers had walked for over a century. The trees on the hill behind the store had been clear-cut and the ones that grew in their place were still seedlings.

There I was, at the end of the stagecoach road. The park by the creek was the perfect place to camp but I pushed on for Toledo. I felt I was testing fate; my luck had been so favorable for so long and I was so close to my goal I didn't want to stop. Aside from that, eventually, I would have gotten moldy out there and didn't want to stick around for the moss to grow in the hood of my poncho.

The afternoon light was yellow; once in awhile the storm would break and the dark gray curtain would open up and the sun would come dazzling through the thick trees. As I passed down the road through Elk City, I saw an old man in a worn brown shirt, faded logger pants and suspenders. He had a great shock of white hair and a long white beard and stood in front of his small silver trailer next to the store motioning to me, with an ancient bony hand, to stop by and say hello. I could hardly help but stare at his beautiful face and he spoke in such a soft tone I had to strain to hear him. His name was Elmer Parks and had lived there all his life. His family arrived in 1889 by wagon train from Arkansas. His Great Uncle Harvey had walked all the way with a team of oxen and a wagon. For years, Elmer had lived on the family homestead a few miles above Elk City and had walked to town nearly every day. When he got too old to make the hike, he moved into the old silver trailer near the store.

We sat on old lawn chairs in front of the trailer as the sky clouded up again and a sheet of rain fell silently. Elmer didn't budge. He was used to the rain.

I got back in the saddle before it got too wet. I looked back at him and waved as I turned Mavis onto the road.

He smiled and said, "Have a good trip." The old man stood there in front of the old trailer as we rode away. "Have a good trip!" he said again in case I hadn't heard, cupping his old rugged hands to his mouth, shouting the words as loud as he could. The words echoed off the trees and I looked back, taking one more look before we turned the corner. That was quite a shout for such an old man. Those were the moments I would miss.

I rode along the river and into Toledo as the mill whistle blew, echoing off the steep fir covered hills. The cedar, spruce, and Douglas fir were thick along the road. I slept on the edge of town in a big grassy lot with a campfire ring. Tiny white diamonds glistened on Yaquina Bay, a wide river that smelled of the sea; a *Rio dulce* or sweet water, where the fresh and salt water mix. White egrets and great blue herons flew low above the river now and then looking over at me as

I rode towards Toledo. I had ridden thirty miles that day. It was the longest day of the whole journey but the land had cast a spell on me and I could smell the ocean. Red tail hawks joined us along the road.

Yaquina Bay Road follows the river and as I rode along the herons skimmed along the gray water circling around, slowing down their flight enough to get a good look at us. I looked up at the wrong moment and a big gray and white seagull welcomed me to the coast with a deposit of white goo on my hat. I took it off and shook it but not before the dropping dried in a perfect line across the front of my cap.

I could hear a truck behind me and it slowed down to keep pace.

"Where are you headed?" a handsome man in his thirties with a thick brown beard smiled at me. His black and red plaid jacket looked so warm I shivered.

"Newport!" I said. I couldn't believe it was only miles away.

"Well," he said, "my wife and I live up the road a few miles and we have a horse corral, if you'd like to put your animals there overnight. It's only about seven miles more. It's the little log cabin overlooking the bay. Can't miss it. Oh, my name's Mark."

"That sounds great."

The bay looked like a big piece of sheet metal pitted by the heavy rain drops that fell hard and fast. It wasn't the kind of rain that would slow down or ease up and because my poncho's finish was starting to wear off, the cold rain was seeping into my wool and I smelled like an old wool sock.

I fought back a creeping sadness. Even though I had tired of the rain, we were coming to the end of our road. I had no doubt that back in Idaho the snow was deep and the little granary I called home would be as cold as an icebox. I had neither hay nor firewood. I would miss the trail, riding along without a care in the world but to find pasture, water, and a dry place to sleep.

Mark's log cabin looked so inviting when I finally arrived there about six. I was cold and hungry. His wife, Marilyn, came running up the driveway to help me unpack.

"We're heading out to a big Halloween party. We're going as California Raisins. Do you want to join us?" Marilyn was a small, energetic woman with a friendly voice. She was a teacher in

Newport, a mother and a horsewoman. The party sounded fun, but I was so cold and tired.

She led me to the shower after I had unpacked. The water revived me. Marilyn made me a big cup of coffee and told me to make myself at home.

Mark was a fisherman, and had fished up and down the coast for years.

"When you get to town you can stay on my boat, the Hazel Lorraine, if you want, as long as you find another place for the mules," he said.

I was still awake when they drove in from the party. Before I left, we made plans to take a ride on the beach together.

The mules stopped at a particularly luscious patch of green grass as I looked out at the Pacific stretching to the horizon. Sarah and Mavis stopped in their tracks when they first saw it, a great band of light gray water, more water than they had ever seen. They eyed it with suspicion. Mavis snorted once and looked back to her lunch.

It was a perfect place to tie them and so I left them there on the little hill. I walked down to the bayfront and found the Hazel Lorraine. The boat must have been sixty feet long and was tied to a dock between two other big boats, the dock creaking and bobbing as I walked down to my temporary home.

The smell of the bay front was so salty and sweet and smelled of old wood and clam chowder. Mo's Chowder House was too tempting to pass up and so I walked up the dock and sat down in the famous old restaurant and ordered a bowl of clam chowder and a cup of coffee. The rain was beating down steadily as it had been all day. It was the first of November and time to be inside.

"Where'd you walk from?" a rusty fisherman with a big white beard asked me in a raspy voice, looking me up and down. "You look like you've been out to sea in a lifeboat," he laughed. "Take off some of that wet gear and dry off. Stay awhile." I knew the mules were standing out in the rain but I hoped they'd find plenty to eat on the hill while I sat a spell. Mo's was warm and the rain and fog started to look nice to me from inside.

"I've been out with my two mules for over two months now. Started up in Clark Fork, Idaho, and rode all the way here."

"That's a heck of a ride. Did you follow the Oregon Trail? The Applegate? That must've been somethin', all by yourself, all that way." He shook his head in disbelief and took a big sip of his beer. The foam stuck to his long beard and he wiped it off with old, rugged fingers.

"I went out there once, out to Idaho. There are a lot of trees between here and there, a lot of country. And a lot of open country, too. But I've been here most of the time. I fished these waters since I was fifteen, started as a deck hand and worked my way up to three boats of my own and now I'm too old to go out. They keep me ashore and say the ocean's no place for an old man. The fish have dropped off so! It's hard to make it now. But we all keep trying. Where are your mules? Don't see 'em!" he said, looking out the window.

"They're up on the hill, grazing, and they're still saddled so I can't stay long."

"Which way'd you come out? The Bay road?" he asked.

"Yep."

"That used to be quite a thing, all those boats going up river as far as they could to Toledo, and the train. Used to bring folks out here to the coast from all over Oregon and even California. You know Newport was quite a tourist destination for the folks from Portland and San Francisco. In the early days, the ladies would dress up in their finery and stroll the long beach to enjoy the good ocean air and then maybe swim in the big pool they had over there on the coast side. It was quite a thing in the old days, with long boardwalks connecting the harbor and the ocean side. Then things changed."

We rode to a stable on the hill where most of the horses in Newport lived because of the big, covered arena and the stalls. The woman who owned the place found me a big corral for Mavis and Sarah, not inside but out near the stable, and sold me a bale of good, dry hay.

I sat quietly on the beach and listened to the sound of the wild ocean breaking and I steamed clams over a small campfire in the shelter of a big rock and ate them with butter and bread. The ocean was stormy and fierce and the wind had a real whip to it. I felt lonely for the first time in a long time. I fondly remembered those warm nights in the high desert, sleeping on my back under a blanket of stars.

I walked down to the bay and had a bowl of chowder at Mo's.

The harbor was quiet and there was no big band or crowd to welcome me. Just me, myself and I sitting in Mo's enjoying the view out the window and the creamy chowder.

Shuffling through my journal, I made a list of all the places I had slept. I started out with the mountain camps. There were twenty of them. I had slept in four trailers, three bunkhouses and one semi truck, in eight real beds and on one living room couch. I had made my bed in three horse stalls, ten barns, on two floors, in the yard of an abandoned house outside of Walla Walla and next to three corrals. I had slept behind a coffee shop under a willow tree, in a stainless steel fish cleaning room and on a fishing boat in Newport harbor.

"Hey, you made it!" Lew yelled enthusiastically as he pulled up in his big car. See, you made it past the Red Dog after all!"

"Hey, Lew!" I yelled. I felt instantly cheered to see my tall, boisterous friend from the trailer park. "How's the water pipe? Did you get it fixed?"

"Not to worry! So, you've been getting rained on, huh?" Lew yelled, from the window of the big car.

"More than a little. Mary's Peak got the best of me!"

"Well, by golly, girl, you amaze me!" Lew said, shaking his head, laughing.

"Can you believe it? No more riding for me. Time to go home."

"How're ya gonna get there? Hitchhike?"

"No, a friend's coming down from Sandpoint with a truck and trailer. He should be here to pick us up in a few days."

"Well, let's go eat," he said in his thundering voice. He was comfortable in all these places, from Toledo to Newport and beyond, and everywhere we walked downtown, people said hello. We walked to a coffee shop and had a nice dinner.

My last night, I slept in the tack room at the stable, on my saddle blankets that still smelled of sagebrush. I buried myself in my bag and under blankets and slept soundly on a big pile of alfalfa. No one ever knew I was there and in the morning, at around six, I heard the barn door open and a girl walked by on her way to feed her horse. I waited until she was gone and crept out from underneath the blankets and out into a day that broke clear and cold. The mules were both lying down, parallel in the corral, enjoying the sun.

I rode Mavis and led Sarah down to the ocean, riding practically bareback with just the green and white Mexican blanket on Mave's charcoal back.

Once we got down on the beach, their ears went flat back and they wouldn't go a step further. I coaxed them and pulled on them and pleaded with them. There was absolutely no way they would gallop up the beach in the surf. They just wouldn't do it. The foghorn would blow and any progress I made was quickly forgotten as they stood stiffly at attention, their long ears pointed towards the biggest river they had ever seen.

They would go nowhere near the water and I wasn't about to try and make them. They pawed at the sand, never taking their concerned gazes off the stormy ocean. Walking any further west was definitely out of the question. They had carried me all that way without mishap. We had come nearly seven hundred miles from our home.

I tugged on their reins and ropes pleading with them to walk down the beach as I had pictured it. I had played that moment over and over in my imagination as we plodded slowly toward Newport, without a care in the world. I knew then that there wouldn't be a spirited run down the beach and I sat down in front of Mavis and Sarah in the sand.

I looked up the beach and saw a stout man walking my way. He stopped at Mavis and scratched her on the neck in the exact right place a mule loves. His hands had oil paint on them and he had two paintbrushes behind his ears. I laughed aloud when I looked into his joyous face with a smile as wide as the ocean and dancing blue eyes.

"I haven't seen many mules since I left the Pyrenees," he said in a strong voice. "For many years, me and my Basque brothers, we packed our mules on the rugged trails that led to the borderlands. All of our trading took place on these high trails and the mules were our life." He stopped and looked out at the ocean. "These two are beautiful. This gray, she will lighten into a coat the color of polished silver. I have seen this type of mule many times, with the dark eye pencil. What a beauty. And the little white one. What an angel!"

The mules were relaxed with this old artist whose red, rugged face told his story. Even though he smelled of oil paint, they didn't shy away. He patted Mavis on the back and Sarah scratched her ears on his thick wool coat leaving white hair all over the front of it.

"I teach an art class, right up there in that building to the right," he said proudly. "I was watching you and laughing as you tugged at them to go towards the water. Don't you know?" he said, patting Sarah on the neck. "The mule will never go in the ocean. They know better. A horse, he will race wildly through the surf. A mule, no. They will not touch the water. For they are the smart ones."

Before I knew what I was doing, I reached out and hugged the old artist. Not surprisingly, he hugged me in return. I closed my eyes, and thought about Nina and how long ago it all seemed, and how hopeful we had been, heading up Dry Creek Road. I thought about the old logger in St. Maries and about Breeze and Orville. And Mary in Condon as she stood in the road and waved goodbye, a halo of large green curlers under her hair net.

"Thank you, old man," I said into his thick coat.

"These mules need some apples. I have some in my car." He turned and walked slowly up the beach.

About the Author

Jody and Mavis   Photograph by Charlie Parker

Jody Foss was born in 1954 and asked her parents for a pony as soon as she could get the words out. When she was thirteen, her fantasy came true. Family friends gave her and her friend Laurie two ponies and from then on they could be found on the fire roads above La Cañada, California, riding the high chaparral.

Things haven't changed much, except now she rides a mule. She has traveled thousands of miles all over the west photographing the people she meets along the way and collecting their oral histories on tape. She lives on a ranch with her husband, Charlie Parker, seven mules, a donkey and a horse, a good dog and cats.

About the Artist

Bonnie and Porter   Photograph by Kayo Frasier

Bonnie Shields grew up in southern Indiana, just west of Louisville, Kentucky. Lots of Thoroughbreds and Standardbreds, but no horse of her own. Like so many little girls, she was "horse crazy," and to endure her horseless state, she drew them constantly. Her first real horse came when she was fourteen, an unbroke mostly Morgan filly. It wasn't until she was in her early twenties and living in Middle Tennessee that she and the mule met. They have neither one been the same since.

She lives in northern Idaho now with her husband, four mules, a donkey and a token horse. They enjoy very much riding and packing into the high country all over the west.

Reader comments on:

Mules Across the Great Wide Open

"Not being a plumb total stranger to the back of a mule, or either end, and having covered down through the years more than one mile on horseback, I figure your book on your experiences derived from that mode of travel should make mighty interesting reading."

E. J. Kirchoff

"I just finished reading your marvelous book. I started it and I couldn't put it down! I have traced the trip on the map from one end to another. What a wonderful experience! Isn't it wonderful that you and Debbie could have had it together? Hope there's going to be another one. When that happens, please place an order for us. Please tell Bonnie Shields how much we enjoyed her clever illustrations!"

Ruth Irby

"We certainly enjoyed the humor in your book. Remember your motto: A rolling Foss gathers no moss. An axiom: 'A rolling Foss mule saves on fuel.'"

Harold Scott

"After strolling along with you and your crew from Park City to Spokane, I feel as if I know you well enough to address you by your first name. I've just had a most pleasant two days with you on your journey (I can read much faster than your mule could trot.) It was a wonderfully warm story and I enjoyed every moment of it. I believe your string passed our motor home in Sandpoint that lovely autumn day as you were nearing the end of your journey and we were just coming out of our mountain camp on Upper Gold Creek."

Pauline Shook

"I just finished reading *Mules Across the Great Wide Open* and I loved it. I didn't want to put it down, but I had to make it last. The illustrations are priceless. I loved the photos, especially all the people you encountered. It was a book I truly loved from cover to cover. Your writing brought up pictures in my mind and feelings that only a good writer can create. I felt it when you were soaking wet, hungry and at those peaceful times sitting alongside a river for hours where the only sound was the call of the birds overhead. I have a new understanding and respect for the marvelous mule. They haven't been given the proper respect they deserve. I sincerely wish for you to continue on with the same determination that took you across the great wide open. May the trails only get happier."

Elaine Dauphin

Jody and her sister Debbie on the trail from Utah in 1976
Photo by: Robert Wuthrich, Henry's Lake, Idaho

Order Page

IN THE COMPANY OF MULES
and
MULES ACROSS THE GREAT WIDE OPEN

To order, send check or money order to:
Mules Across America
Box 225
Tomales, California 94971

For credit card orders:
Telephone or FAX: 707-878-2095
or
E-mail: mules@svn.net

Include name, card number and expiration date, address and telephone number

In The Company of Mules: $19.95
Mules Across the Great Wide Open: $14.95

Orders in California: add 7% tax

Shipping:
United States: add $4.00 for the first book, $2.00 for each additional book
International: add $9.00 for the first book, $5.00 for each additional book
United Parcel Service delivery for bulk orders
If you would like a personalized, signed copy, please say so!